Ton

# Principles of Arable Crop Production

# Principles of
# Arable Crop Production

## F. Harper

**GRANADA**
London Toronto Sydney New York

Granada Publishing Limited – Technical Books Division
Frogmore, St Albans, Herts AL2 2NF
and
36 Golden Square, London W1R 4AH
515 Madison Avenue, New York, NY 10022, USA
117 York Street, Sydney, NSW 2000, Australia
60 International Boulevard, Rexdale, Ontario R9W 6J2, Canada
61 Beach Road, Auckland, New Zealand

*British Library Cataloguing in Publication Data*
Harper, F.
Principles of arable crop production.
1. Field crops
I. Title
631.5          SB185

ISBN 0-246-11741-9

First published in Great Britain 1983 by Granada Publishing Ltd

Printed in Great Britain by
Richard Clay (The Chaucer Press) Ltd,
Bungay, Suffolk

Granada ®
Granada Publishing ®

# Contents

# Preface

Crop production is a major component of courses in general agriculture at degree and higher diploma level. The structure of these courses is such that the basic science subjects related to agriculture are dealt with in the early stages and the production aspects are covered later. This text links the scientific principles of crop production with the practice in a way which should be understandable to students, farmers and advisers. The assumption is made that the reader has a knowledge and understanding of chemistry, botany, soil science, plant physiology, pathology, entomology and the physical sciences relating to agriculture.

Crop production is a broad subject and the title is an ambitious one. It is recognised that there are inadequacies in various areas of the subject. Examples are used extensively in the text to illustrate the principles. These examples are selected to be representative of the practice of crop production in intensive systems in cool temperate climates. Some examples are selected from other climatic zones and it is assumed that the principles described here will be applicable in a wide range of environments.

The preparation of a text of this kind is not possible without the help of a number of other people. I am grateful to Professor N.F. Robertson of the Edinburgh School of Agriculture for encouraging me to write the book and for

making the facilities of the School available for its
preparation. I am also grateful to K. Simpson, formerly
Vice-Principal of the East of Scotland College of Agriculture, for suggesting the idea and introducing me to
Granada Publishing. Several colleagues in the Edinburgh
School of Agriculture have given support and encouragement
during the preparation of this book and I thank them.
Dr G.M. Milbourn, now Director of the National Institute
of Agricultural Botany, encouraged me in the early stages
and I thank him for his support and interest.

I am grateful to Gordon Finnie for his care and
patience in the preparation of the figures. Special
acknowledgement and thanks are due to Mrs Janet Thomas and
Mrs Lena Allan for their care, skill and tolerance in
typing the text on a word processor. I am also grateful
to Ruth Johnson, Librarian, and her staff for their help
in locating references.

Finally I am grateful to my family for their encouragement and patience during this difficult period.

F. Harper

# 1  Introduction to Crop Production

ADAPTATION OF PLANTS TO AGRICULTURE

The supply of food for the human population of the world
depends primarily on the ability of green plants to convert solar energy into carbohydrates through the process
of photosynthesis.  The subsequent storage of the carbohydrates or their conversion to other storage or structural materials through biochemical changes, provides a
direct source of nutrients to man.  Alternatively, the
products of plant growth may be consumed by animals and
provide food for man in the form of meat and other animal
products.  Mineral elements, extracted from the soil, and
vitamins produced in plants provide further requirements
of the human diet.  The production of food from crop
plants is therefore vital to the survival of human and
other forms of life and seventy per cent of the world
population's food comes directly from crops (Williams,
1972).

In addition to producing food for man, a number of
crop plants produce valuable raw materials for industrial
processes.  Oilseed crops produce vegetable oils in their
seeds which, after extraction, can be utilised in a variety of industrial processes.  An example of this is oilseed rape, where the oil is used in the manufacture of
soaps, detergents, plastics, cooking oils and margarine
and as a high-grade lubricant oil.  In addition, rape oil
is combustible and has potential as a substitute for oils

from diminishing stocks of fossil fuels. Linseed oil is used in the manufacture of paints, varnishes and linoleum.

Other products of plant growth may be used as the raw materials for other industrial processes. Starch from potatoes and cereal grains can be converted into alcohols which can then be used for fuel and other purposes. Some plants produce fibre in their stems and roots which can be extracted and used to manufacture textile materials. Linseed (flax) is used for this purpose and is an example of a crop which can be grown to produce more than one useful product but not always from the one crop. Linseed produces fibre, oil and a protein food for farm animals. A number of tropical or sub-tropical crops also produce fibre, e.g. sisal and hemps.

The evolution of systems of crop production has occurred over several millenia, from the simplest form of seed and fruit collection from wild plants by early man to the sophisticated intensive systems of the latter part of the twentieth century. Some crops, such as wheat, have a long history of cultivation, from at least 7000 BC, but others, such as sugar beet, were only exploited in the early nineteenth century. Most crop plants now grown were once wild species and their domestication and distribution by man has brought about changes in their potential to produce food products. Domestication and distribution has required adaptability in the selected plants and the success of the commonest crops has arisen from their adaptability to different growing techniques and climatic conditions. The limited climatic adaptability of many crops has restricted their spread into the temperate regions of the world. The majority of the crops grown in temperate climates originated from warmer areas, particularly the Mediterranean and central and southern America. Only a few, such as sugar beet and oats, originated in the cooler areas of central and western Europe (Table 1.1).

The spread of crops from the warmer areas of their origin has led to problems of production in the different

*Table 1.1 The classification and origin of the major temperate arable crops*

| Family | Crop | | Origin* |
|---|---|---|---|
| Chenopodiaceae | Sugar beet and other beets | (*Beta vulgaris*) | W. Europe |
| Compositae | Sunflower | (*Helianthus annuus*) | Central N. America |
| Cruciferae | Oilseed rape and swede | (*Brassica napus*) | S. Europe/Mediterranean |
| | Turnip rape and turnip | (*Brassica campestris*) | Mediterranean and Pakistan |
| | Kale | (*Brassica oleracea*) | E. Mediterranean |
| Gramineae | Oat | (*Avena sativa*) | C. Europe |
| | Barley | (*Hordeum vulgare*) | E. Mediterranean and Middle East |
| | Rye | (*Secale cereale*) | Middle East |
| | Triticale | (*Tritosecale spp.*) | Canada (hybrid) |
| | Wheat | (*Triticum aestivum*) | Middle East |
| | Maize | (*Zea mays*) | Central and South America |
| Leguminosae | Bean (common, navy, French or haricot) | (*Phaseolus vulgaris*) | Central and South America |
| | Bean (runner) | (*Phaseolus coccineus*) | Central and South America |
| | Bean (field) | (*Vicia faba*) | Near and Middle East |
| Linaceae | Linseed | (*Linum usitatissimum*) | S.W. Asia and Mediterranean |
| Solanaceae | Potato | (*Solanum tuberosum*) | Bolivia and Peru |

* Origin quoted is as close as can be determined from available evidence

3

climatic conditions of temperate regions. Low temperatures have restricted the introduction of crops into
temperate areas in many cases, e.g. maize. In the United
Kingdom, maize cannot be grown reliably anywhere for grain
production and its growth for forage purposes in this
country is restricted to the warmer areas. Soya bean
similarly is not grown widely in north-west Europe because
of low temperatures and its photoperiodic requirement for
flowering of short days found only in the sub-tropics.
Adaptability to photoperiod is therefore a further consideration in growing crops. The frequency and severity
of frosts may also be a restricting factor to crop growth,
and maize, soya bean, *Phaseolus* beans and potatoes may be
severely damaged or killed by frosts. To allow such sensitive crops to be grown at all, growing procedures may
have to be adapted to avoid the worst effects of seasonal
frosts. Temperature is an important consideration in
choosing a crop for temperate areas.

The occurrence of low temperatures at some stage in
the growing cycle of some crops is essential. The requirement of autumn-sown crops for a period of exposure to low
temperatures, to effect the transition from the vegetative
to the reproductive phase of growth, vernalisation, restricts their areas of production to cool temperate climates. The autumn-sown cereals and oilseed rape are
examples of this where good seed yield is dependent on a
period of vernalisation to stimulate the change to reproductive growth. Adaptability to low temperatures can lead
to the problem of attaining the delicate balance between
effecting vernalisation and avoiding death of the plants
by frost damage. Further aspects of the effects of temperature on crop growth and development will be considered in chapter 3. Adaptability of crops to other
weather factors is also an important consideration. The
amount and seasonality of rainfall, and other forms of
precipitation, is important. Tolerance of both drought
and of high rainfall may both be important attributes in

4

plants selected for growth in temperate latitudes.

The climatic conditions in the area of origin of crop plants therefore has an important influence on their successful production in temperate areas. Simmonds (1976) describes over eighty major food and industrial plants in the world, of which less than half are widely grown in temperate climates (excluding forage grasses). The fact that so few of the 200,000 or so angiosperms in the world have shown sufficient adaptability to cultivation for man's use is in itself surprising. Large numbers of plants are excluded from cultivation because they produce no apparent useful product or because they are poisonous to man or farm animals. Others however have not been considered seriously. Hudson (1974) raised the possibility of growing plants, now classified as weeds, for the production of leaf protein and emphasised the fact that many weed species are better adapted to producing green leaf material in periods of low temperature than existing crops. The development of new technologies associated with agriculture, such as leaf protein extraction, may generate the need to examine the adaptability of plants, other than those currently grown, as crops. Furthermore, the need to seek alternative sources of fuel and industrial raw materials may accelerate this process.

OBJECTIVES OF CROP PRODUCTION SYSTEMS

Production systems for arable crops in temperate climates must have objectives which should be met by the growing procedures adopted. A simple summary of the objectives of a system is: to produce the maximum yield of utilisable products as economically and efficiently as possible. This simple definition encompasses a number of individual objectives which will relate to each crop. In a number of crops, food production is the primary objective and this would relate to potatoes and vegetable crops in particular, where the products of growth are directly consumed. However some crops cannot be used directly in this way and require some modification before they are suitable for consumption. Crops such as wheat and sugar beet relate to this category as they both require processing. With such crops maximising the yield is not the only aim; the suitability of the products for processing is also important. Thus yield and quality are both important.

A further consideration is the objective of producing crop products for animal food. Here also yield is not the only objective, as the product must be of suitable quality for consumption by farm animals. Where crops are grown to supply raw materials for industry, the quality requirements for the manufacturing processes must be met. Where crop production systems aim to produce human food, animal feed or industrial raw materials, yield is not the only objective.

A further qualification of the earlier simple objective is that money is often the ultimate product which is required from the system through the sale of the crop material or farm animals. Profit from the system and an adequate return on investment are important considerations. Maximum yield may not be a sensible objective if the level of inputs required to produce high yields results in uneconomic returns. Efficiency in the use of financial resources in growing crops is an important factor. This can be expanded by emphasising the need to market the crops in such a way as to maximise returns.

Crop production involves the use of a number of resources and they all have to be utilised efficiently and effectively. These resources include land, labour, money and physical resources of machinery and buildings. In modern production systems these resources are limited and they must be used sensibly. Wider objectives are introduced through a discussion of resources. Through ownership or tenancy of land, farmers have the power to change the amenity value of that land. This includes changing the nature of the landscape through choice of cropping patterns and aspects of pollution resulting from the use of crop protection chemicals. The preservation of the amenity value of land and its associated wildlife is a further objective of a crop production system.

A simple definition of the objective of a crop production system such as the production of the maximum quantities of a utilisable product is inadequate without some qualifications. The provision of a product is certainly of major importance but consideration of quality and the efficient use of a wide range of resources is also vital.

CROP YIELD

The output from crop production systems is often expressed as yield per unit area. It is convenient to express yield in two ways: *biological* and *economic*. The biological yield is a measure of the total biomass production from the crop and is often used as an expression of yield in experimental work. This is not always a useful measure of yield as not all products of crop growth are useful to the producer or consumer. In only a few cases is the whole plant utilised and examples of such crops are swedes, turnips and fodder beet where the roots constitute the major product of growth but the shoots are also of some value. In other crops, only a specific product of growth is useful and this is the part which is harvested. Examples of the major temperate crops and the harvestable parts of their growth are summarised in Table 1.2. The plant organs which are useful differ markedly with individual crops. In the case of the potato, the underground modified stems or tubers constitute the storage organ which is useful as a human food. In sugar beet, the roots are harvested for the extraction of sucrose, although the shoots and the residue of the roots, after sugar extraction, provide useful by-products for animal feed. In potatoes and root crops, it is the products of vegetative growth which are useful.

In cereals for grain production and oilseed crops, the products of reproductive growth are harvested. In most

7

*Table 1.2  The economic products of growth of the major temperate crops*

| Crop | Harvested part | Economic product |
|---|---|---|
| Sugar beet | Root | Sucrose |
| Potato | Tuber | Tuber |
| Sunflower | Fruit (Achene) | Oil and protein residue |
| Oilseed rape | Seed | Oil and protein residue |
| Linseed  i) | Seed | Oil and protein residue |
| ii) | Stem and roots | Fibre for textiles |
| Field bean | Seed | Seed for animal feed |
| Barley | Seed | Seed for animal feed or alcoholic drinks |
| Oat | Seed | Seed for animal feed or human consumption |
| Wheat | Seed | Seed for animal feed or bread/biscuits |
| Swede | Roots and leaves | Roots and leaves for animal feed and human consumption (roots only) |
| Kale and rape | Stem and leaves | Shoots for animal feed |

cases the seeds from these crops require some degree of processing before they are directly useful to man. With oilseed crops, two major products result from processing, viz vegetable oil and a protein residue for animal feed. Seed is also the major useful product from leguminous crops such as field beans and peas. In these grain-producing crops only a small proportion of the total production is useful and the roots, leaves and stems have little or no financial value at present. It is however conceivable that the stems of such crops could be used as a combustible fuel source in the future. A measure of the efficiency of grain crops to produce a utilisable product is the grain : straw ratio or harvest index. Austin (1980) reported that the yield improvement in barley in recent years has been associated with an increase in the

grain to straw ratio of varieties. Old varieties had a
harvest index of about 40 per cent (i.e. 40 grain : 60
straw) whereas modern ones have values of 50-55 per cent.
Equivalent values for modern wheat varieties are 40-46 per
cent (Austin, 1978).

In well-grown sugar beet crops, Milford *et al.* (1980)
quote ratios for root dry matter and sugar yield to total
dry matter yield in the ranges 0.58 - 0.66 and 0.41 - 0.50
respectively. This example illustrates further the importance of distinguishing between biological yield and
economic yield.

In crops grown primarily for use as animal feed, such
as kale or forage rape, the whole of the growth above
ground is potentially useful and the concept of harvest
index is inappropriate. Furthermore, straightforward
assessment of yield of dry matter is not very meaningful
because quality factors affect intake and animal performance. Yields of digestible organic matter and digestible
crude protein are more appropriate measures of economic
yield in these crops. This approach to quantifying yield
is also appropriate for other forage or fodder crops such
as maize, swedes and grass.

It is important to express crop yields in terms which
reflect the usefulness of the product. In the case of
cereals, this may just be a component of the total yield,
whereas in forage crops the whole of the aerial growth may
be useful.

The expression of yields needs to conform to agreed
standards. In the case of cereals, grain yields are expressed in tonnes/hectare at a moisture content of 15 per
cent. The moisture content of grains at harvest may vary
considerably and yield comparisons can only realistically
be made if the data are converted to a standard moisture
content value. The moisture content for each crop is
usually selected on the basis of the maximum value at
which the grain can be safely stored without further
drying. In the case of oilseed rape, yields are expressed

at 9 per cent moisture content. In addition, with oilseed rape, where oil content is important, it may be appropriate to express the yield at a standard moisture content with a stated oil content, e.g. 3.5 t ha$^{-1}$ at 9 per cent moisture content and 40 per cent oil content.

Yields of sugar beet are expressed as tonnes/hectare of washed roots at a specified sugar content, e.g. 16 per cent. Problems of yield comparisons arise with sugar beet which is harvested over a period of months. Unlike cereals, where the whole crop is harvested in a short period, sugar beet continue to grow in the autumn and yield increases can be interrupted by harvesting early to meet a factory delivery schedule (Figure 1.1).

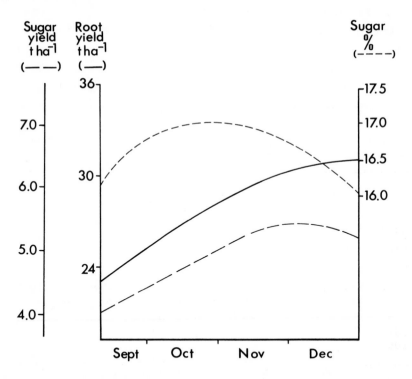

*Figure 1.1  The development of yield and changes in sugar content of sugar beet in the autumn (adapted from MAFF, 1970)*

Potato yields are more difficult to express on a standard basis. The simple approach is to consider total

tuber yield. However, for the ware market, only a particular size grade is considered saleable (> 4.1 cm
diameter) and this inevitably has the effect of reducing
the economic yield. Also with potatoes, a proportion of
the tubers remain in the field as a result of inefficient
harvesting procedures, and yield losses occur there.
Damaged tubers are discarded and storage losses occur,
hence the most useful estimate of the economic yield is
the quantity of marketable tubers which are sold from the
store. This may bear little relationship to the total
tuber weight produced by the crop.

The distinction between biological yield and economic,
or utilisable, yield is important in discussions relating
to the factors affecting yield in all crops.

One of the objectives of any crop production system is
to maximise production of the useful product or products
of growth. Estimates of the maximum yield potential of a
range of important crops have been calculated and these
are summarised in Table 1.3. Average farm yields normally

*Table 1.3 Maximum yield potential of some crops and the average farm
yields obtained in the United Kingdom*

| Crop | Maximum yield potential (t ha$^{-1}$) | Farm yields (t ha$^{-1}$) |
|---|---|---|
| Wheat (Austin, 1978) | 12 | 4–10 |
| Barley (Austin, 1978) | 10 | 3–8 |
| Potato (Alcock, 1967) | 92 | 30–60 |
| Potato (Harris, 1980) | up to 140 (depending on location) | 30–60 |
| Sugar beet (Alcock, 1967) | 78 | 30–50 |

fall well short of the calculated maximum values. However
wheat yields of up to 13 t ha$^{-1}$ have been recorded in the
United Kingdom, which are higher than the theoretical
maximum. This emphasises the difficulties associated with

11

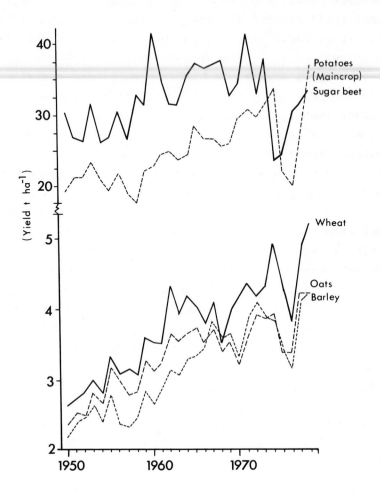

*Figure 1.2   Changes in crop yields in England and Wales.   (Source: MAFF Agricultural Statistics, HMSO, London.)*

calculating maximum yield potential.  Similarly, with potatoes, yields of over 80 t ha$^{-1}$ have been recorded under farm conditions.  Although it is of interest to con-sider the theoretical maximum yields of crops, in practice it may not be realistic because of the high cost of the production systems necessary to achieve them.

An analysis of the national average yield data for some crops in England and Wales, against this background

of maximum potential yields, emphasises the relative biological inefficiency of current production systems (Figure
1.2). It is clear that the yields of all the major crops
have increased in the period 1950-1980 and this has been
most dramatic with cereals, where yields have more than
doubled. Improved production technology and varieties are
the major factors involved in these increases. Yield improvements in sugar beet and potatoes have been less
dramatic. The irregular pattern of the yield increases
illustrated emphasises the importance of seasonal factors
such as weather patterns on crop yields. This is most
clearly demonstrated with the low yields in the mid-1970s
of all crops which were associated with drought conditions
at critical times in the season. This would suggest that
there is a need to examine closely the factors which cause
variation in yields in order to give greater certainty in
production systems of producing consistently high yields.
In addition to the variation in average yields on a
seasonal basis, there is also considerable variation
within years. Average yields for wheat in the United
Kingdom are in excess of 5 t ha$^{-1}$, but the range producing
this average can be 2.5 - 13 t ha$^{-1}$. Explanation of such
a range requires a study of all the factors which influence yields so that the average can be further increased by eliminating very low yielding crops. Later
chapters will consider this aspect further. Wide variations in yields may occur within a farm between fields
and even between different areas within fields. A further
objective of a crop production system should be to reduce
this yield variation to a minimum through improved growing
techniques arising from a deeper understanding of the factors affecting yields.

QUALITY IN CROP PRODUCTS

Quality can be defined simply as: suitability for a purpose. The purposes to which crop products are put are
varied and the criteria for good quality vary with

individual crops. The definition of these quality criteria can influence the suitability of a particular crop
product for a specific market. Any grower must therefore
be aware of the need to achieve certain quality standards
in his production system.

Crops for direct human consumption may have to satisfy
quality requirements appropriate to the human diet and
these are usually based on biochemical criteria in relation to nutritive value. However such criteria may be of
a negative kind in that the absence of toxins may be more
important than positive features such as the protein content. Some potentially productive plants are excluded
from production because of the harmful chemical substances
present in them. This is particularly true of members of
the plant families *Solanaceae* and *Leguminosae*. The biochemical criteria for quality may be more elaborate than
just the quantification of the content of carbohydrate,
protein, fats, minerals and vitamins. In the case of protein and fats, the amino acid and fatty acid composition
respectively may be more important in nutritional terms.

Other criteria may also be important in crops for
direct human consumption and consumer preferences regarding shape, size, colour and cooking characteristics may
have an influence on marketability. These criteria apply
particularly to a range of field vegetable crops such as
carrots and vegetable brassicas and also to the potato.
Potato tubers are consumed in large quantities and the
quality requirements for this crop provide a good example.
The main points relating to potato tuber quality are:

(i) Tuber size — with a preference for tubers in the
    riddle size range of 4.0 - 7.5 cm, except for
    canning.
(ii) Skin characteristics — where colour and thickness
    may influence consumer preference.
(iii) Depth of 'eyes' — which has an influence on the
    ease of peeling and preparation by the housewife.

14

(iv) Greening of the skin — where light-induced chlorophyll formation may lead to the development of
solanidine and a bitter taste.

(v) Shape — where uniformity is important for mechanical processing involving peeling and slicing.

(vi) Nutritive value — where dry matter, carbohydrate,
protein, energy and vitamin C content are important.

(vii) Flesh colour and texture — which may influence consumer preference and cooking quality.

(viii) Non-enzymic browning — where reducing-sugar levels
may influence chip and crisp colour after cooking.

(ix) Enzymic browning — where the discolouration of the
flesh after peeling or cutting may influence consumer acceptability.

(x) After-cooking blackening — where discolouration
after boiling or steaming may influence consumer
acceptability.

(xi) Mechanical damage — where internal and external
damage may affect appearance and keeping quality.

(xii) Tuber diseases — where appearance, cooking quality
and storage characteristics may be affected.

(List prepared from Gray and Hughes, 1978)

This list is not exhaustive but is sufficient to
emphasise the range of problems which the potato grower
has to face when growing the crop for direct human consumption. The control of these quality factors is often
difficult because they may be influenced by varietal,
cultural and environmental factors. Characteristics such
as shape, skin and flesh colour and eye depth are mainly
genetically controlled and the grower can influence these
by choice of variety. Other factors such as dry matter
(DM) content, texture, browning, damage, after-cooking
blackening and nutritional quality are influenced by
varietal, environmental and cultural factors and are not
controlled so easily by the grower.

Quality control of crop products for direct human consumption is also important in crops other than the potato.

15

This is particularly true of vegetables where size, shape, cooking quality and appearance characteristics may influence consumer choice. Some vegetable crops show a seasonality of production and because of a short shelf-life their products may be processed for storage before consumption. The suitability of crops like carrots, peas and potatoes for canning introduces further considerations of quality which may lead to modifications of growing conditions, e.g. the control of carrot root size by growing at high plant population densities to produce small uniform roots for canning. The suitability of crops for freezing or dehydration introduces further quality requirements which are often rigid and specified in contracts between producers and processors.

A large number of other crop products are not suitable for direct human consumption and have to be processed. This applies to the cereal grains which are modified in a variety of ways to produce consumable products. Barley grains form the basis of many alcoholic drinks and they are malted for this process. The malting procedure involves germination of the grains when starch is modified to produce the malt for brewing. The characteristics of good quality malting barley grains are summarised by Kent (1975):

  (i) High germination capacity and energy.
 (ii) Absence of de-husked or broken grains and of grains mechanically damaged in threshing.
(iii) High capacity to produce malt extract.
 (iv) Low husk content.
  (v) Low protein content (generally less than 1.6 per cent N).
 (vi) High starch content.

Some of these requirements are genetically controlled and only varieties recommended for malting should be used to meet this market. Other requirements, such as nitrogen content, can be influenced by the grower through choice of soil type and variety and control of nitrogen fertiliser applications. Germination capacity, freedom from damaged grains, and grain appearance can be controlled by careful choice of harvesting time and method and by the use of suitable drying temperatures (air temperatures of less than 49°C for grain with up to 24 per cent moisture content).

Wheat grains can be processed to produce flour which is then made into bread or biscuits. This process requires different quality criteria. Before flour can be prepared, the grain must be milled. Milling is the separation of the outer layers and germ from the starchy endosperm by a mechanical process. Wheat varieties are divided into two milling categories called hard and soft. Hard wheats are generally easier to mill and a high proportion of the endosperm can be extracted without discolouration from the bran. In soft wheats the outer seed layers may be difficult to separate from the bran and flour yield is reduced. In addition, in hard wheats the flour particles are smooth and flow freely, whereas in soft wheats the flour particles are irregular in size and clump together. Ease of milling is primarily a varietal characteristic and correct choice of variety is essential to attain a grain of milling quality.

The wheat flour can then be used to produce bread or biscuits and different criteria apply for each of these uses. Wheat flour suitable for bread-making must contain adequate levels of protein of the right quality. Approximately 80 per cent of the grain protein is in the endosperm and when mixed with water the majority of this protein forms a complex known as gluten. Gluten has elastic properties and retains carbon dioxide gas bubbles as they form in the loaf during baking. This gives rise to the open-textured loaf favoured by many western societies. Therefore a high level of protein, giving a good yield of gluten, is required for bread-making flour, whereas a lower protein flour with extensible gluten is required for biscuit and cake manufacture. Wheats in the United Kingdom produce grain with a protein content of 8-12 per cent. The protein content of grain is influenced mainly by the amount of nitrogen fertiliser applied to the soil and the time of uptake. Choice of variety is also an important determinant of protein levels. Weather conditions influence protein levels, and wet weather during the development of the grain increases nitrogen uptake. Also high drying temperatures can denature grain protein and cause loss of protein quality.

Levels of the enzyme α-amylase in wheat grains can also affect bread-making quality. High levels of α-amylase are associated with the conversion of starch to soluble sugars and must be avoided in bread-making flour because they give rise to loaves of poor shape and a weak, sticky crumb structure. α-Amylase levels are lowest in the dry ripe dormant grain and highest in sprouted grain. The Falling Number (Hagberg) Test is used to determine α-amylase levels. This test records the time taken for a plunger to fall through a prepared slurry of flour. The result is expressed as the time in seconds taken for the plunger to fall, plus 60 seconds. A minimum falling number of 200 is normally used for determining bread-making quality. α-Amylase levels are influenced by variety (resistance to sprouting) and weather conditions at grain maturity. Dough machinability is a further quality consideration for bread-making wheats.

Quality requirements in wheat grains for bread and biscuit making are clearly identified by the processors. The extra skill required in growing the crops to meet these standards is usually rewarded by a higher price for the grain.

Crops such as sugar beet and oilseed rape require more processing of their economic products of growth than the cereal grains and demand further attention to quality standards. Sugar beet roots, after harvesting and a short period of storage, are delivered to processing factories

18

for extraction of sucrose. The efficiency of this industrial process is dependent on certain quality criteria
which can be controlled by the grower. Furthermore, the
price the farmer receives for his sugar beet roots is influenced by the quality. The main quality characteristics
which are important in beet roots are:

(i) Sugar content — this is usually expressed as a percentage figure of the fresh weight. In the United
Kingdom, 16 per cent is the standard figure around
which premia or penalties are applied to the
farmer's price.

(ii) Dirt tare — the extraction process requires clean
beet and dirty roots require more washing.

(iii) Top tare — the crown and top (leaves and petioles)
contain less sugar and more impurities than the
roots and high top tares are not desirable.

(iv) Juice impurities — sodium, potassium and $\alpha$-amino
nitrogen compounds in the juice extracted from the
roots reduce the efficiency of the sucrose extraction process and these impurities should be as low
as possible.

(v) Frost damage — sugar extraction is more difficult
with frost-damaged roots.

As with cereals and potatoes, these aspects of
quality are influenced by genetic, cultural and environmental factors and the extent to which the farmer can control them is limited. Sugar content for example is influenced by the choice of the variety but the temperature
and solar radiation during the latter part of the growing
season are very important. High nitrogen fertiliser
levels depress sugar content and sugar levels are lower in
large roots than in small ones. Sugar beet crops may be
harvested over a four-month period and the time of harvest
and delivery to the factory may influence quality factors
(Figure 1.1). Sugar beet is a biennial which grows on
longer into the autumn than many crops and the time of

harvest can influence sugar content and root and sugar yields. Dirt tare and top tare are more easily controlled by the farmer through care at harvesting and when cleaning the roots on the farm before delivery.

The vegetable oil from the rapeseed is the useful product and this requires crushing and solvent extraction of the seed before the oil can be refined. The yield of oil is proportional to the oil content of the seed and payment for the crop is based on yield and oil content. The oil content in rapeseed may be in the range 35-45 per cent. This simple criterion of oil content is also important in other oilseed crops such as sunflower, soya and linseed.

The quality of the oil extracted is also important and there has been concern about the quality of rapeseed oil in relation to its fatty acid composition (Bunting, 1974). Rapeseed oil has a high content of erucic acid and this is associated with poor nutritional qualities. Plant breeders have solved this problem and zero erucic acid varieties have been produced. Other oilseed crops contain no erucic acid, but are not so successfully produced in temperate regions (Table 1.4). The fatty acid composition of seed oils may affect their nutritional qualities and also their suitability for blending with other oils for margarine and cooking oil manufacture. Stability at high temperatures, in the case of cooking oils, is important and fatty acid composition may be important here. High erucic acid content may be important for some industrial uses, such as rape oil for lubricant purposes, but, if zero erucic acid types continue to dominate for nutritional reasons, crambe, the other cruciferous crop, could supply oil for this market.

After extraction of the oil, the remainder of the seed provides a valuable high protein animal feed. However, in the case of oilseed rape, the presence of harmful glucosinolates can restrict their inclusion in animal rations, especially for poultry and pigs.

20

*Table 1.4  The fatty acid composition of oilseeds*

| | Fatty acid | | | | | | |
|---|---|---|---|---|---|---|---|
| | Palmitic | Stearic | Oleic | Linoleic | Linolenic | Eicosenoic | Erucic |
| Rape (*B. napus*) normal | 4.0 | 1.5 | 17.0 | 13.0 | 9.0 | 14.5 | 41.0 |
| Rape (*B. napus*) zero erucic | 4.7 | 1.8 | 63.3 | 20.0 | 8.9 | 1.3 | 0 |
| Rape (*B. campestris*) normal | 2.9 | 1.1 | 33.6 | 17.9 | 9.4 | 11.5 | 23.5 |
| Rape (*B. campestris*) zero erucic | 4.4 | 0.1 | 54.8 | 31.1 | 9.7 | 0 | 0 |
| Sunflower | 7.2 | 4.1 | 16.2 | 72.5 | 0 | 0 | 0 |
| Linseed | 6.1 | 3.8 | 15.5 | 15.3 | 59.3 | 0 | 0 |
| Maize | 12.1 | 2.3 | 28.7 | 56.2 | 0.7 | 0 | 0 |
| Crambe | 1.6 | 1.0 | 17.9 | 10.0 | 7.0 | 3.0 | 58.6 |

(Average values quoted by Bunting (1974) from Downey (1966))

21

A large number of crop products are fed directly to farm animals and their nutritional qualities are important in relation to animal growth and production. Cereals form the basis of many supplementary feeds. Different criteria of quality apply here and the metabolisable energy, digestible crude protein and crude fibre contents are important. The three major temperate cereals differ markedly in their content of these and other constituents and average data are summarised in Table 1.5.

*Table 1.5   Composition of cereal grains (g $kg^{-1}$ DM)*

|  | Wheat | Barley | Oats |
| --- | --- | --- | --- |
| Carbohydrate | 786 | 781 | 698 |
| Crude protein | 105 | 118 | 52 |
| Crude fibre | 25 | 53 | 121 |
| Fat | 26 | 18 | 52 |
| Mineral matter | 18 | 31 | 29 |

(Average values from Kent (1975) and
Scottish Agricultural Colleges (1978))

Further quality considerations may apply to other market outlets for products. In member countries of the European Economic Community crop products may be sold into Intervention in periods of oversupply when market prices fall. This requires periods of longer storage and certain quality standards must be met before grain is acceptable for this purpose. Intervention standards for wheat and barley in the United Kingdom are summarised in Table 1.6. Moisture content is an important factor in these standards as it has a profound effect on storage. Limits on various impurities in the standards are designed to maintain purity to protect future buyers. The specific weight is a measure of grain density and reflects individual grain weights and their packing density.

The quality of seeds for establishing future crops is a very important consideration in crop production and this

*Table 1.6  Grain Intervention standards for the United Kingdom (source: Home Grown Cereals Authority, 1979)*

|  | Barley | Feed wheat | Bread-making wheat |
|---|---|---|---|
| Maximum moisture content (per cent) | 15 | 15 | 15 |
| Specific weight (kg hl$^{-1}$)* | 63 | 68 | 72 |
| Maximum total impurities (per cent) | 12 | 12 | 10 |
| of which — | | | |
| broken grains | 5 | 5 | 5 |
| grain impurities | 12 | 12 | 5 |
| sprouted grain | 12 | 8 | 6 |
| miscellaneous impurities | 3 | 3 | 3 |

* hl = hectolitre = 100 litres

will be dealt with in Chapter 6.

The question of quality in crop production is clearly important in determining the suitability of the product for a particular use.  The criteria used to assess quality vary with individual crops and the foregoing examples illustrate the complexity of quality standards for selected crops.  Quality may refer to biochemical criteria such as fatty acid composition in oilseeds or simple factors like shape and size in the potato.  In all cases the criteria are important in securing a market for the product and the grower must use all means possible to meet them, from the initial choice of variety to manipulating growing and harvesting techniques.

CROP PRODUCTION — AN AMALGAM OF DISCIPLINES

The efficient production of crops requires an appreciation of the fact that a wide range of skills and aptitudes is involved.  The use of simple terms such as crop production, crop husbandry and agronomy can oversimplify the fact that any person involved in growing crops requires an understanding of the biological, chemical and physical sciences which can influence growth and production. The multi-disciplinary nature of crop production can be illustrated by listing the importance of the individual subjects involved.

*Soil science* — an understanding of the chemical aspects of soils relating to crop nutrition; physical aspects in relation to soil structure and texture, plant/water relationships, drainage and irrigation; biological aspects in relation to soil pests and diseases and beneficial organisms.

*Climate and weather* — an appreciation of the effects of the major components of climate and weather on crops, e.g. solar radiation, temperature, precipitation, atmospheric composition, wind and pollutants.

*Genetics* — an appreciation of the importance of genetics in relation to plant breeding to increase yield and quality aspects of crops. The importance of choice of variety.

*Plant physiology* — an understanding of the mechanisms controlling plant growth and development with a view to manipulating them to improve crop performance.

*Plant pathology* — an appreciation of the effects of disease-causing organisms and factors affecting their development and control.

*Plant pest science* — an appreciation of the effects of the major crop pests and factors affecting their development and control.

*Weed science* — an appreciation of the effects of weed competition and contamination in crops and their control.

*Management* — an appreciation of the importance of decision-making and timeliness of operations in crop production systems. Attention to detail.

*Economics* — an appreciation of the financial aspects of crop production in relation to investment, purchasing, grants and subsidies and the effects on profitability.

*Marketing* — an appreciation of the importance of marketing in relation to choice of market, method and time of selling.

*Legislation* — an appreciation of relevant legislation, e.g. safety, pollution and employment.

*Resource management* — an appreciation of the value of land as an amenity and recreational facility.

It is clear from this list that crop production systems are not concerned solely with the science disciplines and, for a system to operate effectively, managerial, economic, sociological and marketing skills are necessary. The integration of all these factors into a manageable amalgam is the basis of successful crop production. This text is mainly concerned with the scientific principles involved in crop production and how the application of these principles can improve output. It is however necessary to consider the influence of each scientific discipline against the background of the range of subjects involved in the system as a whole. A change in one area may have repercussions on other components. For example, if the level of nitrogen fertiliser is increased for a particular crop the following results may ensue:

    increased yield
    increased financial return
    increased growing costs
    changes in quality
    increased requirements for other nutrients and water
    changes in disease patterns
    changes in weed-crop competition
    changes in the micro-climate resulting from greater
        vegetative growth
    changes in storage and marketing arrangements result-
        ing from increased yield
    possible pollution of waterways through leaching of
        excess nitrate into drainage water.

This example emphasises the multi-disciplinary nature of crop production and highlights the need to predict the consequences of relatively minor changes in one area to the success of the system as a whole.

REFERENCES AND FURTHER READING

Alcock, M.B. (1967) 'Maximum crop production'. Arable Farmer, September 1967, 42–45.

Austin, R.B. (1978) 'Maximum yield of cereals as determined by plant type and environment'. Proceedings of ADAS/ARC Symposium on Maximising Yield of Crops, Harrogate. Ministry of Agriculture, Fisheries and Food, 18–24.

Austin, R.B. (1980) 'Physiological limitations to cereal yields and ways of reducing them by breeding'. In Opportunities for Increasing Crop Yields, eds. Hurd, R.G., Biscoe, P.V. and Dennis, C. London: Pitman, 3–20.

Bunting, E.S. (1974) 'New arable crops — retrospect and prospects'. Journal of the Royal Agricultural Society of England. 135, 107–121.

Downey, R.K. (1966) Agricultural Institute Review, Canada.

Duffus, C.M. and Slaughter, C. (1980) Seeds and Their Uses. Chichester: John Wiley.

Gedye, D.J., Doling, D.A. and Kingswood, K.W. (1981) A Farmers Guide to Wheat Quality. National Agricultural Centre, Cereal Unit, Stoneleigh, Warwickshire.

Gray, D. and Hughes, J.C. (1978) 'Tuber quality'. In The Potato Crop, ed. Harris, P.M. London: Chapman and Hall, 504–539.

Harper, F. (1981) 'Crop production in England and Wales — 1950-1980: a period of revolutionary change'. Journal of the Royal Agricultural Society of England, 142, 42–54.

Harris, P.M. (1980) 'Agronomic research and potato production practice'. In Opportunities for Increasing

Crop Yields, eds. Hurd, R.G., Biscoe, P.V. and Dennis, C. London: Pitman, 205-218.

Home Grown Cereals Authority (1979) Cereals Statistics 1979. London: Home Grown Cereals Authority.

Hudson, J.P. (1974) 'Weeds as crops'. Proceedings of the 12th British Weed Control Conference, Brighton, 333-335.

Kent, N.L. (1975) Technology of Cereals (2nd edn). Oxford: Pergamon Press.

McDonald, P., Edwards, R.A. and Greenhalgh, N. (1981) Animal Nutrition (3rd edn). London: Longman.

Milford, G.F.J., Biscoe, P.V., Jaggard, K.W., Scott, R.K. and Draycott, A.P. (1980) 'Physiological potential for increasing yields of sugar beet'. In Opportunities for Increasing Crop Yields, eds. Hurd, R.G., Biscoe, P.V. and Dennis, C. London: Pitman, 71-86.

Ministry of Agriculture, Fisheries and Food (1970) Sugar Beet Cultivation. Bulletin 153. London: HMSO.

Scottish Agricultural Colleges (1978) Cereal Grain Quality for Feed and Processing. Technical Note No.15.

Simmonds, N.W. (ed.) (1976) Evolution of Crop Plants. London: Longman.

Spedding, C.R.W. (1977) In The Biology of Agricultural Systems. London: Academic Press, 66-100.

Williams, W. (1972) In Growing Points in Science. London: HMSO, 142.

# 2 Crop Growth and Development

DEFINITIONS

Crop production involves the sowing or planting of a unit
of propagation and the progression, from the young plant,
through the subsequent phases of growth and development to
the harvesting of the economic yield.  During this process
it is important to distinguish between growth and development and to understand the internal and external factors
which can influence them.  Growth is usually defined as
the irreversible increase in size, measured as dry weight,
which occurs throughout the life cycle.  Growth may also
be measured in other terms, such as height and stem diameter, but these are generally not considered to be very
meaningful and may not correlate with dry matter production.

Development is the progression through the morphological changes which occur during the growth of the crop and
is more readily described qualitatively than quantitatively.  A simple example of development stages is in barley
where the seed, seedling, tillering, stem elongation,
flowering and ripe seed stages are easily identifiable
during the growth cycle.  More elaborate description of
the development stages in cereals has been made and this
is referred to later.

An understanding of the patterns of growth and development in crops is important.  Crop production involves

the manipulation of growth and development to make the most efficient use of resources and maximise economic yield. The manipulation of growth can be more effectively achieved if the basic pattern is established. Similarly with development, it is important to provide the optimum conditions to ensure the successful transition from one stage of development to another to provide the basis for a large yield of the economic product required.

The recognition of the major stages of development in crops can also help the grower to use resources more efficiently. The time of application of herbicides in cereals is recommended in terms of the relevant stages of development of the crop and weed flora rather than by a calendar date. In this example, the stage of development selected for application is crucial as, with selective herbicides, the crop and the weed may be damaged or killed if it is too immature or advanced. The most effective use of fungicides and insecticides is also achieved if the stage of development is used as an indicator of timing rather than a calendar. A further example relates to the timing of split-applications of nitrogen fertilisers to cereals. Intensive cereal systems involve the applications of nitrogen fertiliser to stimulate tillering (production of secondary shoots) to increase the numbers of fertile tillers and hence yield. Cereals will only respond to this stimulus if the fertiliser is applied before the onset of the main natural flush of tillering. A knowledge of the development stages in crops can therefore lead to a more precise timing of operations with established crops.

In cereals, the application of fertilisers and crop protection chemicals to established crops is often required in the autumn or spring. Growth and the progression through the development stages may occur at different rates in different years in these periods. A more reliable way of timing applications is achieved through the identification of development stages than from calendar dates or the number of days after sowing.

## GROWTH PATTERNS

The basic growth pattern in annuals is simply described by the curve in Figure 2.1. The S-shaped curve is typical of the growth of many crops and three main phases of growth can be identified. The first phase relates to the germination of the seed and the seedling growth. Crop seeds

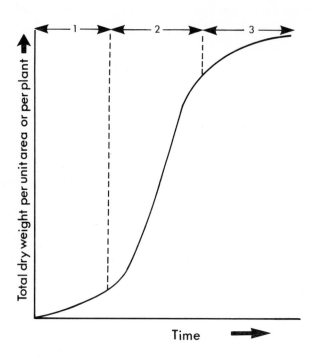

*Figure 2.1  The basic pattern of growth in annuals.  (1) Establishment and seedling growth.  (2) Period of rapid growth, stem elongation and flowering.  (3) Ripening and senescence.*

vary in weight from 2-5 mg for the true seed of the sugar beet to 500-700 mg for the field bean. This difference in initial dry weight, largely due to differences in cotyledon weight, influences the rate of early growth, assuming that environmental conditions are favourable, although final yields may not be affected by seed size. Crop seeds

which germinate below ground are dependent on the stored
materials in the cotyledons until the seedlings emerge
into the light and photosynthesis starts. In these early
stages the dry weight may decrease as storage materials
are respired. By the earlier definition, no growth has
occurred in this period but the tissues have undergone
differentiation into roots, leaves and stems and development has occurred at the expense of dry weight increase.
Once the expanded cotyledons or first true leaves develop
chlorophyll, photosynthetic increases in dry matter exceed
respiratory losses and growth proceeds rapidly.

The second phase of growth is characterised by a rapid
and often linear increase in dry matter production. This
is associated with vegetative growth in annuals and ter-
minates with the onset of flowering (anthesis). In
cereals the early part of this phase is associated with
the production of tillers and leaves. The completion of
tillering is followed by a period of stem elongation with
associated expansion of leaves. As the final or flag leaf
expands the rate of stem elongation is reduced and the
emergence of the previously formed inflorescence occurs.
During this phase of growth the root system increases in
size. In oilseed rape, the development pattern in this
phase of growth is different. Initially the seedling
develops a rosette of leaves which undergo expansion before the onset of stem elongation. The stem development
of rape plants is different from cereals and is characterised by the formation of a branched structure with the
production of a large number of smaller leaves. The production of a large number of flower buds signifies the end
of the rapid phase of growth and the onset of flowering.
The duration of the period of inflorescence production
varies with different crops. Cereals complete this phase
in a short period of time and display a determinate habit
of growth. Some other crops produce flower buds over a
longer period of time and are described as indeterminate.
Field beans, peas, lupins and oilseed rape all show

31

indeterminate growth habits to some degree and this results in lack of uniformity of ripening.

The third phase of growth is marked by a reduction in
growth rate until growth ceases at crop maturity.  After
flowering in cereals the seeds develop and the growth of
stems and leaves ceases.  During this period re-
translocation of assimilates, stored in leaves and stems,
occurs to partially sustain seed growth.  At the end of
the growth period, water is lost from the aerial parts of
the plants, photosynthesis stops and the crop ripens.

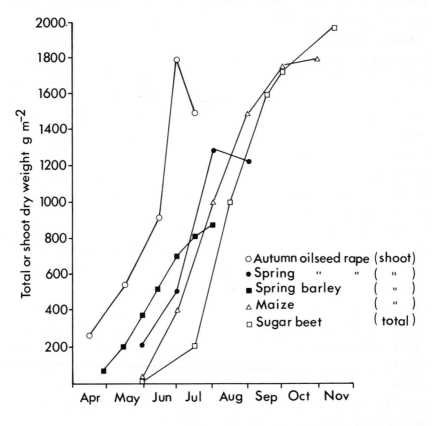

*Figure 2.2   Crop growth patterns in the Midlands and the south-east of
England*

The basic growth pattern described for annual plants
is evident from studies of the major field grown crops.
Figure 2.2 shows examples of the growth patterns,

measured as total or shoot dry weight, of some major
crops grown in the Midlands and the south-east of England.
In all the examples, the shape of the growth curve is
similar and reflects the basic pattern described in
Figure 2.1. However, because of the differences in sowing
date and adaptability to cool spring and early summer temperatures the curves for different crops occupy different
time scales. Autumn-sown oilseed rape is sown in late-
August to early-September and substantial growth occurs in
the autumn of the year preceding harvest. This accounts
for the relatively large amount of shoot dry weight present in April. With this crop, spring growth is rapid and
maximum shoot weight is achieved by the end of June.
Flowering commences as early as late-April to early-May.
Shoot dry weight decreases after late-June with leaf senescence and loss. This decrease in dry weight at the end
of the growth cycle is found with other crops, e.g. winter
wheat. Spring oilseed rape exhibits a similar growth pat-
term although the maximum dry weight is reached approximately one month later at the end of July. The maximum dry
weight of spring-sown rape is substantially less than that
of the autumn-sown crop.

The growth pattern for spring barley is similar to
that for spring oilseed rape although growth occurs
earlier from similar sowing dates. The maximum dry weight
of barley occurs towards the end of July and there is no
evidence of a decline. The growth patterns presented are
selected to show general trends; changing husbandry and
environmental factors may alter the position of the curve
in time and the magnitude of the maximum total or shoot
dry weight values. Spring cereals, for example, are sown
from February to April and sowing date has a large effect
on the position of the curve in time.

The growth pattern of sugar beet is spread over a long
period of time and starts much later in the spring. Sugar
beet is grown from small seeds which are slow to establish
in cool seedbeds in the spring. Seedling growth and the

33

development of the rosette of leaves is slow.  Consequently the efficiency of light interception by the leaves is
low in late-spring and summer and the early phase of
growth is prolonged.  Rapid growth does not occur until
the end of June to early-July when cereals and autumn-sown
oilseed rape are entering the ripening phase.  From July,
growth proceeds at a rapid rate until the end of September
with the onset of declining temperatures and solar radiation.  There is no evidence of a reduction in total dry
weight and growth continues into November.  The fundamental difference between sugar beet and cereals is the fact
that it is a biennial and normally completes its growth
cycle in two years.  The first year of growth is normally
the result of vegetative development and senescence is
restricted to a few of the older leaves.  In temperate
winters sugar beet are vernalised and flower and produce
seed in the second year of growth.

The maize crop also exhibits slow growth in the early
summer, despite its large seed, and requires temperatures
above 10°C to germinate and grow successfully.  Growth of
maize proceeds rapidly in June, July and August before
cool autumn temperatures cause a reduction in the growth
rate.  Maize is killed by autumn frosts and the time of
attainment of maximum yield is determined by the date of
the first severe frost.  In temperate climates, maize
rarely produces ripe grain suitable for mechanical harvesting and the growth cycle may not be completed in the
season.

These examples of growth patterns illustrate the variation between different crops in the time scales involved.
Information of this type can be useful to the grower in
helping him to understand the requirements of the crops
and to give precision to the timing of husbandry operations
in the production system.  The different environmental
requirements of the crops also emerge from analysis of the
growth patterns, and the slow early growth of maize and
sugar beet in cool springs and early summers emphasises

the difficulties of growing these crops in temperate regions.

## DEVELOPMENT AND THE PARTITION OF DRY MATTER

The growth patterns described relate only to shoot or total dry weight. During the growth of crop plants substantial morphological changes occur and the distribution or partition of the total dry matter amongst the major plant organs is of interest to the grower. Emphasis has already been placed on the importance of economic yield in crops and growing procedures should aim to maximise the apportionment of dry matter to the economically useful parts of the plants. Examples of the development changes and the partitioning of dry matter during growth in some major crop plants are described below.

*Table 2.1  The principal stages of development of cereals. (after Tottman and Makepeace (1979))*

| Code | Stage of Development |
| --- | --- |
| 0 | Germination |
| 1 | Seedling growth |
| 2 | Tillering |
| 3 | Stem elongation |
| 4 | Booting (swelling of the flag leaf sheath) |
| 5 | Inflorescence emergence |
| 6 | Anthesis (flowering) |
| 7 | Milk development of the seed |
| 8 | Dough      "          "      "      " |
| 9 | Ripening of the seed |

The stages of development in cereals have been described in detail and ten major stages can be identified (Table 2.1). The first five stages relate to the period from the dry seed through germination, seedling growth, tillering and stem elongation to the point of emergence of

the ear. After ear emergence, the production of pollen
(anthesis) and fertilisation occurs before the development
of the seed to ripeness. Further stages of development
within the major categories are described by the authors
providing a very detailed description of the whole development sequence in cereals.

The components of yield in cereals are well known and
can be summarised:

  (i) Ear number per unit field area — determined by
     tillering and seed rate.
 (ii) Grain numbers per ear — determined at ear initiation
     and ear development.
(iii) Grain weight — determined by conditions during grain
     growth.

Ear numbers can be manipulated by husbandry practices
during the tillering phase by application of nitrogen fertiliser. In this case the grower can control a component
of yield if he can identify the stage of growth in the
field crop. The number of spikelets on each ear determines grain number and this is controlled by environmental
and internal factors in the seedling stage. The survival
of the grains formed can however be controlled by ensuring
adequate water and nutrient supply during grain development after anthesis. Grain size is similarly affected by
water and nutrient supply during the seed development
stages. It is apparent that a knowledge of the main
stages of cereal development and the ability to recognise
them can help the grower to achieve high yields.

Development throughout the growth of cereals can be
quantified by analysis of the components of the plants at
intervals throughout the season. Figure 2.3 illustrates a
typical pattern of growth and development in a well-grown
wheat crop. In most examples of this kind, the data are
restricted to analysis of the shoot because of the difficulties of extracting the root system efficiently. It is
clear from the example that, in early spring, the dry

36

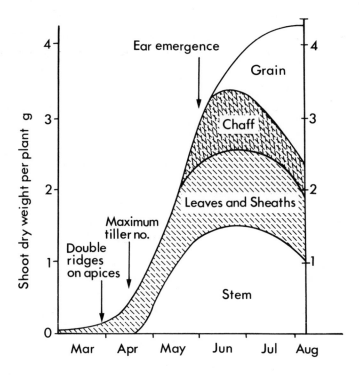

*Figure 2.3 Growth and development pattern of winter wheat (after Austin and Jones, 1974)*

weight consists mainly of leaf from the seedlings. During this period the spikelets are initiated on the apex (double ridges on diagram) and tillering occurs.

The maximum number of tillers is reached by mid-April and the elongation of the stems is signified thereafter by the increasing contribution to the total dry weight by stem tissue. By the middle of May the inflorescence begins to contribute to total shoot weight although ear emergence does not occur until the end of May. In the period from mid-May to early-June the inflorescence consists mainly of chaff (glumes, lemmas and paleas) but after anthesis, the seeds begin to develop. Grain growth progresses from late-June to early-August and at harvest accounts for over 40 per cent of the total shoot weight.

During grain development, the weight of stem, leaf, leaf sheath and chaff tissue decreases indicating re-translocation of assimilates to the developing grain. The leaves senesce rapidly after ear emergence and the leaf weight present at harvest is made up of dead and dry material.

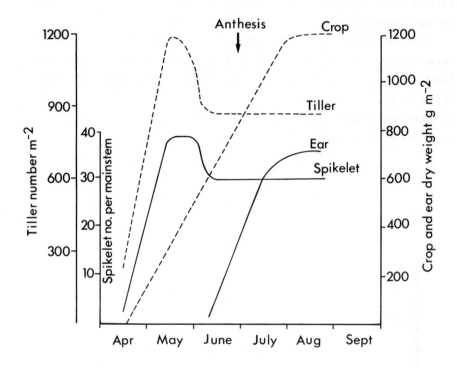

*Figure 2.4  Aspects of growth and development of early-sown spring barley (after Scott and Dennis-Jones, 1976)*

Growth and development in spring barley is similar to that in wheat although data in the example provided are presented in a different way (Figure 2.4). Crop growth (g m$^{-2}$) continues from late-April to late-July when ripening occurs. Ear dry weight, as with wheat, increases from early-June before anthesis at the end of June. Ear weight continues to increase until early-August and constitutes over 50 per cent of the total shoot weight at the end of the period. Tiller numbers increase from early-April to

38

a maximum of almost 1200 m$^{-2}$ by mid-May and then decline to less than 900 m$^{-2}$ in early-June. After anthesis, fertile tiller numbers remain constant. This pattern of excessive production of tillers in cereals with the subsequent death of a proportion from competition is widely documented. The number of fertile tillers is an important determinant of yield, and grain yield is directly related to ear numbers in many experiments with cereals.

Grain number is a product of ear numbers and the numbers of grains per ear. Spikelets are formed on the apex from the seedling stage and increase to a maximum in mid-May (38 per ear). Not all of the spikelets formed survive to produce grain and, in the example quoted (Figure 2.4), only 30 spikelets per ear remain at harvest.

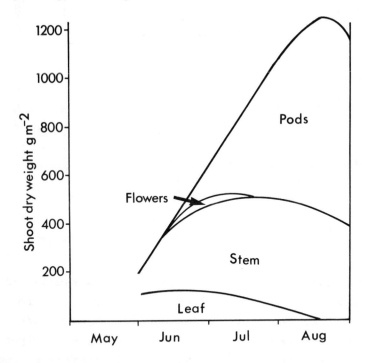

*Figure 2.5 Growth and development of spring-sown oilseed rape (after Scott, Ogunremi, Ivins and Mendham, 1973)*

Development in spring-sown oilseed rape (Figure 2.5) follows a different pattern from cereals. Young plants in

the spring consist mainly of leaf with some stem. With
extension of the stem towards flowering, the proportion of
leaf dry matter declines. Flowering occurs over a longer
period in rape from early-June to mid-July, but the contribution to total shoot weight from the flowers is small.
With the onset of flowering, pods develop, with the associated seed growth, until at harvest they constitute
approximately two-thirds of the total shoot weight. The
decline in leaf weight continues until, at harvest, all
leaves have senesced and been lost from the plant.

The components of yield in oilseed rape are different
from those of cereals. Tillering does not occur and
therefore it is important to have adequate plant numbers
established. Adequate leaf growth is essential to sustain
early growth although, after flowering, photosynthesis in
the stems and pods contributes to seed growth. The number
of flowers formed is important but more so, in yield terms,
is the proportion of flowers which are fertilised and produce pods which survive to harvest. Seed numbers per pod
and individual seed weight are further important components of yield in oilseed rape. The oilseed rape grower
therefore has to ensure that adequate plant numbers are
established and thereafter try to manipulate growth to di-
vert most of the assimilates produced into pod and seed
growth.

The growth and development pattern of a maize crop,
grown in southern England, is illustrated in Figure 2.6.
Seedling growth occurs throughout June when mainly leaf
tissue is present. The development of the stem proceeds
from late-June and evidence of inflorescence formation is
apparent from husk dry matter in late-July. Maize is a
monoecious plant producing separate male and female
flowers. Pollen is produced from the male flowers at the
top of the plant (tassels) in late-July and the female
flowers (silks) are receptive to this pollen in the first
week of August. The rachis is the structure on which the
seeds are situated and this is formed in a short period in

40

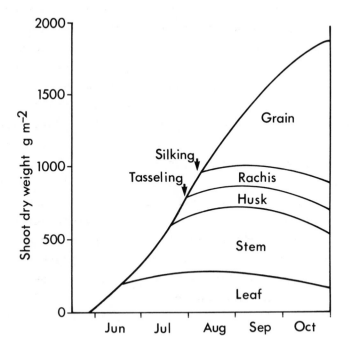

*Figure 2.6   Growth and development of maize (adapted from Milbourn, 1975)*

early-August.  After silking, grain development takes place until at harvest in the autumn grain dry weight accounts for almost 50 per cent of the total shoot dry weight.  There is evidence of a decline in stem and leaf dry weights later in the season indicating re-translocation of assimilates to the grain.  However, un-like cereals, leaf material may remain green late into the season in temperate climates, unless it is killed by frosts.

The development of the sugar beet crop is quite dif-ferent from the grain crops mentioned so far.  Sugar beet plants grow vegetatively throughout the first year pro-ducing roots, leaves and stem and petiole components.  The tap root nature of beet means that most of the root system can be extracted and measured more accurately than with

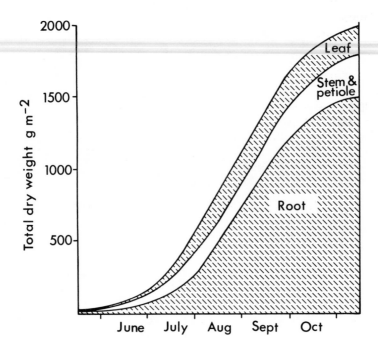

*Figure 2.7  Growth and development of an early-sown sugar beet crop (adapted from Scott, Harper, Wood and Jaggard, 1974)*

other crops.  The slow early growth is apparent (Figure 2.7) until late-June when leaf, stem and petiole tissues are the major components of the total dry weight.  The stem of the vegetative beet plant is a small component and occupies the portion between the lowest leaf scar and the apex.  From July the dry weight of the root increases rapidly until, at the beginning of November, it may comprise 70 per cent or more of the total dry weight.  Leaf, stem and petiole weights also continue to increase throughout the season.  The leaves remain green into the autumn although the lower ones may senesce.  The objective of the sugar beet grower is to produce a large canopy of leaves as early as possible to intercept the maximum amount of solar radiation.  When a large leaf canopy has been produced the dry matter should then be diverted into root growth.

In the second year of growth, after vernalisation, the stem elongates to produce a branched flowering structure on which seeds are formed after wind-pollination.  With the development of the seeds, the plant senesces and the two-year cycle is completed.

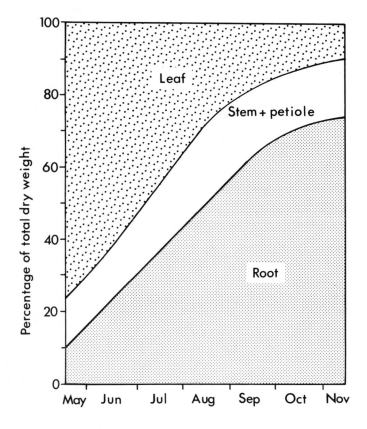

*Figure 2.8  The distribution of dry matter within early-sown sugar beet plants (adapted from Scott, Harper, Wood and Jaggard, 1974)*

Development in the sugar beet root crop is presented in a different way in Figure 2.8.  The data were collected from a series of harvests throughout the season and the dry weights of the component parts are expressed as a percentage of the total dry weight.  This form of data presentation emphasises the dominance of leaf tissue in

43

the seedling stage in May and June and of root tissue in
the autumn.  The leaf proportion declines from 75 per cent
of total dry weight in May to 10 per cent in November.
Over the same period the proportion of root increases from
10 per cent to over 70 per cent.  The proportion of stem
and petiole remains relatively constant at approximately
15-20 per cent throughout.

The examples quoted illustrate the importance of considering growth and development together throughout the
life of the crop.  Husbandry techniques should not be
designed just to promote growth but also to manipulate the
development of the crop to ensure that the maximum amounts
of the dry matter produced are diverted or partitioned
into the economically useful products.

GROWTH ANALYSIS AND MEASUREMENT

Crop physiologists have derived means of quantifying the
growth of crops in an attempt to explain the variation in
yields and to understand the mechanisms of responses to
applied agronomic treatments.  The objective of analysing
growth quantitatively is to seek an understanding of the
factors which are likely to influence yield so that models
can be produced to help to clarify the objectives for
plant breeding and to formulate appropriate husbandry
plans.  Growth analysis techniques have been applied to
all of the major crops and the growth and development patterns referred to earlier are examples of the type of
information which can be obtained.  Growth anaylsis is
also valuable in explaining the response of plants to
changes in various environmental factors.  Growth is dependent on external environmental and internal physiological factors and the agronomist is concerned with
trying to understand and control the interactions between
these groups in order to improve yield.  Considerable
progress has been made in understanding the physiology of
plant growth and development and the examples of plant
nutrition and chemical growth regulation emphasise the

44

relevance of this work to crop production.  The crop productionist has been more concerned with the identification of environmental factors affecting crop growth and the reaction of plants to variation in the environment.

The collection of data on crop growth and development involves the establishment of field experiments where treatments are imposed on the crop.  The growth is subsequently analysed by harvesting small and randomly selected areas at regular intervals.  The harvested plants are usually destructively analysed by dividing them into the major component parts.  After drying in an oven, dry weights can be determined and the response of the crop to the treatments examined.  The major methods of analysing growth which are used in studies of this kind are described below.

Crop growth rate (C) is simply a measure of the rate of dry matter production per unit of time.  Crop dry weight per unit area at one harvest ($W_1$) is deducted from that at the next harvest ($W_2$) and the difference divided by the number of time units between the harvests, ($T_2 - T_1$ in days).  The formula for C is:

$$C = \frac{W_2 - W_1}{T_2 - T_1}$$

*Example*  Total dry weight of sugar beet on 31 July ($T_1$) = 600 g m$^{-2}$ ($W_1$)
Total dry weight of sugar beet on 13 August ($T_2$) = 860 g m$^{-2}$ ($W_2$)
Number of days ($T_2 - T_1$) = 14

$$C = \frac{860 - 600}{14}$$

$$= \frac{260}{14}$$

$$= 18.6 \text{ g m}^{-2} \text{ day}^{-1} \quad \text{(data from Figure 2.2).}$$

Growth rates can be compared at different times in the season and for different treatments, e.g. at a later stage

45

in Figure 2.2:

$$W_1 \text{ on 30 September } (T_1) = 1730 \text{ g m}^{-2}$$
$$W_2 \text{ on 13 October } (T_2) = 1820 \text{ g m}^{-2}$$
$$C = \frac{1820 - 1730}{14} = \frac{90}{14}$$
$$= 6.4 \text{ g m}^{-2} \text{ day}^{-1}$$

In this example the crop growth rate in the cool temperatures of early October is only about one-third of that in the warmer month of August. This example illustrates how the calculation of growth rate can help to quantify the effect of changes in environmental factors.

Monteith (1978) has demonstrated that crops which exhibit the $C_4$ photosynthetic pathway (e.g. maize and sorghum) show greater short-term maximum crop growth rates than the $C_3$ types (potato and rice) but this only occurs in the cloudy weather of temperate climates. In cloudless weather there is little difference between the two groups. The mean crop growth rate over the whole season for a range of $C_4$ crops of 22.0 g m$^{-2}$ day$^{-1}$ is however greater than that for the $C_3$ group of 13.0 g m$^{-2}$ day$^{-1}$. These differences are associated with a 40 per cent better solar energy conversion efficiency in $C_4$ (2.0 per cent) than $C_3$ (1.4 per cent) groups.

Crop growth rate is affected by a range of factors including temperature, radiation levels, water and nutrient supply and the type and age of the plant. These factors affect the size and efficiency of the leaf canopy and hence the ability of the crop to convert solar energy into useful growth.

Relative growth rate (R). Crop growth rate is an absolute measure of growth, and similar values could be obtained for crops of different initial weights. Blackman (1919) proposed that growth rate could be compared with the law of compound interest where the rate of increase is proportional to the initial amount of money (or dry weight) present. Thus a measure of the efficiency of a plant as a producer of new dry matter can only be made if the initial size of the plant is taken into account. The relative growth rate (R) is used to measure the efficiency of dry matter production and the formula used is:

$$R = \frac{\log_e W_2 - \log_e W_1}{T_2 - T_1}$$

where W and T are the same as in the formula for crop growth rate.

Data are usually expressed on a per plant basis for calculating R even though a large number of plants may have come from the harvest area. The units of expression of R are grams per gram per day (or week).

*Example*

$$W_1 = 75 \text{ g}$$
$$W_2 = 108 \text{ g}$$
$$T_2 - T_1 = 7 \text{ days}$$

$$R = \frac{4.682 - 4.317}{7}$$
$$= 0.052 \text{ g g}^{-1} \text{ day}^{-1}$$

To illustrate the importance of initial dry weight a further example is given where the same crop growth rate would apply, but a quite different value of R results:

$$W_1 = 15 \text{ g}$$
$$W_2 = 48 \text{ g}$$
$$T_2 - T_1 = 7 \text{ days}$$

$$R = \frac{3.871 - 2.708}{7}$$
$$= 0.166 \text{ g g}^{-1} \text{ day}^{-1}$$

In this case, although C is the same, the value of R for the second example is more than three times that of the first indicating that the plants in the hypothetical second example have been much more efficient producers of dry matter.

The calculation of values of R is only really useful

47

for short harvest intervals where growth is assumed to be linear and for comparisons under similar environmental conditions, i.e. between treatments within a trial. R tends to decline as plants age and care is needed in interpreting comparisons of R as plants reach maturity (Hunt, 1978).

Leaf area ($L_A$).    Growth analysis usually involves the measurement of the area of the leaf surface to quantify the photosynthetic component.  A range of techniques for measuring the area of leaves is available and has been described by Bleasdale (1973).  The development of the leaf surface (leaf area per plant or per square metre) can be plotted with time and related to dry matter production.

Net assimilation or unit leaf rate (E) is a measure of the productive efficiency of the leaf surface of the plant or crop.  It is normally expressed as grams per square metre per week.

Formula:    $E = \dfrac{W_2 - W_1}{T_2 - T_1} \times \dfrac{\log_e L_{A2} - \log_e L_{A1}}{L_{A2} - L_{A1}}$

where $L_A$ is the leaf area.

*Example*

$$W_1 = 380 \text{ g}$$
$$W_2 = 500 \text{ g}$$
$$L_{A1} = 3.0 \text{ m}^2$$
$$L_{A2} = 3.6 \text{ m}^2$$
$$T_2 - T_1 = 2 \text{ weeks}$$

$$E = \frac{500 - 380}{2} \times \frac{1.281 - 1.100}{3.6 - 3.0}$$

$$= 60 \times \frac{0.181}{0.6}$$

$$= 60 \times 0.302$$

$$= 18.1 \text{ g m}^{-2} \text{ week}^{-1}$$

Watson (1947) showed that E varies with time for a

number of agricultural crops and, if the seasonal trends
are smoothed, E has low values in the autumn and winter
and increases in the spring to reach maximum values in
June and July. It is therefore important to have an
adequate leaf surface by early summer to benefit from the
higher potential rates of E. E is also affected by temperature, light intensity and water and nutrient supply.
Values for E differ between and within crop species and
decline with increasing plant maturity.

Leaf area ratio (LAR) is the ratio of the total leaf area
to the whole plant dry weight and is a further measure of
the efficiency of the leaf surface in producing dry matter.

$$\text{Formula: } LAR = \frac{(L_{A1}/W_1) + (L_{A2}/W_2)}{2}$$

*Example* (values used in example for E)

$$LAR = \frac{(3.0/380) + (3.6/500)}{2}$$

$$= \frac{(0.008) + (0.007)}{2}$$

$$= \frac{0.015}{2} = 0.008 \text{ m}^2 \text{ g}^{-1} \quad \text{or}$$

$$80 \text{ cm}^2 \text{ g}^{-1} \text{ over the 14-day period.}$$

Values of LAR decline as the crop increases in dry
weight when leaf area remains relatively constant.

Specific leaf area (SLA) is a measure of the change in
leaf area per unit of leaf weight between harvests and is
calculated from the formula:

$$SLA = \frac{(L_{A1}/L_{W1}) + (L_{A2}/L_{W2})}{2}$$

where $L_W$ is the leaf dry weight.

Leaf weight ratio (LWR) is a ratio of the leaf dry weight
to total dry weight and is calculated from:

$$LWR = \frac{(L_{W_1}/W_1) + (L_{W_2}/W_2)}{2}$$

LWR decreases as growth proceeds in most crops and is simply a measure of leafiness.

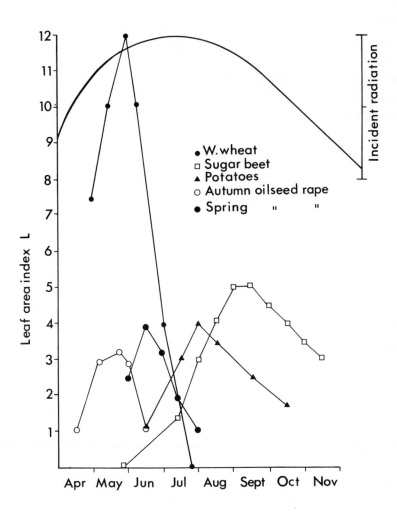

*Figure 2.9 The development of leaf area index (L) in some temperate crops*

Leaf area index (L) is the ratio of the leaf area to the area of ground covered. If in a crop there are 3.6 m$^2$ of leaf above 1.2 m$^2$ of land then the leaf area index is 3. L has been measured in many crops and some examples are illustrated in Figure 2.9. It is clear that patterns of L typically increase after crop emergence to a maximum and then decline. The maximum value of L varies for different crops but is typically in the range 3-6 for most temperate environments. The example for winter wheat shows an exceptionally high value of maximum L (12) and reflects the situation in well-grown crops receiving large quantities of fertiliser nitrogen. L has been related to crop growth rate and C is generally high when L is high.

Figure 2.9 shows a typical pattern of incident solar radiation in the United Kingdom and the potential for crop growth is highest in June, July and August. Crop production systems aim to produce high values of L when incident radiation is at its highest to ensure maximum interception of light energy by the leaf canopy. Winter wheat attains maximum L values at the end of May and can be considered efficient in terms of utilising radiation. Similarly autumn- and spring-sown oilseed rape maximum L values are well synchronised with the pattern of radiation. In autumn-rape, L is declining by the end of May, but by this time there is a good canopy of photosynthesising pods to intercept radiation. The pattern of L development for maincrop potatoes shows that maximum L values are not reached until late-July when radiation levels are beginning to decline. Furthermore this coincides with the rapid phase of tuber bulking, although maximum tuber numbers are determined by the end of June (Figure 2.10). The main period of tuber bulking occurs in conditions of declining L and incident radiation. The potato is therefore less efficient in terms of light interception when conditions for growth are optimal. The situation with sugar beet is less desirable where the leaf canopy is even slower to develop. Maximum L values for beet are not

51

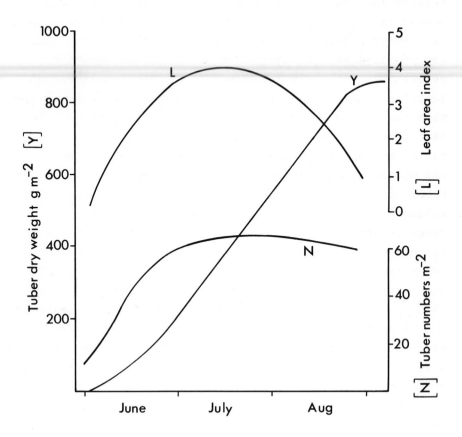

*Figure 2.10  Changes in leaf area index, tuber numbers and tuber dry weight in the potato*

reached until late-August.  However unlike the potato, where L declines rapidly in the late summer, sugar beet retains high values of L into the autumn allowing the crop to utilise radiation in the late summer and autumn while temperatures are favourable.

Crops differ markedly in their patterns of L development and therefore in their efficiency of use of light energy throughout the season.  Attempts have been made to change the patterns of L development in crops to achieve a more favourable use of resources.  For example, early-sowing in sugar beet advances the L curve and usually

52

results in higher yields. However with potatoes early sowing may simply mean earlier attainment of maximum L and an earlier decline. Changes in the sowing date may shift the position of the L curve but this may not have the desired effect on yield. Changing the level of nitrogen fertiliser may also change L and this has been demonstrated with the potato crop. High nitrogen levels give rise to a faster development of L and a greater maximum value which may or may not result in a higher yield. High nitrogen can encourage excessive haulm growth at the expense of tuber growth. Irrigation can have a similar effect. High values of L may not therefore be desirable because the lower leaves in the canopy are shaded and their efficiency is reduced. Where light levels to the lower leaves are below the compensation point (respiratory losses exceed photosynthetic gains) they may actually be 'parasitic' on the upper leaves. Careful manipulation of L is therefore necessary in crop production to attain adequate values when radiation is maximal but not to achieve values so high that the leaf canopy functions less efficiently as a producer of dry matter.

The use of L as a means of elucidating the causes of variation in yields has been challenged. The measurement of green leaf area to produce a value of L is subject to deficiencies. It is often difficult to get accurate estimates of leaf area in practice. Also it is assumed that all leaves are capable of making an equal contribution to growth. This may not be so and it has been established that leaves decline in their efficiency of light conversion as they age. The arrangement and position of the leaves in the canopy also affects their efficiency. Furthermore the angle of presentation of the leaves to incoming radiation can affect their ability to intercept it. Plants with more erect leaves (erectophile) are generally considered to be more efficient than those with the leaves positioned horizontally (planophile), and higher maximum L values may be more appropriate for the former. A further

argument against the use of L in growth analysis is that
crop growth rate is not directly related to it for the
whole life of the crop and this limits its usefulness as a
tool for explaining variation in crop yields. Also the
efficiency of the leaf area as a producer of dry matter
(E) is inversely related to L for much of the life of the
crop (Allen and Scott, 1980).

Leaf area duration (LAD) is a measure of persistence of
the leaf canopy. L declines rapidly in some crops and
this may restrict growth. Treatments which prolong the
duration of the leaf surface in an active state may increase yields. LAD provides a means for comparing treatments on the basis of their leaf persistence. It is
usually determined by measuring the area beneath leaf
growth curves for selected parts of the season.

From this analysis of the methods for measuring growth
it is apparent that many of them give only crude estimates
of aspects of growth but they may be useful for comparing
the effects of treatments on crops. Many of the methods
described are interdependent and interrelated. For
example crop growth rate (C) is dependent on the area of
the leaf surface (L) and its efficiency as a producer of
dry matter (E). Also yield may be proportional to the
efficiency of the leaf surface (E) and its duration (LAD).
The difficulties associated with understanding these relationships and the relative lack of usefulness of them in
explaining differences in crop yields has led crop physiologists to use conventional growth analysis techniques
less and less since the late 1960s.

Monteith (1977) has suggested a new approach which has
been supported by Allen and Scott (1980). This approach
considers that variation in crop yields is almost entirely
due to variation in the amounts of intercepted radiation,
as measured by tube solarimeters placed in the crop. They
propose that the efficiency of radiation conversion is
constant throughout the season and that, once a closed
leaf canopy is formed, rates of crop photosynthesis and

growth rate are largely independent of temperature in the range 10-25°C. The dependence of total crop dry weight on the amount of radiation intercepted is shown for sugar beet, potatoes and barley in Figure 2.11. Crop growth

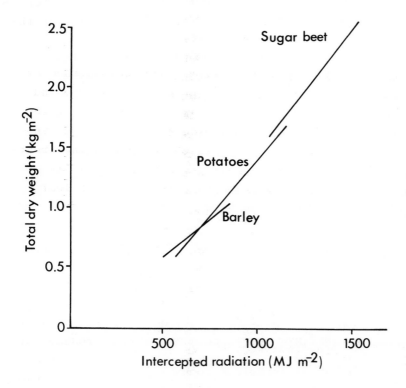

*Figure 2.11 The relationship between total dry weight produced and intercepted radiation in the United Kingdom (after Monteith, 1977)*

rate in wheat, maize and soya beans is also linearly related to the amount of intercepted radiation in the early stages of growth. The lesson from this approach is that production systems should strive to produce a leaf cover early to intercept the maximum amount of radiation throughout the season. Light interception is related to L and in sugar beet 80-85 per cent interception occurs at an L value of 3.0, and 95 per cent when L is 5.0. Biscoe and Gallagher (1977) confirmed the fact that the proportion of light intercepted is dependent on L and suggested that for most crops when L reaches values of 4-5 more than 80 per cent of the photosynthetically active radiation is intercepted. Treatments which encourage early development of L in temperate climates and which result in longer LAD periods are therefore likely to increase yields.

A knowledge of the factors which control growth and development in crops is valuable to the farmer in helping him to attain high yields. Once the desired patterns of growth and development are known, an understanding of the environmental, physiological, genetic and husbandry factors which affect them is helpful in making decisions on the best way of growing crops to maximise the utilisation of resources and achieve high yields. The following chapters explore the limitations to increasing crop yields in a temperate climate.

REFERENCES AND FURTHER READING

Allen, E.J. and Scott, R.K. (1980) 'An analysis of the growth of the potato crop'. Journal of agricultural Science, Cambridge, 94, 583-606.

Austin, R.B. and Jones, H.G. (1974) 'The physiology of wheat'. Report of the Plant Breeding Institute, Cambridge for 1974, 20-73.

Biscoe, P.V. and Gallagher, J.N. (1977) 'Weather, dry matter production and yield'. In Environmental Effects on Crop Physiology, eds. Landsberg, J.J. and Cutting, C.V. London: Academic Press, 75-100.

Blackman, V.H. (1919) Annals of Botany, 23, 353-360.

Bleasdale, J.K.A. (1973) Plant Physiology in Relation to Horticulture. London: Macmillan.

Evans, G.C. (1972) The quantitative analysis of plant growth. Oxford: Blackwell Scientific Publications.

Hunt, R. (1978) Plant Growth Analysis. Institute of Biology. Studies in Biology No.96. London: Edward Arnold.

Milbourn, G.M. (ed.) (1975) Maize Growers Handbook (3rd edn). London: Home Grown Cereals Authority.

Milthorpe, F.L. and Moorby, J. (1981) An Introduction to Crop Physiology (2nd edn). Cambridge: University Press.

Monteith, J.L. (1977) 'Climate and the efficiency of crop production in Britain'. In Agricultural Efficiency. London: The Royal Society.

Monteith, J.L. (1978) 'Reassessment of maximum growth rates for $C_3$ and $C_4$ crops'. Experimental Agriculture, 14, 1-5.

Osafo, D.M. and Milbourn, G.M. (1975) 'The growth of maize. III. The effect of date of sowing and bitumen mulch on dry matter yields'. Journal of agricultural Science, Cambridge, 85, 271-279.

Scott, R.K., Ogunremi, E.A., Ivins, J.D. and Mendham, N.J. (1973) 'The effect of sowing date and season on growth and yield of oilseed rape (Brassica napus)'. Journal of agricultural Science, Cambridge, 81, 277-285.

Scott, R.K., Harper, F., Wood, D.W. and Jaggard, K.W. (1974) 'Effect of seed size on growth development and yield of monogerm sugar beet'. Journal of agricultural Science, Cambridge, 82, 517-530.

Scott, R.K. and Dennis-Jones, R. (1976) 'The physiological background of barley'. Journal of the National Institute of Agricultural Botany, 14 (1), 182-187.

Scott, R.K. and Jaggard, K.W. (1978) 'Theoretical criteria for maximum yield'. Proceedings of 41st Winter Congress of Institute Internationale de Recherches Betteravieres, Brussels, 179-198.

Tottman, D.R. and Makepeace, R.J. (1979) 'An explanation of the decimal growth code for the growth stages of cereals with illustrations'. Annals of Applied Biology, 93, 221-234.

Wareing, P.F. and Cooper, J.P. (eds.) (1971) Potential Crop Production. London: Heinemann Educational Books.

Watson, D.J. (1947) 'Comparative physiological studies on the growth of field crops'. Annals of Botany, 11, 41-76.

Watson, D.J. (1952) 'The physiological basis of variation in yield'. <u>Advances in Agronomy</u>, <u>4</u>, 101–145.

Watson, D.J. (1968) 'A prospect of crop physiology'. <u>Annals of Applied Biology</u>, <u>62</u>, 1–9.

# 3  The Effects of Climate and Weather

INTRODUCTION

The physical environment in which crops are grown can have
large effects on the type and rate of growth and development.  In the controlled environment of a glasshouse, temperature, radiation, photoperiod, water supply and the
gaseous composition of the atmosphere can all be regulated
to meet the changing requirements of a crop as it develops.
Temperature can be controlled by the use of heating systems and ventilation, and with crops like tomato and
cucumber, this is important to secure high yields.  Radiation levels can be controlled by the use of various
sources of supplementary lighting to influence growth and
development.  Supplementary lighting for young lettuce and
tomato plants is a good example of this.  Day-length can
be controlled to give year-round production of sensitive
crops, such as chrysanthemums which require short days to
induce flowering, by covering the plants with blackout
screens to give artificially short days in summer.  The
supply of water to plants can be more easily regulated in
the glasshouse by means of different types of irrigation
systems.  The gaseous composition of the atmosphere can
also be manipulated and the classic example of this is
carbon dioxide enrichment of glasshouse 'air' to promote
more vigorous growth by supplementing a limiting factor to
photosynthesis.  However the control of these aspects of

the physical environment in field-grown crops is more
difficult and often impossible.

The lack of control and the variable nature of the
physical environment is a limitation to crop production in
temperate regions.  Temperature varies on an annual cycle
and wide ranges can be experienced within a single day.
Low temperatures restrict the types of crops which can be
grown through direct freezing damage or by retarding
growth and development, to the extent that the crop is immature when autumn temperatures decline below those necessary for growth, e.g. maize.  Moisture supply is irregular
and unpredictable and crops may be damaged by excessive or
insufficient amounts of water.  The amounts of incident
radiation, in the photosynthetically active range, may be
insufficient for maximum growth.  In addition, low temperatures may restrict leaf development in the spring so that
a high proportion of the incident radiation is not intercepted by the leaf canopy and is wasted.  Photoperiod
varies on an annual cycle and can restrict the growth and
development of some sensitive crops.  The cycle of photoperiod may not synchronise with that of temperatures.  An
example of this is the short-day soya bean where the
growth of the crop in the spring is restricted by low temperature and it emerges into days which are too long to
induce flowering.  Wind is a further variable of the
physical environment which can affect crop growth.

The variable nature of the physical factors of the
environment in temperate regions imposes limitations on
crop production systems and growth patterns can be unpredictable.  The weather patterns are therefore an important consideration.  Components of the weather can be
identified and quantified, and to some extent predicted,
but the ways in which these components interact and the
consequences for crop growth are not well understood.  The
temperate zones of the world share a similar climate,
which will be described later, but within this, local
weather patterns can vary markedly and generalisations

need cautious acceptance. However Watson's proposal (1963) that climate determines the crops that can be grown and weather determines the yields, is a useful one. Quantification of weather and its components has received considerable attention from mathematicians and physicists but often the findings are not easily understood by biologists and agronomists (Hudson, 1977). It is not the intention of this text to adopt a mathematical approach but to emphasise the effects of weather components on biological processes in crop plants in general terms.

*Table 3.1  A summary of the factors of the plant environment (after Hudson, 1977)*

| Aerial | Soil |
|---|---|
| Radiant energy | Temperature: gradients with depth |
| Light: day-length | Soil moisture: amount and availability |
|     spectral composition | |
|     intensity | Composition of soil atmosphere: $CO_2 : O_2$ ratio |
| Temperature: seasonal and daily fluctuations | |
|     incidence of frost | Nutrients: concentration and availability |
| Humidity | Soil pH |
| Wind: speed | Physical characteristics of the soil |
|     gustiness | |
|     direction | |
| Cloud, mist and fog | |
| Precipitation: dew, rain, sleet, snow, hail | |
| Composition of the atmosphere: | |
|     $CO_2$ | |
|     pollution | |

The main factors of the plant environment have been
summarised by Hudson (1977) and are presented in Table 3.1.
This illustrates the wide range of factors involved in the
aerial and soil environment and emphasises the difficulty
of interpreting the likely effects on crop growth when
they are all operating together.

THE COOL TEMPERATE REGIONS OF THE WORLD

The distribution of the major climatic zones of the world
is represented in Figure 3.1.   Four main zones are identifiable.   The cold arctic region occupies large areas of

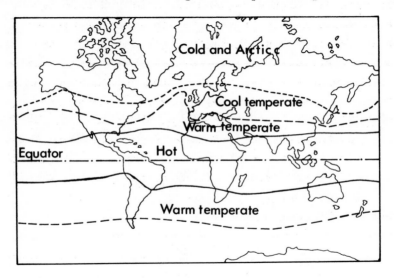

*Figure 3.1.   Distribution of the major climatic zones of the world
(after Miller, 1963)*

Canada, Greenland, Scandinavia, Iceland and the northern
parts of the Soviet Union.   The northern parts of Japan
and China also experience this climate.   In contrast, the
hot zone occupies a belt north and south of the equator
including central America, northern South America, Africa,
southern Asia and northern Australia.   Sandwiched between
the two zones are the warm and cool temperate climates.
In the southern hemisphere, the warm temperate zone occupies a large part of South America, southern Africa and

62

southern Australasia. In the northern hemisphere a warm temperate climate is found in the southern USA, southern Europe, North Africa, the Middle East and the mid-south of Asia.

This text is mainly concerned with crop production in a cool temperate climate which is found mainly in the northern hemisphere. Parts of the USA and Canada, the United Kingdom, north-west and central Europe and the southern parts of the USSR and China all experience a cool temperate climate. In addition southern Japan and the South Island of New Zealand share the same climate.

The main difference between the cool and warm temperate climates is the presence of an identifiable cold season in the former which restricts plant growth and limits some agricultural activities. Proximity to marine influences reduces the severity of the cold season and permits a wider range of crops to be grown. The amount and seasonal distribution of precipitation is also influenced by the position of land masses relative to the seas. The main features of the cool temperate climate are illustrated more clearly by reference to specific locations. Average monthly air temperatures are summarised in Figure 3.2. The data for London are typical of a maritime influence in the northern hemisphere. Temperatures are at their lowest in January when averages are 4-5°C. However large variation about this general mean is apparent on days within the month and between years, and values lower than -10°C are commonly recorded. Temperatures increase progressively through the spring to a maximum of 17-18°C in July or August and the highest temperatures may reach 30°C in this period. In March and April, when most spring-sown crops are sown, temperatures of only 7-9°C are common and this results in slow early growth. Frosts are also a limitation and can occur as late as May when some susceptible crops have emerged.

After August, temperatures decline to approximately 10°C in October and autumn growth is then reduced. A

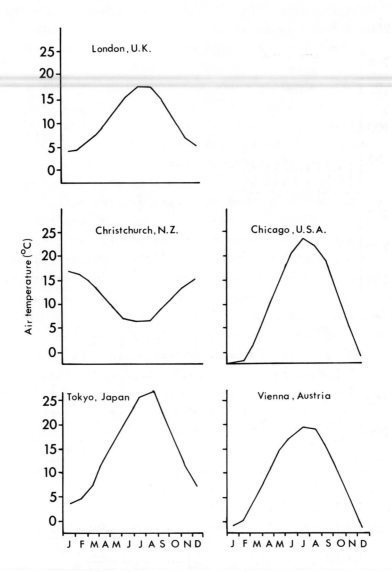

*Figure 3.2   Average monthly temperatures (at sea level) in cool temperate climates*

similar pattern of average monthly temperature is evident for a maritime cool temperate climate in the southern hemisphere in Christchurch, New Zealand.

Similar temperature records are presented for continental cool temperate areas of Vienna in Austria and

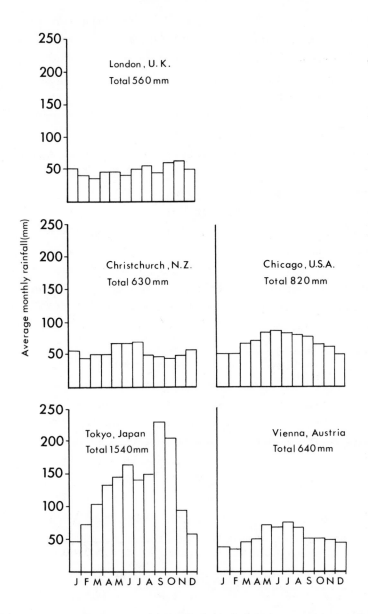

*Figure 3.3  Average monthly rainfall in cool temperate climates*

Chicago in the USA.  In these situations the seasonal pattern of temperatures is similar but the range is greater.
In Chicago, for example, the summer maximum average is
nearly 25°C and the winter minimum is -2°C.  Corresponding

figures for Vienna are 20°C and -1°C. The data for Tokyo
show winter temperatures similar to London, but with a
higher summer maximum of 26°C. The more severe winter in
continental areas means that winter hardiness in crops is
an important consideration and spring-sown crops are
commonly grown which mature rapidly in the warmer summers.
Autumn-sown crops are more common in the maritime areas.

Average monthly rainfall patterns for the same five
locations are presented in Figure 3.3. London and Christchurch have similar monthly patterns of rainfall. There
is no distinct dry or wet season but a tendency for the
winter months to be wetter. Total rainfall amounts of
560 mm and 630 mm are also similar and low, resulting in
periods of water shortage in the higher summer temperatures. The continental locations of Chicago and Vienna do
not have markedly different total amounts of rainfall
(820 mm and 640 mm) but in both cases there is a distinct-
ly wetter part of the year. The summer months of May to
August are the wettest with the winter months of December
to March the driest. Rainfall in Tokyo is much higher
than the other locations (1540 mm) and also shows a marked
seasonality with the highest amounts falling in the summer
months, especially September and October. In this case,
the influence of the monsoon in south-east Asia is important. These few examples illustrate that both the total
amounts and monthly distribution of rainfall (or other
forms of precipitation) can vary markedly within the cool
temperate zone. Both of these factors influence crop
growth and the need for irrigation.

The following sections consider in more detail the
components of the weather in cool temperate climates and
their effects on biological processes in plants.

TEMPERATURE

General patterns of temperature changes have already been
described. However a more detailed examination reveals
the extent of the variation about these general trends.

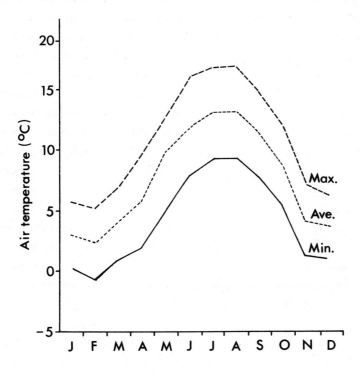

*Figure 3.4  Monthly average air temperature (1965-74) at Bush Estate,*
*Midlothian, Scotland*

Figure 3.4 shows the monthly average maximum and minimum
air temperature over a ten-year period in south-east Scotland.  It is clear that there is commonly a range of 3-4°C
above and below the monthly average.  As a result, although the February average is approximately 2°C, the
range may be from -1°C to +5°C.  In reality the range is
greater than this because daily temperatures may be as low
as -15°C (minimum) or as high as +10°C (maximum).  Similar
ranges exist for other months of the year.  Therefore data
of this kind are of limited use, but they do provide
guidelines in a form that can be easily understood.

Soil temperatures are also important as they influence
root growth and function.  Figure 3.5 shows average
monthly soil temperatures at three different depths.  At
all depths, the basic pattern of change is similar to that

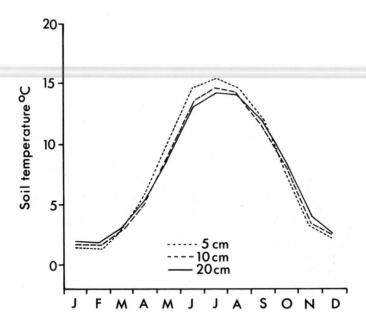

*Figure 3.5 Average of monthly soil temperature at 5, 10 and 20 cm depths at Bush Estate, Midlothian, Scotland (1965-75)*

of air temperatures. However the range is greater at the 5 cm depth than at 20 cm; at 20 cm depth, temperatures in the winter months do not fall so low and do not achieve such high levels in the summer. The rate of change of soil temperatures and the annual range is not as great as that experienced with air temperatures and the buffering effect becomes greater with increasing depth.

Soil temperatures are particularly critical during the establishment of crops in the autumn and spring. The numbers of seeds which germinate and eventually produce established seedlings depend in part on temperature. The speed of germination and emergence is also dependent on temperature and this can determine the survival of seedlings in seedbeds which are rapidly losing moisture (see chapter 6). Most seeds are sown at depths of 10-50 mm and the soil temperatures in this range can influence the success of crop establishment. Large diurnal fluctuations

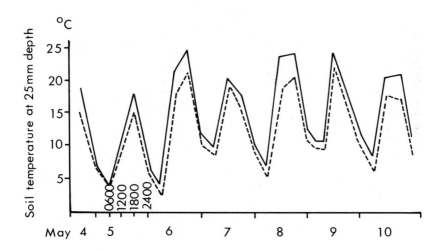

*Figure 3.6  Daily variation in soil temperature (25 mm depth) in early May in south-east Scotland under bare soil (broken line) and bitumen mulch (solid line) (Harper and Ferguson, 1979)*

in temperature can occur at these depths in temperate climates in the spring (Figure 3.6). The data show that, in early May in northern Britain, soil temperatures at sowing depth may range from 3–25°C during a 24 h period. The use of a black bitumen mulch, applied after sowing, in the example demonstrates that temperatures at 25 mm depth can be increased by 4–5°C in this critical period.

Seeds of most crop plants germinate readily at temperatures of 6–10°C, e.g. wheat, barley and brassicas, but other crops such as maize require a minimum soil temperature of 10°C. Information on soil temperatures is therefore valuable in determining appropriate sowing dates for crops. Wheat germination will occur between 4°C and 37°C, but the optimum range for germination percentage is

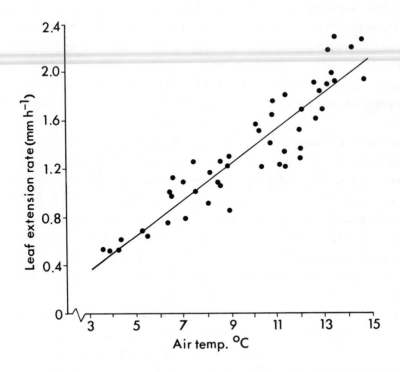

*Figure 3.7  Effects of air temperature (day and night) on the rate of leaf extension in the early growth of barley (Biscoe and Gallagher, 1978)*

20-25°C.  Seedbed temperatures at normal sowing depths are typically 5-10°C (Figure 3.5) when wheat is sown in October and November and thus, in temperate climates, establishment occurs in sub-optimal conditions.

Şoil and air temperatures have effects on other aspects of crop growth and development.  Leaf growth and expansion in many crops is correlated with air temperature. This is exemplified by the leaf extension rate of spring barley in the Midlands of England (Figure 3.7).  Within the range 3.5 - 15°C, leaf extension rate is directly correlated with day and night temperatures.  A six-fold increase is evident over the range and this has important practical implications in that the establishment of an early leaf cover is desirable to intercept incident

70

radiation early in the growing season to maximise yield.

In the soyabean the rate of appearance of leaves is also dependent on temperature and increases over the range 18-30°C. This emphasises the high temperature requirement of this crop and illustrates why it is not widely grown in cool temperate regions. Photosynthesis and development in the leaves of maize plants are slow at 10°C and fastest at 30-33°C.

The rate of appearance of leaves in sugar beet increases with temperature over the range 5-15°C before reaching a plateau, and then declines above 30°C. In this example rapid leaf expansion in the cool temperatures of late-spring and early summer is essential to improve yields of roots and sugar. It has been estimated that a 1°C drop in average temperature in the spring reduces radiation interception and, by implication, sugar yield by 10 per cent.

Temperature effects on root growth are not so clearly defined but are nevertheless important. In maize for example, the rate of elongation of the seminal roots increases between 10°C and 30°C, after which it declines. These effects influence the rate of development of the root system and ultimately its ability to absorb water and nutrients from the soil to support aerial growth.

The initiation of flowering in many crop plants is stimulated by exposure to low temperatures. This is in contrast to other plant responses to temperature where an increase results in a faster reaction. This flowering response is known as vernalisation. Most autumn-sown crops, which behave as biennials, require a period of exposure to low temperatures to change the development of the apex from vegetative to reproductive growth. Physically the apex changes from the smooth dome structure producing leaves to a small version of the inflorescence with the differentiation of florets.

Autumn-sown cereals require vernalisation. In winter wheat, the most effective temperatures for vernalisation

71

in the early growth stages are 3-8°C.  Sub-zero temperatures are not required although vernalisation can occur
over the range -3°C to +13°C.  This requirement is normally met during cool temperate winters and usually occurs
within 4-6 weeks of sowing in cool weather.  Imbibed seeds
can be vernalised on the mother plant but in practice it
is the young seedlings which respond to the low temperature stimulus.  Exposure to high temperatures after
vernalisation can reverse the effect, but this is not
usually a problem in the field.

   The vernalisation requirement of wheat has important
practical consequences.  The climatic areas where winter
wheat can be grown are restricted by this requirement and
in warm temperate and hot climates the autumn varieties of
wheat are not suitable.  The choice of sowing date can
also be critical.  In normal conditions wheat would be
sown in the autumn but, because of difficult soil and
weather conditions, this may not be possible.  In such
cases it is possible to sow in early spring and still obtain vernalisation.  Varieties differ in their requirements for low temperatures and some recommended variety
lists specify a latest safe sowing date for spring-sowing
of autumn varieties.  Autumn varieties of barley, oats and
rye respond in a similar way to wheat in their vernalisation requirement.  Oilseed rape and field beans also
exist in autumn and spring forms and require vernalisation.
In all of these crops vernalisation is an important requirement to achieve satisfactory seed yields.

   In biennial crops, grown for their vegetative growth,
vernalisation is undesirable.  A consequence of early sowing of sugar beet, to ensure early leaf development, is
that the young seedlings will be exposed to cool spring
temperatures.  This may result in vernalisation of a proportion of the crop and the subsequent production of
flowering stems or bolters in the first year.  Bolting in
sugar beet produces fibrous roots which are low in sucrose content and difficult to harvest mechanically.  A

high proportion of bolters can reduce the yield and value of the crop and aggravate the problem of weed beet by seed-shedding before harvest. Sugar beet varieties differ in their resistance to bolting and some are better suited to early sowing than others.

Bolting can also present problems in swedes and turnips where early sowing, to increase root yields, may result in vernalisation of seedlings. The financial consequences of bolting in these crops are less severe but health problems in animals grazing bolted brassicas may result from the higher levels of the kale anaemia factor (s-methyl cysteine sulphoxide) in the flowers.

The initiation of inflorescences in spring-sown crops is also affected by temperature but in these cases higher temperatures are generally beneficial.

In some crops the geographical areas suitable for growth can be determined by a knowledge of the temperature requirements and weather patterns. The use of accumulated temperatures over the season is valuable for this purpose to predict suitable areas for maize (for grain and silage) in the United Kingdom. Two systems have evolved for maize. Accumulated average daily air temperatures above 10°C provide an approximate guide to suitable areas, if the crop requirements are known. The Ontario Unit system is however considered to be more closely related to maize development and is now more widely accepted. Ontario Units (OU) are calculated as follows (Hough, 1978):

Day term:  $Y = 3.33 (T_{max} - 10) - 0.084 (T_{max} - 10)^2$ for $T_{max} \geq 10°C$.
For temperatures of $Y < 10°C$, $Y = 0$

Where $T_{max}$ is the day maximum air (screen) temperature in °C.

Night term: $X = 1.8 (T_{min} - 4.4)$ for $T_{min} \geq 4.4°C$.
$X = 0$ otherwise

Ontario Unit = $(Y + X)/2$

73

*Example*

For a particular day, assume that $T_{max}$ = 16.7°C and $T_{min}$ = 7.8°C

$$Y = 3.33 (16.7 - 10) - 0.084 (16.7 - 10)^2$$
$$= 3.33 (6.7) - 0.084 (44.9)$$
$$= 22.3 - 3.8$$
$$= 18.5$$

$$X = 1.8 (7.8 - 4.4)$$
$$= 1.8 (3.4)$$
$$= 6.1$$

$$OU = (18.5 - 6.1)/2$$
$$= 6.2$$

Values for each day are then added together to give the accumulated total.

Accumulated OUs can then be determined for the whole season for different areas of the country where weather data are available. Experimental data have shown that identifiable development stages in maize coincide with a specified number of OUs for varieties within the same maturity group as the variety LG11 as follows:

| Stage | OUs |
| --- | --- |
| Sowing to silking | 1400 |
| Sowing to 25 per cent whole crop dry matter | 2300 |
| Sowing to 30 per cent whole crop dry matter | 2500 |
| Sowing to grain moisture content of 40 per cent | 2700 |

(These values are minima required for each development stage.)

Areas of England and Wales have been mapped for their suitability for growing maize on the basis of OUs (Figure 3.8). The use of temperature data for this purpose is a

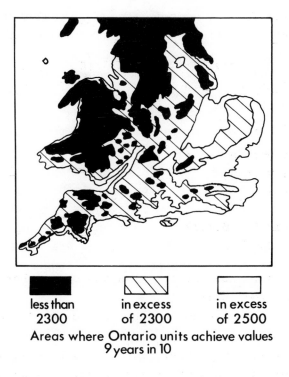

less than 2300    in excess of 2300    in excess of 2500

**Areas where Ontario units achieve values 9 years in 10**

*Figure 3.8   Areas of England and Wales suitable for maize growing based on Ontario Units (average 1941-1970) (after Hough, 1978)*

valuable aid to farmers contemplating growing maize. This approach to using information on the effects of tempera- ture on crop growth and development is helpful for crops which are considered marginal for cool temperate climates. A similar system has been developed for outdoor tomatoes.

The accumulated degree system has also been used with other crops, e.g. vining peas. The value of the system for vining peas is in predicting harvest dates and sowing dates to allow large areas of crops to be vined when the quality is optimal. Peas for processing quickly pass through the optimum 'tenderometer' value as they mature in summer and, if sowing dates are not staggered, large areas of the crop would be ready for harvest in a short period of time and harvesting would be impossible. Information on the accumulated day degree requirement for different varieties allows sowing dates to be planned to avoid a concentrated harvest period. The base temperature for peas is 4.4°C (40°F) and consequently they can be grown in a wider geographical area than maize.

Some crops are sensitive to frost damage and a knowledge of the severity and frequency of occurrence of temperatures below freezing in a particular area can help to avoid damage to such crops. There are three situations when crops may be at risk from frost damage. Firstly the early-sowing of sensitive crops may well result in the crop emerging when frosts occur. Potatoes are a good example of this where the emerging shoots may be temporarily damaged with the consequent· delay of the normal crop development pattern. *Phaseolus* beans are also in this category. Secondly crops requiring a long growing season can be damaged by early-autumn frosts which may kill them before they are fully mature. Maize is a good example of this category in temperate climates where harvesting often occurs into November. Although maize plants are killed by severe autumn frosts, the resulting cell damage and loss of water from the leaves increases the dry matter content making them more suitable for ensilage. Thirdly, crops which are autumn-sown may be adversely affected by freezing temperatures over a long period throughout the winter. Death of plants from this cause is commonly referred to as winter kill. Winter cereals are at risk from winter kill and some varieties of barley and particularly oats can be severely damaged to the extent of total crop losses. Wheat varieties are generally hardier and survive severe frosts in temperate winters.

Freezing damage results from the formation of ice crystals inside plant cells. The cell membranes are then punctured and, on thawing, they collapse and the tissues decompose. Resistance to damage of this kind depends not only on species and variety but also on the age of the tissues and the degree of acclimatisation to low temperatures before freezing. Protection of certain high-value crops can be achieved by applying water during periods of frosts. The latent heat of fusion produced when the applied water changes to ice is sufficient to prevent the tissues from freezing.

## LIGHT

Light is a further component of the environment which has a large influence on crop growth and development. Three aspects of light are important:

  (i) How much? - the intensity
 (ii) How long? - the duration or day-length
(iii) The quality - the spectral distribution

Some of the more important physiological processes in plants which are affected by light are summarised in Table 3.2. It is clear that light is important from the germination of the seed, through the vegetative phase of growth to flowering and the induction of seed and bud dormancy.

*Table 3.2 Some light-controlled processes in plants (after Fitter and Hay, 1981)*

| Process | Effects of light |
| --- | --- |
| Germination | Effects on dark and light-requiring seeds |
| Stem extension | Etiolation effects |
| Leaf expansion | Prolonged illumination required for full expansion |
| Chlorophyll synthesis | Illumination required for development of green pigments |
| Stem and leaf movements | Of little significance in crop production |
| Flower induction | Photoperiodism and the control of flowering |
| Bud dormancy | Photoperiodic response induced in short days |

THE IMPORTANCE OF QUANTITY OF LIGHT

The fundamental process of photosynthesis in green plants
depends on light intensity. The basic relationship between the rate of photosynthesis and irradiance has been
established (Gaastra, 1962) (Figure 3.9). Assuming that

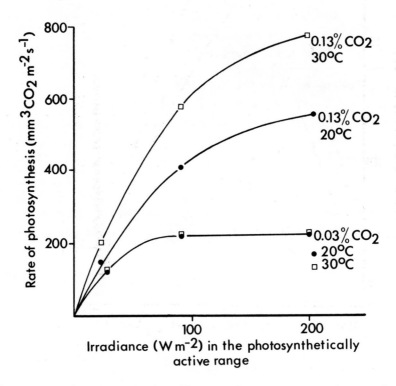

*Figure 3.9  The effect of irradiance and $CO_2$ concentration on the rate
of photosynthesis at 20° and 30°C (after Gaastra, 1962)*

temperature and concentration of carbon dioxide are not
limiting, the rate of photosynthesis increases with increasing irradiance levels. Consequently the rate of
growth of crops in the early stages is related to light
intensity and the proportion of it which is intercepted.
The importance of the proportion of the incident radiation
intercepted by the leaf surface to increasing crop yields
has already been stressed in chapter 2. The total amount
of radiation reaching the surface of the soil or crop is a

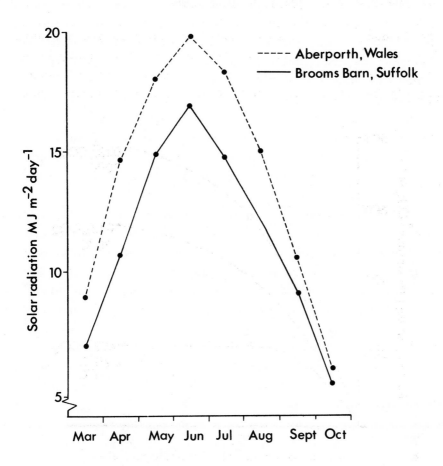

*Figure 3.10   Radiation receipts at two sites in the United Kingdom during the growing season (average of 11 years from 1968-1978) (after Allen and Scott, 1980)*

function of the intensity and duration (day-length). Radiation receipts can vary markedly within short distances and this is illustrated by the data from south Wales and East Anglia in the United Kingdom (Figure 3.10). It is evident that, at any time of the year, the radiation receipts at Aberporth are consistently higher than at Broom's Barn. In consequence the potential for photosynthesis and higher crop yields is greater in the former. It is also evident that monthly radiation receipts differ throughout the growing season. The amounts are highest in June and it is therefore important to have an adequate leaf surface to intercept the radiation before this time. After June, radiation levels decline rapidly. This pattern of radiation receipts is particularly important for sugar beet and potatoes where full leaf cover may not be achieved until radiation levels are declining. A high proportion of the radiation received in April to June is not intercepted and is wasted. In sugar beet, as much as 50 per cent of the incident radiation is not intercepted by the crop.

The efficiency of light interception by a crop is dependent on a variety of factors. The ability of a crop to produce a full leaf cover in the cool temperatures of spring and early summer increases this efficiency. Cereals are generally superior to root crops in this respect. The plant population density is also important and crops grown in wide rows, to facilitate mechanical harvesting, are less efficient, in the early part of the season, than those grown in narrow rows. In addition the arrangement of the leaves is important. The rosette leaf arrangement of sugar beet results in an inefficient light interception system. In contrast, the cereals produce a leaf canopy which is more efficient in these terms. Leaf angle also determines the efficiency of interception of radiation but this aspect is not under the control of the grower and can only be effectively manipulated by plant breeders. Plants with more erect leaves are generally more efficient as light interceptors and give rise to a canopy structure with less mutual shading than those with a leaf angle closer to the horizontal.

Leaf development is also affected by radiation levels. In cereals, the rate of leaf expansion and the final breadth and thickness increase with increasing radiation. In contrast, the final area and length of individual leaves declines at higher light intensity.

A further effect of light intensity on growth of

80

plants is evident in tillering of cereals. Tillering is
the production of secondary shoots from the axils of
leaves on the main stem and is also influenced by nitrogen
supply. The number of tillers produced increases linearly
with increasing irradiance. This effect can be observed
in cereals which have lodged before they are mature.
Lodging allows light access to the base of the crop and
this stimulates the production of further tillers which
are unproductive and cause difficulty at harvesting.

Light can also control the type of growth which occurs.
At very low levels of irradiance, or in darkness, etio-
lation of shoots occurs which results in weak and spindly
growth. Sprout growth in potatoes, prior to planting, can
be controlled by manipulating the storage temperature and
light levels. Low temperatures and relatively high light
intensity produce sturdy sprouts, with chlorophyll development, which are less likely to be damaged during planting.

## THE IMPORTANCE OF LIGHT DURATION

The duration of exposure to light periods (known also as
day-length and photoperiod) affects crop growth and
development. In temperate latitudes, the seasonal pattern
of variation in day-length illustrates that crops may be
exposed to light periods of 8 to 22 hours depending on
latitude and calendar date (Figure 3.11). In the northern
hemisphere the longest days occur in the summer coinciding
with the period of highest temperatures and irradiance.
The range of day-lengths experienced throughout the year
is greater with increasing distance from the equator. The
effects of such variations in day-length on crop growth
and development are well documented and are of practical
significance.

Photoperiodism is defined as the effect of day-length
on flowering. Early studies with soyabean demonstrated
that flowering occurred at a similar date irrespective of
when they were sown. With progressively later sowings
the period of vegetative growth before flowering was

81

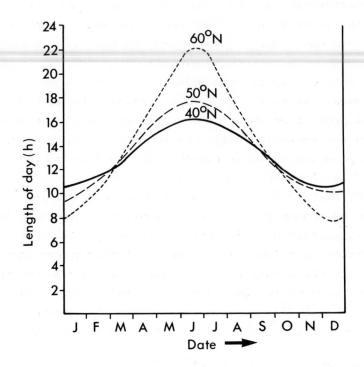

*Figure 3.11  Effect of latitude on the seasonal variation in day-length in the temperate zones of the northern hemisphere (after Canham, 1966)*

shortened and this was associated with a photoperiodic influence.  Cultivars differ in their critical day-length for flowering and this restricts the areas and season in which soyabean can be grown successfully; although some are not affected by day-length.  When sensitive soyabean cultivars are grown in northern latitudes (above 40°) they are sown in cool springs and make considerable vegetative growth before flowering is induced by declining day-length in late summer.  Under such conditions the crop does not ripen before low autumn temperatures cause growth to cease.

Most temperate crops exhibit a long-day photoperiodic response.  In winter wheat, long days promote flowering, assuming that vernalisation has been effected, but this requirement for an appropriate day-length is not essential in all varieties. In this case wheat can be described as a facultative or quantitative long-day plant as opposed to an obligate one. Other cereals and grasses exhibit similar long-day requirements to promote flowering and in barley the rate of ear primordia initiation increases with longer days. In wheat, long days decrease the duration of the leaf production phase, the number of true leaves per stem and the number of spikelets produced. Other crops such as peas are known as day-neutral and flower over a range of day-lengths.

Other aspects of crop growth and development are affected by photoperiod. Tuber formation in potatoes is a short-day response. In contrast runner production in strawberries is a long-day response. Although day-length effects in crop plants are important there is nothing that the grower can do to control them in field crops. The value of this information is in enabling the grower to select appropriate crops for the latitude of his farm.

THE IMPORTANCE OF LIGHT QUALITY

It is well established that not all parts of the light spectrum are important in plant growth. In the case of photosynthesis, light in the wavelength range 400-700 nanometres is considered to be the only useful part (photosynthetically active radiation). Within this range it is known that different pigments, involved in photosynthesis, have different wavelengths where absorption of light is maximal. In addition, other physiological processes are dependent on light from different parts of the spectrum, e.g. the red and far-red end is most effective in photoperiodic responses. However, in practice light quality cannot be manipulated in field cropping systems.

WATER

Water is essential for plant growth and, during the actively-growing phase, it may constitute between 70 and

83

95 per cent of the total fresh weight. At maturity, grain crops have normally lost most of their water and the levels decline to 5 to 30 per cent. In addition, water is constantly being lost through transpiration and replenished by uptake from the soil by the root system. A hectare of vegetation in full sunlight, on a summer day, loses approximately 25 tonnes of water. This may necessitate irrigating with 25 mm of water as frequently as every 10 days.

This constant movement of water through the plant is essential for its survival. The transpiration stream carries essential nutrients from the soil to the sites where they are needed in the shoot. Also water flow permits the translocation of assimilates produced in the leaves to other parts of the plant to support new growth or for storage. Water serves an essential transport role in plants.

Water also confers mechanical strength to the plant in non-woody tissues. The osmotic pressure of the plant cells means that water is taken up and they become turgid and rigid. If excessive water loss occurs then the cells show partial collapse which leads to wilting. If water shortage occurs for long periods, permanent wilting and death may ensue.

A number of physiological processes in crop plants respond to water stress conditions. Cell growth, cell wall and protein synthesis are all very sensitive to water stress and are adversely affected. Stomata close when moisture stress occurs and this reduces the rate of exchange of $CO_2$ and hence photosynthesis. The levels of the hormone abscisic acid increase under water stress conditions and this causes stomatal closure and effectively reduces further water loss from the leaves. Respiration increases and sugar levels in plants accumulate under moisture stress.

The effects of water stress on the physiological processes listed can result in reduced crop yields. It is therefore important in crop production to ensure adequate supplies of water when they are needed. Critical stages of growth can be identified when moisture stress can be more damaging. The establishment of crops is one such stage and late-spring or summer sowings may require irrigation of the seedbed to ensure satisfactory germination. Water is required during the vegetative phase of growth to sustain leaf and stem growth. In the potato crop, water is required to ensure the survival and growth of the tubers. Similarly in high value root crops the provision of irrigation water may be necessary to achieve good growth.

In cereals and other seed-producing crops there is a further critical stage for water at flowering. Adequate production of viable pollen and the fertilisation process require water, and stress at these stages can reduce the numbers of seeds produced. After fertilisation, development of the seeds also requires adequate water to avoid the production of small and shrivelled grains. In crops grown for their fleshy pods and immature seeds, e.g. vining peas, water supply after flowering is also critical to sustain normal growth.

Seasonal patterns of rainfall in cool temperate climates have already been discussed but these data are not very useful in predicting irrigation requirements. As crops grow their water requirement increases and, even if summer rainfall appears to be adequate, additional water may be required. The rate of water loss depends on solar radiation, temperature and wind, and when crops are growing fast in the summer the loss of water is also great.

Spring and summer are the seasons when irrigation is likely to be needed most. Calculation of potential transpiration and rainfall levels in specified geographical areas is helpful in predicting irrigation need (MAFF, 1974). Meteorological data can provide information on soil moisture deficits and give more precision to irrigation. Irrigation requirements are based on weather data

85

and a knowledge of the requirements of the crop. In practice, small soil moisture deficits are allowed to accumulate before irrigation is recommended as this reduces the
frequency of application and avoids wastage from natural
rainfall which may follow. Further aspects of irrigation
are considered in chapter 4.

Water can have other effects on crops. The humidity
of the atmosphere varies and high humidities can increase
the risk of infection by some plant disease organisms. A
good example of this is potato blight (*Phytophthora infestans*) where outbreaks can be forecast from a knowledge of
the effects of high humidity and temperature on the
infecting-ability of the pathogen. Downy mildew infection
of brassicas is also favoured by high humidity. In both
these cases, the high humidity provides a favourable environment for spore germination. Bacterial diseases
thrive in wet conditions.

Prolonged periods of exposure to too much water can
also damage crops and areas prone to flooding should be
avoided or drained.

GASES

The gaseous composition of the aerial atmosphere remains
relatively constant over a wide range of conditions. Carbon dioxide is rarely a limiting factor to photosynthesis
in the field and there is usually sufficient air movement
within crop canopies to quickly replenish temporary reductions.

Oxygen is essential for respiration but deficiencies
in the aerial environments are not a problem. In the soil,
oxygen deficiencies can occur in periods of waterlogging
and root growth can be adversely affected. In extreme
cases of prolonged waterlogging, root death occurs emphasising the need for good drainage. The build-up of toxic
products from anaerobic respiration (acetaldehyde, ethanol
and lactic acid) is responsible for the restriction of
root growth in association with high levels of ethylene

production. Root extension in barley is progressively
reduced with increasing ethylene concentration over the
range 0.1 - 10 ppm.

Gaseous aerial pollutants can adversely affect crop
growth in some areas. Sulphur dioxide is the most common
pollutant and can reduce photosynthesis in cereals and in
acute cases give rise to interveinal chlorosis. Nitrous
and nitric oxide similarly affect photosynthesis, but to
a lesser extent, and may cause interveinal or marginal
leaf damage.

## WIND

Wind is a further variable of the physical environment
which affects crops. Plant responses to wind have been
extensively reviewed by Grace (1977). Surface wind speeds
over the earth's surface have been mapped. In the United
Kingdom, the range of average annual wind speed at 10
metres height is from 4 m/s to 12 m/s. The lowest speeds
are found at low altitude sites away from coasts. The
highest wind speeds are recorded in coastal areas or in
high altitude mountainous areas. Average data are again
misleading and, in severe storms, speeds of up to 50 m/s
have been recorded. This variation and the gustiness of
wind makes it difficult to predict the effects on crops.
Weather forecasting and the use of the Beaufort scale help
to warn the grower of impending wind damage.

In its severest form, wind damage can physically
damage plants through the removal of leaves and breakage
of stems. However more subtle effects of lower wind
speeds over longer periods can have serious consequences
for plant growth.

Air movement over the plant surface increases the rate
of water vapour loss through transpiration which can
accelerate the onset of drought in dry periods. This can
then lead to stomatal closure and a reduced rate of
gaseous exchange which then reduces photosynthesis and
crop growth rates. Wind also has a cooling effect on

leaves and this can further reduce the rate of photo-synthesis.

Prolonged exposure to wind results in a decrease in stem length of crops and may then indirectly change the structure of the leaf canopy, thus making it less effic-ient in photosynthesis. In addition, wind increases the bending strength of stems which may protect them from strong winds at a later date. Strong winds can however cause stem breakage and this is particularly evident in cereals. Lodging is often a result of wind and heavy rainfall together. In areas which are prone to these con-ditions stiff-strawed varieties are useful.

The assessment of the effects of wind on crop yields is difficult but comparisons of crops which are exposed with those provided with shelter give an idea of the mag-nitude of reduction. In cereals, the yield increases from providing shelter vary from 10 to 30 per cent. Recorded ranges for sugar beet, potatoes and soyabeans are 1 to 23, 11 to 50 and 4 to 22 per cent respectively (from Grace, 1977). Precise figures are difficult to establish because of the effects of the variation in wind speed and the dis-tance from the shelter. There is sufficient evidence to suggest that the provision of shelter is worthwhile in exposed areas.

Wind can also cause serious erosion of soil in dry periods. The loss of soil, and seeds and seedlings, is most apparent on the light-textured soils in coastal areas and on high organic matter soils such as the peat Fens of East Anglia. In these areas preventative measures may be necessary to avoid soil and crop losses. Various chemi-cals have been used to stabilise the soil surface after sowing to allow crops to establish. In addition some pro-tection can be given by planting quick-growing crops bet-ween the rows to give initial protection. After the main crop is established these crops are removed. Straw, placed vertically in the soil between the rows, serves the same purpose.

The physical and chemical aspects of the cool temperate environment can be defined for particular locations but regional variations can be large. The producer of field crops has little or no control over the aerial environment and he can only describe his local conditions and adapt his production systems according to the sensitivity of the crops which can be grown. The annual variation in air and soil temperatures and precipitation imposes restrictions on the growth of some crops and in the extreme areas some crops cannot be grown at all. The effects of temperature on crop growth and development are well known and the grower must select appropriate crops for his locality. Similarly the effects of shortage or excess of water supply on growth and development can be large and the use of drainage and irrigation has to be considered.

The grower can exert some influence over temperature and water in his environment, but he has no control over the three main aspects of light. In this case he can only select crops which will perform well under his conditions of radiation receipts and photoperiod. In crops with an obligate photoperiodic requirement this can be a very important aspect.

The adverse effects of wind can to some extent be overcome by the provision of shelter and by careful selection of crop and cultivar. Gaseous pollutants are only likely to be a problem in certain localities.

This text has only considered some of the effects of the physical aspects of the environment in isolation, but in practice they are interacting. The relationship between yield and radiation receipts in crops will not hold if crop growth is being limited by water shortage, wind damage or low temperatures. The grower can only hope to develop a production system which is well adapted to his particular set of interacting factors.

REFERENCES AND FURTHER READING

Allen, E.J. and Scott, R.K. (1980) 'An analysis of the growth of the potato crop'. Journal of agricultural Science, Cambridge, 94, 583-606.

Austin, R.B. and Jones, H.G. (1974) 'The physiology of wheat'. Report of the Plant Breeding Institute, Cambridge for 1974, 20-73.

Biscoe, P.V. and Gallagher, J.W. (1978) 'A physiological analysis of barley yield. I. Production of dry matter'. Agricultural Progress, 53, 34-50.

Canham, A.E. (1966) Artificial Light in Horticulture. Eindhoven: Centrex Publishing Company.

Evans, L.T. (ed.) (1980) Crop Physiology (2nd edn). Cambridge: University Press.

Fitter, A.H. and Hay, R.K.M. (1981) Environmental Physiology of Plants. London: Academic Press.

Gaastra, P. (1962) 'Photosynthesis of leaves and field crops'. Netherlands Journal of Agricultural Science, 10 (5), 311-324.

Grace, J. (1977) Plant Response to Wind. London: Academic Press.

Harper, F. and Ferguson, R.J. (1979) 'The effects of bitumen mulch and sowing date on the establishment and yield of oil-seed sunflower (*Helianthus annuus* L.)'. Journal of agricultural Science, Cambridge, 93, 171-180.

Hough, H.N. (1978) 'Mapping areas of Britain suitable for maize on the basis of Ontario Units'. ADAS Quarterly Review, 31, 217-221.

Hudson, J.P. (1977) 'Plants and the weather'. In Environmental Effects on Crop Physiology, eds. Landsberg, J.J. and Cutting, C.V. London: Academic Press, 1-20.

Johnson, C.B. (ed.) (1981) Physiological Processes Limiting Plant Productivity. London: Butterworth.

Miller, A.A. (1963) Climatology. London: Methuen.

Milthorpe, F.L. and Moorby, J. (1981)  An Introduction to Crop Physiology (2nd edn).  Cambridge: University Press.

Ministry of Agriculture, Fisheries and Food (MAFF) (1974) Irrigation, Bulletin 138.  London: HMSO.

Smith, K. (1975)  Principles of Applied Climatology. Maidenhead: McGraw-Hill.

Sutcliffe, J. (1977)  Plants and Temperature.  Institute of Biology's Studies in Biology, No.86.  London: Edward Arnold.

Wareing, P.F. and Phillips, I.D.J. (1981)  Growth and Differentiation in Plants (3rd edn).  Oxford: Pergamon Press.

Watson, D.J. (1963)  'Climate, weather and plant yield'. In Environmental Control of Plant Growth.  London: Academic Press.

# 4 Site Considerations

The effects of weather on crop growth and development have
been described. The choice of site for a particular crop
or, in more practical terms, the choice of crop for a particular site, is dependent on the adaptability of the crop
to the local weather. Weather patterns in cool temperate
climates vary from year to year and this unpredictability
makes the choice of crop and site difficult.

Temperature and rainfall are the two most important
factors of the weather affecting the performance of a crop
at a particular site. The influence of temperature on the
growth of a sensitive crop, such as maize, is well known
and suitable areas of the country for growing it have been
mapped on the basis of accumulated temperature data (chapter 3). This approach has risks associated with it and
growing areas are defined on the basis of the probability
of suitable temperatures prevailing in nine years out of
ten. The temperature occurring at particular locations
can affect the suitability for growing crops which have
their origins outside cool temperate climates.

The length of the growing season is important. The
date of attainment of suitable soil temperatures determines the sowing date of maize. In eastern Northumberland,
the soil temperature, under grass at 0.3 m depth at sea
level, reaches 10°C on average on May 8 or 9. In eastern

Kent the equivalent dates are April 24 or 25. Maize growth ceases with the first air frost and in equivalent sites in Northumberland and Kent this occurs on November 24 and December 8 respectively. Thus the length of growing season is very different in these two areas and the Ontario Heat Unit totals are also different, 2100 and 2900. The effect on the crop is that, in Northumberland it may achieve a 25 per cent whole crop dry matter and be suitable for ensilage, and in Kent it may achieve a grain moisture content of 40 per cent and be suitable for harvesting for grain.

Maize is an extreme example of the effect of temperature and its importance to the choice of site. Temperate cereals can be grown successfully throughout the lowland areas of the United Kingdom although temperature patterns will affect the length of the growing season. This usually means a later harvest in northern areas and the production of grain with a higher moisture content at harvest, which requires more drying before storage. Wheat requires a longer period to ripen than barley and is not so well-suited to the most northerly areas.

Temperature in the spring affects the early leaf development of crops and determines their ability to efficiently intercept solar radiation. Sugar beet produces higher sugar yields if the period of effective light interception is extended by higher spring temperatures. Potatoes similarly display slow early growth and the period of tuber bulking is shortened with cool spring and early summer temperatures. Higher yields are therefore achieved in areas where spring temperatures are higher and more radiation is intercepted due to a faster development of the leaf canopy. In these examples temperature does not limit the areas where a crop can be grown but does determine the yield potential.

Within cool temperate areas, accumulated temperature units vary. This has two main effects on the choice of site or crop. Firstly the temperature determines whether or not a crop can be successfully grown, e.g. maize. Secondly, with less sensitive crops, temperature determines the length of time from sowing to harvest and the potential yield, e.g. wheat and sugar beet. The effect on yield influences the profitability. The effect on the length of growing season affects the management of subsequent crops, such as determining the date of sowing of autumn cereals or oilseed rape.

Temperatures vary with latitude: the further away from the equator the site is, the lower the temperature and the shorter the growing season will be. Altitude also has an influence on temperature and this aspect of the site should be considered as well. Mean monthly air temperature falls by about 1°C for every 160 m increase in altitude. This means that high areas in southerly latitudes of the northern hemisphere can experience temperatures below those optimal for the crop. An example of this is the chalk downlands of southern England which are not well-suited to maize production because of altitude and low soil temperatures resulting from reflection of solar heat from the light-coloured chalky soil.

The risk of frost damage should also be considered when choosing a site. Prolonged periods of freezing temperatures can kill overwintering crops, such as winter cereals, and the risks of such losses should be considered in selecting a crop for a particular area. Meteorological data can supply information on the likely risks from winter kill or late-spring frosts. Within an area, the topography can influence the occurrence of frosts. Cold air is heavier than warm air and falls down slopes. Where natural hollows or obstructions occur at the bottom of slopes, 'frost pockets' can develop. These sites should be avoided for sowing sensitive crops.

Rainfall patterns are also an important consideration in the choice of site. The seasonal distribution and amounts of rain affect the workability of the soil and the irrigation requirement of the crop. In both cases the

soil and crop type influence the degree of effect. High
rainfall in autumn and spring, on heavy-textured soils,
leads to difficulties of seedbed cultivation and may result in later-than-optimal sowing for some crops. Timeliness of operations is a crucial part of a crop production system. The requirement for irrigation is affected
also by summer temperatures and the rate of water loss
from the crop. Most temperate crops respond to irrigation
during drought periods and the need for it must be
assessed for each site and crop.

Irrigation requirements can be calculated from
meteorological, soil and crop data relating to the site.
Rainfall data are valuable in determining the input of
water to the crop within a period. The equation has to
consider also the losses of water from the soil and crop.
A growing crop, with good water supplies, loses 2-3 mm
of water per day during warm but dull summer weather. On
hot summer days the water loss can increase to 3-6 mm.

The ability of a soil to hold available water is important in this context. Soils of different textural
groups can hold different amounts of water. Sandy and
shallow soils, and those containing a high proportion of
gravel, have a low available water-holding capacity,
within 500 mm depth, of < 60 mm (12 per cent by volume).
Organic, peat and deep silt soils can hold more available
water (> 100 mm (20 per cent by volume)). An intermediate
category, of medium water-holding capacity, can be identified and includes a wide range of textural groups.

Rainfall data, water losses from evapotranspiration
and the degree of crop cover, permit the calculation of
the soil moisture deficit (SMD). SMD values can then be
used to calculate the irrigation needs of the crop.
Examples of the irrigation requirements for a range of different crops, on soils of the three water-holding capacity
groups, are given in Table 4.1. In potatoes, which are
susceptible to drought, irrigation is recommended for all
soil categories from the early stages of tuber growth.

Table 4.1 Irrigation requirements of some arable crops in a temperate climate (UK) (source: Ministry of Agriculture, Fisheries and Food, 1979)

| Crop | Response periods and growth stages | Irrigation plan for 3 soil types* mm water at mm Soil Moisture Deficit (SMD) | | |
|---|---|---|---|---|
| | | Low | Medium | High |
| Maincrop and early potatoes | From tuber marble stage onwards | 25 at 25 | 25 at 25-40 | 25 at 25-40 |
| Sugar beet | Maximum SMD 5 mm in June | – | 25 at 40 | No irrigation |
| | Thereafter maximum SMD 75 mm | – | 50 at 75 | – |
| Cereals | From late tillering onwards | 25 at 50 | Irrigation not normally required | |
| Field beans | Early flowering | 35 at 40+ | 35 at 40+ | No irrigation |
| Vining or dried peas | Early flowering | 25 at 25+ | 25 at 25+ | 25 at 25+ |
| | Pod swelling | 25 at 25+ | 25 at 25+ | 25 at 25+ |

* Low, medium and high available water-holding capacity.

96

SMDs are not allowed to reach very high levels with this crop before they are made up by the application of irrigation water. Irrigation of sugar beet is only recommended for the medium soil group. In June, when the root system has not developed fully, irrigation is recommended at a SMD of 40 mm. Thereafter further irrigation is not beneficial unless the SMD reaches 75 mm. Cereals are rarely irrigated except in soils with a very low available water-holding capacity. Field beans only benefit from irrigation after the early-flowering stage when SMDs exceed 40 mm.

The harvestable product of peas for vining is a fleshy pod and seeds of a high water content. Consequently soil moisture deficits should not be allowed to exceed 25 mm during the flowering and pod swelling stage.

The examples in the table illustrate the different requirements of each crop for irrigation water. The stage of growth for which irrigation is necessary is different for each crop. The choice of site should therefore be made with the water requirements in mind. Crops which respond to irrigation should not be grown in areas where rainfall is low and evapotranspiration losses are high during the critical stages of growth, unless irrigation water can be supplied.

Wind damage to crops has already been referred to (chapter 3). Sensitive crops should not be grown in areas which receive high winds unless shelter can be provided.

The topography and aspect of the site can affect the local environment. South-facing slopes warm up more quickly than north-facing ones and this can affect crop growth. This aspect of choice of site is particularly important with crops which require high temperatures.

THE IMPORTANCE OF SOIL FACTORS

Three aspects of soil are important when considering the choice of site for a particular crop: physical, chemical and biological.

The physical characteristics of the soil can affect

crop performance and the use of machinery. Soil texture
is an important concept of the physical characteristics.
In general terms, texture is referred to in relation to
the ease of cultivations, e.g. light, medium or heavy
soils. More specifically, soil texture can be described
as the distribution of particle sizes. Soil can be considered as having three main particle size groups which
are referred to as sand, silt and clay. Mechanical analysis of soils in the laboratory provides information on the
proportions of these three categories, and the use of the
widely-accepted texture diagram (Figure 4.1) allows the

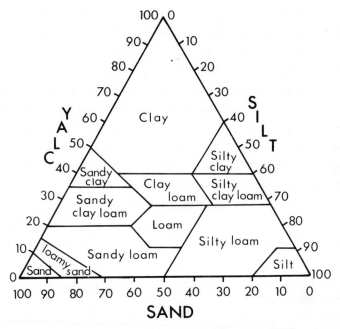

*Figure 4.1 The textural classes of soil used by the United States Soil Survey*

soil to be described in textural terms. The use of the
concept of soil texture relies on there being a close
correlation between the textural class and the 'workability' of the soil. Clay soils are considered difficult
to work and may not be suitable for crops such as potatoes

and vegetables. Sandy and loam soils are generally easier to work by machinery and are suited to a wider range of crops. The ability to work the soil when required in the spring or autumn can have a great effect on the time of sowing of crops and the success of establishment.

Soil texture influences the drainage characteristics of the soil and the water movement through sandy soils is faster than through clays. The differences in water-holding capacity of soils can also affect the likely need for irrigation. The risk of erosion of surface soil is greater with sands and silts especially during periods of heavy rainfall on sloping land. Silt soils are prone to 'capping'; this is the production of a surface crust when they dry out after periods of heavy rain. This physical barrier can impede the emergence of seedlings. Soil texture can therefore affect many aspects of crop production and is an important consideration in the choice of site.

Soil structure is the other main physical character-istic of a soil which determines its suitability for arable cropping. Soil particles are held together in aggregates, the size and shape of which varies. These aggregates are referred to as peds. The size distribution of the peds and that of the pore spaces between them determines the soil structure. Soil structure can in turn influence soil tilth. The structural characteristics of soils can influence several aspects of crop production. Water movement through the soil is by gravity and water only moves freely if the pores between aggregates are greater than 0.3 mm. It is important to maintain a good structure to allow drainage to occur and permit adequate aeration. The ped and pore size distribution of soils also affects root development and the efficiency of water and nutrient uptake by plants.

Small aggregates of soil, of less than 5 mm diameter, are called crumbs. It is important that a good crumb structure is obtained during cultivations to provide a good seedbed. Larger aggregates of more than 10 mm diameter are classified as clods and need to be broken down to produce a good seedbed. With crops which have small seeds, it is important that a soil is selected which will produce a good crumb structure or tilth during cultivations. The ease with which this is achieved depends on the water content of the soil.

Soil structure, unlike texture, is not a stable phenomenon and changes with time and weather factors. Heavy rainfall can break down aggregates and structure can be destroyed. The stability of soil structure is important and can be influenced by the grower. The addition of decomposable organic matter improves crumb stability and farmyard manure is helpful in this respect. Crops which leave large weights of roots and residues behind after harvest also improve structure stability, e.g. cereals. In mixed farming systems, grass and lucerne are valuable in improving structure.

Soil structure can be damaged by the use of heavy machinery when the soil is wet. This is a particular problem on heavy clay soils where the compression and smearing from implements and tractors destroys the aggregate structure. Heavy textured soils should not be worked by machines when they are wet. Autumn ploughing is useful with these soils as it allows the action of frost to create a better structure before spring cultivations. Long-term damage to structure is difficult to remedy and the timing of cultivations is very important. Poor structure results in restricted root growth and drainage problems which give lower yields.

Chemical aspects of soils are also important in site considerations. Soil pH is crucial and analysis should be done regularly to determine the lime requirement. Most arable crops have an optimum soil pH for growth of 6.0 - 6.5, whereas the range found in soils may be 4.0 - 8.0. Crop failures can occur at pH values below 5.0. Over-liming must also be avoided as trace element deficiency problems can occur.

Soil analysis provides estimates of the levels of available nutrients. Potassium and phosphorus are the two elements most commonly determined and levels vary from site to site. A knowledge of the levels of available nutrients can be useful in determining the suitability of the site for a particular crop and in formulating more precisely the fertiliser requirement. Nitrogen residues can be estimated from a knowledge of the previous cropping.

Other elements are required for normal growth of certain crops, e.g. manganese, magnesium and boron for sugar beet. A knowledge of the levels of these elements in soils can help to avoid deficiency problems.

Biological characteristics of soils are complex and will not be dealt with in detail here. The most important aspects which affect the choice of site for crops are the levels of disease organisms and pests which damage crops.

The soil fauna is diverse and includes both beneficial and damaging organisms. Beneficial soil animals are those which break down and incorporate crop residues. This group includes mites and earthworms. Earthworms confer a further benefit in aiding water movement and aeration through the creation of channels in the soil.

The larval stages of many insects are spent in the soil and their feeding habits can result in damage to crops. The larvae of the click beetle (*Agriotes* spp) are called wireworms and they feed for more than two whole seasons before pupating. During this time they feed on the roots of crop plants with serious effects. The risk of wireworm damage to arable crops is greater after grassland is ploughed. Chafer grubs (larvae of chafer beetles) similarly live in the soil and feed on roots and tubers.

The larval stage of many of the true flies is spent in the soil. The crane fly (*Tipula* spp) larvae, or leatherjackets, are most numerous under grassland and can present a problem to succeeding crops. There are a number of root fly pests of arable crops which feed for shorter periods of time in the soil but which are equally damaging. The

101

carrot (*Psila rosae*) and cabbage (*Erioischia brassica*) root fly larvae feed on the root systems and weaken or kill the host crops. The adult egg-laying patterns, and subsequently the feeding periods of the larvae, are predictable and a reduction in the damage can be achieved by manipulating the sowing date to avoid times of high risk (Figure 4.2). Wheat bulb fly (*Leptohylemyia coarctata*) is a further example of this kind of pest.

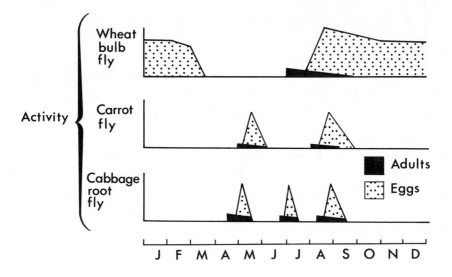

*Figure 4.2 Diagram of the adult activity periods and egg stages in the life cycles of three 'root' fly pests.*

The larvae of some moths live in the soil and cutworms can cause serious damage to young plants and potato tubers. Adult millipedes live in the soil and can cause seedling losses in sugar beet. Slugs are important soil pests of many crops.

A further group of soil-inhabiting pests which can cause crop damage are the eelworms or nematodes. Free-living eelworms cause damage by feeding on roots and in some cases transmitting virus diseases. The most important

Table 4.2 Cyst nematode pests of arable crops (after Jones and Jones, 1974)

| Species | | Host family and crops affected |
|---|---|---|
| Globodera rostochiensis | Solanaceae | Potato and tomato |
| " pallida | | |
| Heterodera schactii | Chenopodiaceae | Sugar beet, fodder beet, mangel |
| | Cruciferae | All brassicas |
| | Polygonaceae | Rhubarb |
| | Caryophyllaceae | Weeds |
| | Labiatae | " |
| | Scrophulareaceae | " |
| " goettingiana | Leguminosae | Pea, field bean, broad bean |
| " carotae | Umbelliferae | Carrot |
| " cruciferae | Cruciferae | All types of brassicas |

103

eelworm pests are the cyst-forming types (Table 4.2). These are usually host-specific, e.g. potato and sugar beet, but they can survive on alternative weed hosts. At a certain stage in the life cycle, the female eelworms are fertilised and their bodies become distended with eggs. After this stage, the females develop into the cysts which can remain in the soil, in a viable state, for five years or more until the eggs are stimulated to hatch by the root exudates of a suitable host plant. The young larvae then feed on the roots of the host plant. The persistence of the cysts in the soil creates problems of control by rotations. When susceptible host plants are grown on a site, the risk of cyst eelworm attack should be assessed. This can be done by considering the occurrence of susceptible hosts in the previous cropping programme or by analysis of the soil for viable cysts.

A number of important diseases can survive in the soil for long periods between crops and the choice of site should take this into account. Cereal diseases such as take-all (*Gaeumannomyces graminis*) and eyespot (*Cercosporella herpotrichoides*) can survive on root and straw residues and infect the following cereal. This does not preclude the growing of a further cereal crop, but yield losses may occur. In the case of eyespot in succeeding wheat crops, the effects of the disease can be reduced by the use of fungicides. Take-all cannot be controlled in this way.

Club root disease of brassicas (*Plasmodiophora brassicae*) is a persistent soil-borne disease and can survive in the resting spore stage for long periods. Susceptible brassica crops should not be grown on infected land for at least five years. Club root survives better in acid and poorly-drained soils and its incidence can be reduced by good soil management. Other soil-borne diseases such as *Sclerotinia* root rot, which affects a range of crops, and *Fusarium* rots of cereals can cause serious crop losses.

The risk of pests and disease attack on particular

sites should be carefully assessed. Because of the host-specificity of most of the organisms, previous cropping programmes provide an indication of the risks and, in some cases, soil analysis is helpful. Rotational aspects of crop production are considered later in this chapter.

DRAINAGE

The effects of excessive soil water on the growth of plants have already been referred to. A feature of the weather in cool temperate climates is the variation in the seasonality of rainfall. Large amounts of rainfall can result in waterlogging of the soil for periods of time which can cause damage to crops. This is particularly true with the heavy-textured clay soils in wet areas and where the soil water table is consistently high. In these situations crop growth can be improved by draining the land.

There are a number of situations where drainage could be implemented. In the reclamation of previously un-cropped land, drainage may be necessary to allow intensification. Drainage may also be used where a change in the farming pattern is envisaged. An example of this is where grassland is ploughed out to make way for arable crops such as cereals. Drainage may also be necessary where a breakdown in the existing system occurs and the problems of difficult cultivation and low crop yields arise. Under marginal conditions on arable land drainage may be employed to improve yields (Calvert and Morris, 1974).

Yield improvements from drainage are difficult to quantify and few good experiments have been carried out. On clay soils, yield benefits of approximately 20 per cent have been recorded with cereals from draining. The use of pipe drains and moling on a clay soil in the West Midlands of England increased the yields of winter wheat by up to 27 per cent (Trafford and Oliphant, 1977) (Table 4.3). Other work with winter wheat has shown different results, with yield losses from waterlogging ranging from 0 per

105

Table 4.3  Effect of drainage treatments on a heavy clay soil on winter wheat yields in tonnes per hectare (after Trafford and Oliphant, 1977)

| | Control | Drains @ 15 m | Drains @ 30 m | Drains @ 60 m | Mean | % |
|---|---|---|---|---|---|---|
| Control | 3.69 | – | – | – | 3.69 | 100 |
| Drains only | – | 4.17 | 4.47 | – | 4.28 | 116 |
| Drains and subsoiling | – | 4.63 | 3.80 | 4.16 | 4.20 | 114 |
| Drains and moling | – | 4.81 | 4.62 | 4.67 | 4.70 | 127 |
| Means | 3.69 | 4.45 | 4.29 | 4.42 | | |
| % | 100 | 121 | 116 | 120 | | |

cent, with crops of below average yields, to 15 per cent, with high yielding crops.  Wheat is most sensitive to waterlogging after germination, and seedling establishment may be only 10 per cent of the target value.  Wheat can partly compensate for such losses by tillering (Belford and Cannell, 1980).  Peas are very sensitive to waterlogging and yields can be reduced by 50 per cent after only five days exposure at the sensitive stage just before flowering.  The optimum water table depth varies for different crops; for cereals it is 100-120 cm and for potatoes 50-60 cm.  There is sufficient evidence to suggest that substantial yield benefits result from good drainage and lowering of the water table.

Other benefits result from good drainage.  A good soil structure is easier to maintain on drained heavy soils. An important benefit of drainage is that field operations can be done at the correct time with the minimum of damage to soil and crops.  This is particularly important with cultivations and in the application of fertiliser and crop protection chemicals.  The efficiency of fertiliser use is increased through deeper rooting of crops.  Drainage also increases the range of crops which can be grown and gives more flexibility in the system. Drained soils warm up quicker in the spring and good crop establishment is more readily achieved.

Several aspects of mechanisation are also improved by drainage. Machines can be used at the right time, which avoids damage to the machine and soil and saves on fuel. The speed of work is increased by good traction and fewer cultivations are necessary to produce a tilth. Management of well-drained farms is easier and the value of the land is increased.

The financial benefits of drainage are difficult to quantify but in arable farming systems the other benefits described are undoubtedly valuable.

The type of drainage system employed needs to be carefully assessed for individual sites and expert advice should be sought. In many countries, drainage schemes qualify for government grants and these are not provided unless the plans are made by specialists. The drainage system employed depends on the texture of the soil and the topography of the land and also the rate of water movement through the soil (hydraulic conductivity). Three main methods are available:

(i) *Pipe systems* — these systems involve the use of plastic or clay pipes which collect the water moving through the soil and carry it away to an open ditch. The pipes are laid in trenches and may be covered by a layer of permeable backfill before the topsoil is returned. The arrangement of the pipe system and the depth at which it is placed should be assessed for individual sites.

(ii) *Moling* — this involves the creation of channels by dragging a cylindrical metal object (bullet) through the soil. The cylinder is attached to a blade which is fixed to a tractor-drawn implement. A ball may be attached to the cylinder by a chain. In addition to creating a channel for drainage water, the operation may also create fissures in the surrounding soil, if it is done under the right conditions, which further aids water movement. Moling is more suitable for heavy textured soils where the channels will remain open and functional for a long period. It is often used over pipe systems with soils of low hydraulic conductivity. This technique is only suitable for soils which show stability to water and which are plastic over a reasonable range of moisture contents to allow the formation of the mole channel. Soil moisture contents of between 14 and 16 per cent of water by weight are optimal for moling.

(iii) *Subsoiling* — this involves the use of a machine consisting of a toolbar with a blade mounted vertically into the soil. Attached to the bottom of the blade is a 'foot' with an angled leading edge. As the machine moves through the soil the foot lifts and shatters the soil forwards at an angle of about 45°. The foot may also have wings attached to increase the effective width. Deep subsoiling (> 40 cm) is intended to improve horizontal water movement in the subsoil which allows wider pipe drain spaces to be used. Shallow subsoiling (< 30 cm) is usually used to break up compaction pans, caused by cultivations, or chemical pans. In both cases the subsoiler allows water movement down the profile to the permanent drainage system. Pans can occur in soils of all textures and they not only affect water movement, but also restrict rooting depth. Land should only be subsoiled when it is dry. The distance between passes varies between 60 cm and 1 m.

Sensible use of these drainage methods can result in the benefits described earlier. The drainage characteristics of a soil are an important factor in deciding on a suitable site for sensitive crops.

## THE IMPORTANCE OF ACCESS TO A MARKET

The choice of site for particular crops can depend on the accessibility of a market for the product. In the case of cereals, the market structure is well-developed and there is usually easy access to a grain merchant, maltster or miller. In many cases cereals can be stored on the farm for long periods of time without deterioration and quick access to a market is not necessary. In the United Kingdom, large quantities of grain never go to a market and are used on the farm for feeding livestock. Where grain is sold off the farm, transport costs to the market or store can affect the profitability of the crop and these can be substantial. Movement of grain for particular market outlets, such as wheat for breadmaking and barley for malting, can involve long distances, but this is usually the responsibility of the merchant and not the producer. A similar situation exists with exported grain.

The market structure with other crops is often not so simple. In the case of sugar beet in the United Kingdom, the crop has to be processed through a factory. The area of beet grown is controlled by a quota system on a contract basis. Although haulage costs may be built into the contract price, the bulk of crop which has to be moved in this case makes transport over long distances prohibitively expensive. Nearness to a processing factory is therefore essential. Originally there were 18 beet processing factories in Scotland and England but, by 1982, this had been reduced to 13. The factories are situated in the areas most-suited to growing the crop in eastern England, the east and west Midlands and Yorkshire (Figure 4.3). Reliance on processing outlets of this nature can make growers vulnerable to economic and political changes which may require the closure of a factory.

Other crops may also need to be grown on farms close to processing factories. Vining peas are grown for the frozen food market and the farms must be near enough to

109

*Figure 4.3  Location of sugar beet growing areas and factories in England*

the factory to allow quick transport after harvest, before
the quality declines.  The location of such factories may
not be based on purely agricultural considerations and
this prevents farmers growing such crops in potentially
productive areas.  The seasonal nature of the freezing pea
product means that other crops are required in the area to
provide a continuous flow of products to the factories.
This usually means the production of large-scale vegetable
crops, e.g. Brussels sprouts and green beans, which in-
jects diversity into the farming of an area.

In the case of crops yielding a product for the fresh
market, which has a short shelf-life, it is important for
the producing-farm to be near a market.  Field vegetable

110

crops such as cauliflowers and cabbages are in this category. Areas of these crops are usually concentrated
around large centres of population. The concentration of
vegetable growers around London illustrates this point.
A further example is the vegetable growing area in the
Vale of Evesham which supplies fresh vegetables to the
urban areas of the west Midlands. This pattern is not
always followed and the vegetable growing areas of the
Fens of England are not near to any centres of population.
The suitability of the soil and climate for vegetables in
this area is the main reason why they are grown. Nevertheless good rail and road links to the industrial areas
to the north and south allow rapid transport of perish-
able products to a market. In the absence of a nearby
market, special storage arrangements may be necessary on
the farm. This inevitably means the use of refrigerated
stores and these are costly to install and operate.

Market considerations are not so important in the
choice of site for potatoes. In the case of earlies,
climatic considerations are much more important to achieve
early lifting to obtain the highest price. A high price
for the product can offset the extra costs of haulage
needed to market it. Similarly with seed potatoes, the
extra returns for the product can in part meet the cost of
transport from the area of production to the area of use.
It is preferable to produce disease-free tubers in remote
areas which are climatically suitable and incur the extra
cost of haulage. In this situation growers must be compensated for lower yields and higher growing costs.

Markets for ware potatoes are more uniformly distributed in the United Kingdom and the merchant link with the
retailer relieves the grower of the additional transport
costs. In addition there is no great urgency to market
ware tubers which can be stored on farms for long periods.
However the bulky nature of this crop requires that haulage distances are not too great. In the case of potatoes
for crisping, canning or other processing outlets, a

higher price is usually paid for a higher quality product and greater haulage costs can be justified.

Oilseed crops have increased in importance in the European Economic Community since 1970. The extraction of oil from the seeds of rape and sunflower is an industrial process and the seed may have to be transported long distances. The use of subsidies to guarantee a high price and the development of marketing co-operatives have helped to offset high transport costs with the rape crop.

Consideration of these examples has illustrated the importance of marketing arrangements to the choice of site. In the case of cereals in mixed farming systems, the grain is consumed on the farm and the problem of marketing does not apply. However with crops such as sugar beet and vegetables for processing, easy and cheap access to a factory is crucial. Thus the choice of site for many crops is an important decision which can affect the profitability of an enterprise.

CROP SEQUENCES OR ROTATIONS

The practice of growing a sequence of crops on the same piece of land or field has been employed for a long time. Towards the end of the nineteenth century, fixed rotations developed which were typified by the Norfolk four-course rotation. This employed the following sequence of crops: roots, barley, clover ley and wheat.

The reasons for adopting a particular sequence of crops are numerous. A common objective is to disrupt the life cycle of persistent pests and diseases by avoidance of susceptible crops for a number of years. The cyst nematodes referred to earlier provide a good example of this, where a break of five years between susceptible crops reduces the pest level below one at which economic damage occurs. Club root disease of brassicas is a further example of where long breaks from susceptible host crops can reduce the level of inoculum of the organism in the soil. In both of these cases, the rotation only

fulfils this objective if intervening crops are kept free
of alternative weed hosts.  Club root, for example, infects a wide range of cruciferous weed plants such as
charlock and shepherd's purse.

A further argument for adopting a sequence of crops is
based on soil fertility considerations.  The inclusion of
a legume in a cereal system certainly confers a short-term
benefit to the succeeding crop through the residual nitrogen that it leaves in the soil.  However fertiliser nitrogen can be substituted for this benefit, and this argument
is largely of historical interest while the price of
nitrogen fertiliser remains competitive.  Soil organic
matter levels are depleted in all-cereal systems and this
can be detrimental to soil structure and water-holding
capacity in the longer term.  The inclusion of a grass ley
in the rotation will help to temporarily replenish soil
organic matter levels but this is only attractive on farms
with livestock enterprises.  On mixed-arable farms, there
is a stronger case for rotations, where the use of more
productive short-term leys necessitates reseeding areas of
the farm and this is often most easily achieved by under-
sowing a cereal crop.  In this example, both the forage
and arable parts of the system benefit from the rotation.
In addition, grazing livestock on grass, or other forages,
results in recycling of nutrients and the return of
organic matter through the faeces.

Modern arable farming systems, in developed countries,
do not adhere so rigidly to the former rotations.  In many
areas, farming systems, through the decline in the labour-
force and the increase in mechanisation and use of crop
protection chemicals, have been simplified.  This simpli-
fication has led to monoculture in some crops.  Continuous
cereal cropping is common in many parts of the cool temperate countries.  This is not a surprising development
and the famous Rothamsted experiments of continuous wheat
and barley have provided evidence that yields can be maintained at reasonable levels if the fertiliser input is

113

high enough. These experiments, now concluded, were
carried out for over 100 years. There are a number of
advantages of continuous cereal cropping which have led
to its adoption:

  (i) simplicity of management
 (ii) reduction in the range of machinery required
(iii) low labour requirement
 (iv) a ready market for the product at a guaranteed price
      within the European Economic Community
  (v) yield levels can be maintained with the currently
      available fertiliser and crop protection products
 (vi) field operations can be planned with greater
      precision.

   However, there are many crops where continuous production is not possible or permitted. Before 1983 contracts for sugar beet growers required that the crop
should not be grown for a period of years on fields known
to be infected with the cyst nematode or where other host
crops have been grown. Similar constraints apply to
potatoes and peas. In these cases and in mixed farming
systems there are still strong arguments for a specific
sequence of crops of different botanical families.
   It is also evident with cereals that there are serious
disadvantages associated with continuous cropping. These
include:

  (i) a greater incidence of soil-borne fungal diseases.
      This is particularly the case with take-all and
      eyespot, although other diseases may be influenced.
 (ii) problems of weed control. This is particularly
      true for grass weeds such as couch (*Agropyron
      repens*), wild oats (*Avena fatua* and *A. ludoviciana*)
      and blackgrass (*Alopecurus myosuroides*). Where
      these weeds become a problem, control is difficult
      and expensive. Grass weed problems have been
      aggravated by the reduction in cultivations for

114

cereals which has accompanied the move towards monoculture.

(iii) problems of soil-borne pests, such as the cereal cyst nematode, wheat bulb fly and slugs.

(iv) decline of soil fertility and organic matter levels. This may require additional inputs of expensive fertilisers and make the crops more prone to drought in dry periods.

(v) continuous cereal growers are more vulnerable to changes in market trends and prices.

(vi) the labour demands are highly concentrated with peaks at sowing and harvesting times and in the early summer when crop protection chemicals are applied.

(vii) straw disposal is a problem. Burning can be beneficial, but it is socially and environmentally undesirable. Ploughing-in is costly and may result in increased fertiliser requirements and disease problems.

(viii) combine harvesters can spread weed seeds around the farm unless precautions are taken.

These disadvantages have to be weighed against the advantages of a cereal monoculture. If one or more of the disadvantages becomes unacceptable then another crop may have to be grown to reduce the effects. In cereal systems, other crops grown to reduce the damaging effects of monoculture are called break crops. In order to be acceptable, break crops must satisfy a number of criteria:

(i) produce satisfactory yields

(ii) produce a product of sufficiently high quality to meet market requirements

(iii) produce an economic return for the farmer

(iv) provide an opportunity to control persistent weeds either by cultivations or the use of a wider range of herbicides than was available for the previous crop.

    (v) disrupt the life cycles of pests and diseases
   (vi) allow the use of the same machinery and storage
        facilities as the main crop in the rotation
  (vii) show adaptability to the climate of the area
 (viii) provide consistency of yield and quality from year
        to year
   (ix) fit in with the work programme of the farm and not
        create labour peaks at the same time as other crops.

    Few crops will fulfil all these requirements. However
in cereal systems, oilseed rape is a useful break crop
and, although it has its own production problems, fits in
well. Other crops which are suitable in cereal systems
include field bean, sunflower, linseed, dried peas,
herbage seed and other seed crops. Sugar beet and potatoes
do not fulfil many of the criteria listed and in particular require a higher investment in machinery and storage
facilities. Large areas of these crops need to be grown
to justify the extra investment, despite the potentially
high returns. Grass and other forage crops are only suitable as break crops if livestock enterprises exist on the
farm.

THE EFFECTS OF PREVIOUS CROPPING

The preceding crop in a sequence can have a number of
implications for the subsequent one. The problem from
pests and diseases through continuous cropping has already
been referred to. A further good example is the increased
risk of wheat bulb fly in crops grown after the soil has
been bare for some time, which encourages egg-laying, e.g.
early harvested potatoes. Residues from a previous crop
can cause problems. If trash from a crop is not disposed
of adequately, problems may result with cultivations for
the next crop. Straw disposal causes problems in this
respect, especially where the succeeding crop is autumn-
sown and there is only a short period between harvesting
one and sowing the next. The haulms of vining peas and

potatoes can also cause cultivation difficulties. Where the previous crop is grass it is important to kill the old turf, either by a herbicide or by good ploughing-in. If this is not done, cultivations are difficult, poor establishment of the next crop can occur in old pieces of turf and the grass may regrow and compete with the succeeding crop.

A further reason for good disposal of crop residues is the problem of crop establishment which results from chemical breakdown products. Chemicals produced from the breakdown of cereal straw (acetic and other fatty acids) can adversely affect the establishment of the following cereal crop.

A further consequence of previous cropping to subsequent management is the need to modify fertiliser policies according to the amounts of nutrients removed. This aspect will be dealt with in more detail in chapter 9. Nitrogen fertiliser levels can be reduced where the previous crop was a legume, grazed grass or forage or potatoes. In contrast, with second or third cereal crops, the nitrogen levels are increased to compensate for the large quantities removed and the unavailability of that present from residues. The quantities of elements removed are proportional to the size of the previous crop and its fertiliser input. The fertiliser policy for the subsequent crop should be calculated with this in mind. The removal of potassium and phosphorus also has to be taken into account. Where large quantities of potassium have been removed, as with grass which is conserved, kale or sugar beet, extra consideration should be given to the requirements of the next crop. Potatoes remove large quantities of phosphorus and potassium.

The time of harvest of the previous crop can affect the field operations for the next one, especially if it is autumn-sown. In continuous autumn cereals, there is a short period between harvest and the next sowing. During this period crop residues have to be disposed of, weeds

117

have to be controlled and cultivations carried out for the next crop. This leads to a concentration of work in the late-summer and early-autumn. This problem is aggravated where the next crop has an early optimum sowing date, e.g. mid- to late-September for winter barley. In the case of autumn-sown oilseed rape, where sowing in August is desirable, this problem is particularly acute. The earlier harvest of winter barley, relative to other cereals, permits August sowings and provides a good example of the importance of selecting an appropriate sequence of crops. Late-harvested potatoes and sugar beet are not ideally suited as previous crops for oilseed rape and winter barley. A further consequence of the short period between some crops is that there may not be time to complete a full set of cultivations, and some form of reduced cultivation or direct drilling may be necessary.

An awareness of the weed populations in the previous crop is helpful in planning a future herbicide programme. Perennial grass weeds, such as couch, cannot be effectively controlled in a growing crop and pre-sowing treatment is necessary. This may have to be done in the short period between crops or, as in the case of the herbicide glyphosate, in the mature preceding cereal crop. Black-grass and wild oat seeds can be shed in the previous crop and this burden of weed seeds must be catered for in a future cropping programme. Annual broad-leaved weeds are more easily controlled with the wide spectrum of herbicides available. The risk of problems from plants of the previous crop must also be considered, e.g. volunteer cereals, which can carry diseases, and potatoes.

The effects of previous cropping on subsequent crops can have important consequences. The management of a crop must therefore consider the range of factors involved.

REFERENCES AND FURTHER READING

Belford, R.K. and Cannell, R.Q. (1980) Crop Response to Waterlogging and Drainage. Report of Conference on

Field Drainage Research. Aberdeen: North of Scotland College of Agriculture.

Bunting, E.S., Pain, B.F., Phipps, R.H., Wilkinson, J.M. and Gunn, R.E. (eds.) (1978) Forage Maize Production and Utilisation. London: Agricultural Research Council.

Calvert, J.T. and Morris, J. (1974) A Financial Cost/Benefit Study of Selected Drainage Projects in the Eastern Part of England. Occasional Paper No.2 of National College of Agricultural Engineering. Silsoe, Bedfordshire.

Eddowes, M. (1976) Crop Production in Europe. London: Oxford University Press.

Ellis, F.B. and Lynch, J.M. (1976) Crop Establishment in the Presence of Straw Residues. Report of Agricultural Research Council Letcombe Laboratory for 1976, 53-54.

Jones, F.G.W. and Jones, M.G. (1974) Pests of Field Crops. London: Edward Arnold.

Ministry of Agriculture, Fisheries and Food (1974) Irrigation Bulletin 138. London: HMSO.

Ministry of Agriculture, Fisheries and Food (1979) Irrigation Guide. Booklet 2067. Pinner, Middlesex: MAFF (Publications).

Ministry of Agriculture, Fisheries and Food (1981) Drainage Benefits. Leaflet 722. Alnwick, Northumberland: MAFF (Publications).

Ministry of Agriculture, Fisheries and Food (1981) Subsoiling. Leaflet 730. Alnwick, Northumberland: MAFF (Publications).

Ministry of Agriculture, Fisheries and Food (1981) Mole Drainage. Leaflet 731. Alnwick, Northumberland: MAFF (Publications).

Roy, M.G. and Hough, M.N. (1978) 'Effects of weather and climate on modern British farming'. Journal of the Royal Agricultural Society of England, 139, 43-53.

Russell, E.W. (1973) Soil Conditions and Plant Growth

(10th edn).   London: Longman.

Smith, C.V. (1979)  'Weather and field work planning'.
Agricultural Progress, 54, 57-65.

Sutcliffe, J. (1977)  Plants and Temperature.   Institute
of Biology's Studies in Biology No.86.   London:
Edward Arnold.

Taylor, J.A. (ed.) (1968)  Weather and Agriculture.
Oxford: Pergamon Press.

Trafford, B.D. and Oliphant, J.M. (1977)  'The effect of
different drainage systems on soil conditions and crop
yield of a heavy clay soil'.   Experimental Husbandry,
32, 75-85.

Trafford, B.D. (1977) 'Recent progress in field drainage.
Part I'.   Journal of the Royal Agricultural Society
of England, 138, 27-42.

Trafford, B.D. (1978)  'Recent progress in field drainage.
Part II'.   Journal of the Royal Agricultural Society
of England, 139, 31-42.

# 5 The Importance of Plant Breeding

The evolution and domestication of crop plants has been referred to in chapter 1. It is clear that a number of plants have been grown as crops for several millenia, e.g. cereals, although many are of more recent introduction, e.g. sugar beet. Throughout the period of domestication growers have selected superior individuals from large populations for seed for the succeeding crop. Gradual improvements in crop performance, based on this simple selection process, have been achieved. Natural selection in plant populations has also occurred with domestication.

The manipulation of the genetic variability in crop plant populations by man has been more recent and in western Europe gained momentum in the first two decades of the twentieth century. Plant breeders have improved the yield and quality of most of the major crops substantially since that period and plant breeding is now a large industry.

The methods and techniques employed in plant breeding are complex and will not be dealt with here. Other texts deal in detail with these aspects (Allard, 1960; Simmonds, 1979). However, the grower should have a basic knowledge of the principles of plant breeding and of their significance to crop production. The correct choice of cultivar for a particular site is an important management decision and can have a large effect on the profitability of an enterprise.

The extent of improvement in crop yields over a period of time from using improved genotypes is difficult to evaluate. One of the reasons for this is that the technology of production also changes with time and it is difficult to separate out the contribution to improved yields from any one source. Furthermore, the expression of the genotype characteristics is modified by environmental influences in the field and straightforward analyses of genotypic effects are difficult.

One example of an attempt to quantify the contribution to increasing national average yields from the use of improved varieties is a study with barley and wheat in the United Kingdom by Sylvey (1978). Data were collected on national average yields and the popularity of different varieties over a thirty-year period. Estimates were made of the effect of variety on yield. From 1947 to 1977 the five-year moving average yields of wheat increased at a rate of 3 per cent per annum. Barley increased at a rate of more than 2 per cent over the same period.

The contribution to increased yields from varieties and other sources in barley is illustrated in Figure 5.1. From 1947 to 1975, the yields increased by approximately 63 per cent, of which 30 per cent is attributable to the use of improved varieties. Most of this increase due to variety occurred in the ten-year period 1947-57 (16 per cent). The improvement in wheat yields over the same twenty-eight-year period was 84 per cent, of which 50 per cent is attributable to variety. In contrast to barley, most of the improvement due to variety with wheat occurred in the period 1967-1975 (24 per cent). These estimates provide a useful indicator of the value of better varieties to improving cereal yields and emphasise the need for the grower to choose his varieties carefully. The increases from sources other than from improved varieties, in the example, can be attributed to improved technology, such as the use of crop protection chemicals and higher fertiliser inputs.

122

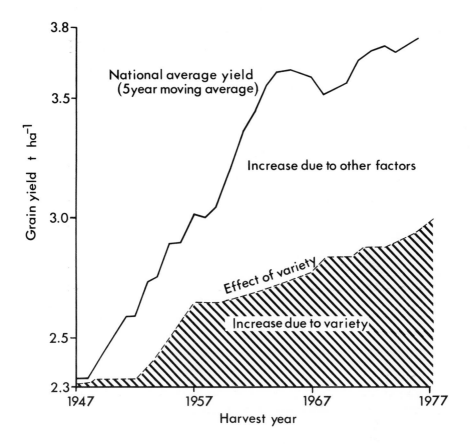

*Figure 5.1  The estimated effects of variety on increases in national average barley yields in England and Wales (1947-1977) (after Sylvey, 1978)*

Examples for other crops are lacking, but an estimate of the effect of variety on maincrop ware potato yields suggests that the contribution from variety is much smaller at 21 per cent over the period 1957-1977 (Harris, 1980) in England and Wales.

THE CHANGING VARIETY SCENE

The state of varieties or cultivars is dynamic and new varieties are constantly appearing as others go out of use. The progressive grower, who is aiming to achieve high

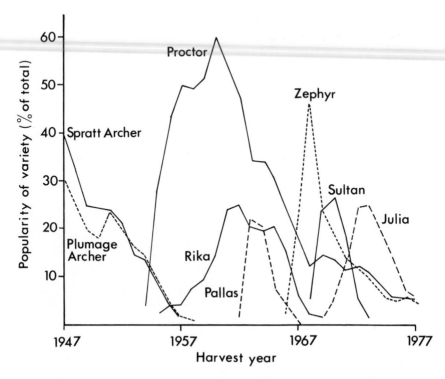

*Figure 5.2  Changes in the popularity of some spring barley varieties in England and Wales (1947-1977) (estimates from seed sample data from the Official Seed Testing Station and MAFF seed sales survey) (after Sylvey, 1978)*

yields on a regular basis, should therefore review his selection of varieties annually.  The changing nature of the popularity of varieties over time is illustrated for spring barley in Figure 5.2 (Sylvey, 1978).  For simplicity, a number of other varieties which were grown in the period in question have been ommitted.  In 1947, the spring barley area was dominated by the varieties Spratt Archer and Plumage Archer but these declined to low levels over the next ten years.  In 1954, Proctor was introduced and this increased rapidly to occupy over 60 per cent of the area in 1960.  After this date, the popularity of Proctor declined steadily through to 1977 when it occupied approximately 5 per cent of the area.  Rika and Pallas occupied significant areas in the 1960s but these also declined. The area of Zephyr increased rapidly from 1966-1968 and then declined rapidly. Sultan and Julia showed similar patterns of popularity to Zephyr but were introduced later. The rapid decline of Zephyr and Sultan was largely due to a breakdown in the resistance to powdery mildew disease.

Proctor is unusual in that it has had a useful life of over twenty-five years and this is largely attributable to its suitability for malting. Zephyr, in contrast, was only popular for about five years. Numerous other varieties were grown in the period but few exceeded 10 per cent of the total area grown. A similar changing pattern of variety use is evident with wheat (Sylvey, 1978), which emphasises further the need to review constantly the range of varieties available and select the most appropriate one for the site in question.

Changes in the popularity of maincrop ware potatoes from 1968 to 1979 are shown in Figure 5.3 (the list is incomplete). The most dramatic change has been the rapid decline in the area of Majestic grown, from nearly 35 per cent to 1 per cent. Pentland Crown increased rapidly from 1968 to 27 per cent in 1973 and thereafter the area fluctuated between 21 and 27 per cent of the total. Maris Piper and Desiree increased steadily over the twelve-year period to 16-19 per cent in 1979. Pentland Squire increased from its introduction in 1977 to approximately 5 per cent in 1979. The area of King Edward has declined steadily, while the crisping variety Record increased slowly to approximately 10 per cent in 1979. The variety situation with maincrop ware potatoes, like barley and wheat, is a changing one and in the short twelve-year period some varieties have virtually disappeared while others have increased markedly.

Other examples could be quoted to illustrate the constantly changing picture of crop varieties, but cereals and potatoes serve to emphasise the need to keep pace with

125

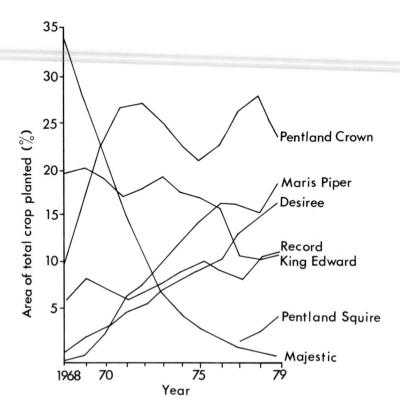

*Figure 5.3   Changes in the popularity of selected maincrop ware potatoes in the United Kingdom, 1968-1979 (National Seed Development Organisation, 1980)*

the rapid developments in plant breeding.

LEGISLATION AND VARIETY TESTING

The competitive nature of the plant breeding industry requires that some form of legal protection is given to
breeders of new varieties.   This became increasingly important from the 1950s with the increased trade in seeds
between countries in western Europe.   The result was the
Plant Varieties and Seeds Act (1964) in the United Kingdom, which gave the breeder the facility to register a
variety in his name and control its multiplication and

126

sale.

The development of testing schemes to evaluate new
varieties, as they become available, has afforded some
protection to the grower and breeder.

Within member countries of the European Economic
Community, new varieties cannot be marketed until they
have been accepted on to a National List. Each country
has its own National List detailing varieties of crops
which have been tested and approved. In order to satisfy
the National List Testing (NLT) requirements new varieties
must undergo two types of test. Firstly, the variety must
be subjected to DUS (Distinctness, Uniformity and Stability) testing which is carried out by an authorised independent establishment, e.g. National Institute of Agricultural Botany (NIAB) for England and Wales. To be distinct,
the variety must be morphologically distinguishable from
varieties already on the list. The uniformity test effectively restricts the variability of the material. The
stability test is designed to ensure that the variety will
breed true from year to year. DUS testing assigns an
identity to a variety and demonstrates that it is potentially certifiable in any seed production or testing
scheme.

Secondly the variety must be subjected to VCU (Value
for Cultivation and Use) tests. This involves field testing to compare the performance of the variety relative to
others on the list. To satisfy the VCU requirements the
new variety must show some advantages over others. This
is usually assessed in yield terms although other criteria
such as quality and disease resistance can be used. VCU
testing effectively eliminates inferior varieties before
they enter the market and ensures a restricted list of
good ones. This helps to reduce the confusion associated
with selecting a variety from a large list.

If a new variety satisfies the NLT criteria, it can
then be marketed. The NLT procedure has protected the
breeder, by definition of the detail of his new variety

127

(DUS), and the grower, by eliminating inferior types (VCU). After NLT trials, the variety is then evaluated in further trials, alongside established varieties, to produce a recommended list from which farmers can make their choice. The recommended list trials are carried out by independent organisations, such as NIAB or the Scottish Agricultural Colleges, at a number of sites. The sites are selected to cover a range of soil types and weather patterns and, in the case of the NIAB, up to fifteen sites are involved. Data from all sites are considered and the recommended list is produced. These lists provide an independent assessment of a variety's worth and are a useful aid to the grower. Recommended list trial sites are often open to the farmer, on selected days, and he can go and see for himself the performance of varieties in his area and make his own judgement. The recommended lists not only contain yield comparisons but also provide useful information on quality characteristics, disease resistance and other important criteria for selection.

The logistics and expense of conducting trials mean that yield data for recommended lists are of necessity collected from a limited number of sites and from small-scale plots. Caution is therefore needed in interpreting such data.

CRITERIA FOR VARIETY SELECTION

Yield

Yield is often of major importance when selecting a variety. Reference to recommended lists of crops provides information on the relative yield performance of a range of varieties. The absolute yields are rarely given as these will vary from site to site. Yields of individual varieties are expressed relative to that of a control or the average yield of all varieties in the trials. In both cases the standard is expressed as 100. The yields of the best varieties may be 12-15 per cent higher than the

control in cereals and this can represent a large increase
in output if transferred to a commercial farm situation.
In contrast the worst varieties may be lower yielding by
12-15 per cent. In the case of a wheat trial where the
average or control yield is 7 t ha$^{-1}$, a 15 per cent increase would result in a yield of 8.05 t ha$^{-1}$ and a similar order of decrease would give 5.95 t ha$^{-1}$. Transformed
into financial terms this can make a substantial difference to the gross margin and profitability. This is an
extreme example but quite small percentage differences in
high yielding crops can have a large effect on output.

*Table 5.1 The effect of site on the yield performance of spring
barley (yield expressed as percentage of the control = 100) (data
from Scottish Agricultural Colleges cereal trials, 1981)*

| | Variety | | | |
| --- | --- | --- | --- | --- |
| | A | B | C | D |
| Site 1 | 109 | 106 | 100 | 107 |
| Site 2 | 99 | 104 | 105 | 104 |
| Site 3 | 103 | 101 | 99 | 101 |
| Site 4 | 86 | 104 | 97 | 115 |
| Mean of all sites (18) | 99 | 101 | 95 | 107 |

Reference has already been made to the limitations of
recommended list trials and the need to treat the information with caution. Table 5.1 illustrates the effect that
site can have on the relative yield of four spring barley
varieties. The data are taken from trials carried out in
Scotland in 1981. The yields of Variety A vary considerably with site and at Site 1 it is superior to other
varieties but at Site 4 it is inferior. Variety B shows
greater stability of yield over a range of sites and, on
average, is similar to the control. Variety C is 5 per
cent lower-yielding than the control over all eighteen
sites, but in these four its performance is similar to
that of the control. Variety D is consistently higher-

yielding than the control especially at Site 4 where a
15 per cent advantage is apparent. Data of this kind
emphasise the effect of local conditions on the yielding
ability of individual varieties and, where possible, local
information on variety performance should be obtained.

In the case of cereals, field beans, oilseed rape and
other grain crops, yields are assessed by weighing the
amounts of seed collected from combine harvesting. This
effectively is the total harvestable grain or seed yield.
Total yield may not be such a useful criterion in crops
like potatoes where the market demands a particular size
grade of tubers. In this case yields are better expressed
as 'marketable yields'. Recommendations for potato
varieties adopt this terminology and, for maincrop ware
varieties, the yield of tubers in the size grade 40-80 mm
is used. In potatoes, and other crops, yields need not be
expressed relative to a control of 100, but can be graded
within an arbitrary scale, which is usually 0-6 or 0-9.

Different yield criteria may be used for other crops.
In sugar beet for example the yield of washed roots and
sugar are more valuable criteria.

Quality

Yield is not the only criterion used for variety selection
and quality can be very important in determining the suitability of the product for a particular market. Genotype
can have a large influence on quality but environmental
influences can be important. In many cases the choice of
variety is of overriding importance in determining the
quality of the product for a particular market. Buyers of
malting barley are only interested in grain from certain
varieties and, in the United Kingdom, the Institute of
Brewing determines which ones are suitable. Golden
Promise barley is favoured by maltsters in Scotland but
others such as Midas and Piccolo may be accepted. Unfor-
tunately for the grower, malting quality varieties are not
necessarily the highest-yielding ones, but the yield

penalty is compensated by a higher price for the product.

Wheat grain sold for milling, bread-making or biscuit-making also has to meet quality requirements and the variety has a big influence here. The National Association of British and Irish Millers determines the acceptability of varieties for the market outlets. Different varieties may be needed for each of these markets. The winter wheat variety Bounty is of good milling and bread-making quality but is not suitable for biscuit-making. The high-yielding variety Brigand is of average milling quality and unsuitable for bread-making, but it is well-suited to biscuit-making. The examples named here may be short-lived, but they serve to illustrate the importance of variety choice in determining the suitability of grain for processing outlets.

Quality in potatoes is also important. The variety Record has long been accepted for crisping, because of its high dry matter and low reducing sugar content. Variety choice also influences the degree of discolouration and disintegration after cooking and this may affect the acceptability of the tubers to the consumer.

The choice of variety is very important in determining the quality of a crop product and careful consideration must be given to this important decision.

Disease resistance
<u></u>

Plant breeders have produced a number of varieties of crop plants with resistance to one or more important diseases. The choice of variety, with disease resistance in mind, is an important part of a disease control strategy. Examples of crops where varieties can be selected on the basis of disease resistance are given in Table 5.2.

Farm surveys have shown that cereal yields are reduced by an average of 12 per cent each year by diseases. Varieties are available with resistance to most of the important diseases except for take-all. Some cereal diseases such as mildew are widespread and the risk from

Table 5.2 *Examples of crops where choice of variety can influence resistance to specific diseases*

| Crop | Diseases |
|------|----------|
| Wheat | powdery mildew, yellow rust, brown rust, *Septoria*, eyespot, loose smut |
| Barley | powdery mildew, yellow rust, brown rust, *Rhyncosporium*, loose smut, net blotch |
| Oats | powdery mildew, crown rust |
| Potato | gangrene, foliage blight, tuber blight, common scab, powdery scab, skinspot, dry rot, leaf roll, severe mosaic, spraing |
| Oilseed rape | stem canker, light leaf spot, downy mildew |
| Sugar beet | downy mildew |

infection is likely to be high. In this case resistance to mildew in a variety is important in most localities. *Rhyncosporium* is more prevalent in the wetter areas and near coasts and thus is more restricted in its distribution. Choosing varieties with resistance to *Rhyncosporium* is important only in areas of high risk. Previous cropping can be an indication of disease risk and resistance to eyespot can be an important consideration in intensive wheat growing systems.

Disease resistance in varieties is only one aspect of a disease control strategy and may not be an adequate measure to reduce economic loss. Resistance to foliage blight in maincrop potatoes is not high and chemical control measures are needed to eradicate the disease. Similarly chemical control of eyespot in wheat may be necessary even where varieties with some resistance to this disease are grown. Even though the use of variety resistance to control diseases may not be completely effective, it may help to reduce the yield losses and save on the use of costly fungicides.

Further aspects of the use of varietal resistance in

disease control strategies are considered in chapter 11.

## Pest resistance

There are few examples of crops where resistance to pests is an important factor in the choice of variety. The best example is resistance to cyst nematodes in potatoes and cereals. The varieties of potatoes resistant to the $RO_1$ pathotype of the cyst nematode include Pentland Javelin, Pentland Lustre, Maris Piper and Cara. The spring barleys Tyra and Tintern, the winter oat Panema and the spring oat Trafalgar are all resistant to the cereal cyst nematode. Resistance to the stem eelworm (*Ditylenchus dipsaci*) occurs in some spring oat varieties.

Other examples of pest resistance in arable crops are lacking, although there is some resistance to slug damage in the tubers of different potato varieties.

## Environmental adaptability

A number of characteristics of crops are important in determining their ability to withstand a range of environmental influences and the choice of variety is important here also. Selected examples are briefly considered here.

Lodging in cereals, and other crops, is influenced by stem diseases and adverse weather conditions of wind and heavy rain. In the absence of diseases, the characteristics of the stem determine the incidence and extent of lodging under bad weather conditions and in systems which use high levels of fertiliser nitrogen. Varieties of cereals differ markedly in stem length and standing power and, in high-risk situations, varieties should be selected which are stiff-strawed. Lodging resistance, or standing power, is important in maize, field beans and oilseed rape and in all cases varieties can be selected with this in mind.

Loss of seed yield and quality can occur, as a crop nears maturity, from ear and grain shedding and from the sprouting of grain in the ear or pod. Varieties of wheat and barley differ in their resistance to shedding and ear loss, and in areas of high risk careful selection of variety can keep these losses to a minimum. Seed shedding is also important in oilseed rape. Sprouting of grains in the ears of cereals or of seeds in the pods of oilseed rape can be reduced by careful choice of variety.

In areas which experience very cold winters, careful choice of variety can reduce plant losses due to frost damage. Selection of variety for winter hardiness is important in winter barley and winter oats in northern areas.

Selection of varieties on the basis of drought resistance can be important with sensitive crops in dry areas. Potatoes are the best example of a crop where varieties differ in their resistance to drought in temperate climates.

In cool temperate climates the short growing season can be a limiting factor to the successful production of a crop. Earliness of maturity is an important consideration in this context. With all the cereal grain crops there is scope for selecting early varieties which are more appropriate for use in the colder areas. In Scotland, the difference in the date of maturity of the latest and earliest spring barley varieties can be six days. The use of varieties which ripen one week earlier than the latest ones can mean that the crop is harvested in better weather conditions and that drying costs can be reduced. Earliness of ripening is also genetically controlled in field beans. In forage maize, varieties differ in their earliness of tasselling and this can influence the period of time available for grain development.

In addition to the examples quoted above, other aspects of crops can be influenced by the choice of variety. Examples of these are resistance to mechanical damage in potato tubers, tolerance of manganese deficiency in cereals and uniformity of shape and colour in vegetables, which can all be determined to some extent by the choice of variety.

It is clear that the choice of variety is an important decision in crop production systems. The genetic variation which exists within crop species has been exploited by plant breeders to present the grower with a range of varieties which exhibit different agronomic characteristics. Selection of varieties on the basis of yield and quality is important but consideration should be given to disease and pest resistance and a wide range of other characteristics. Inevitably no single variety combines all of the desirable characteristics of an ideal crop. Selection for quality invariably results in a penalty in yield or lack of disease resistance. All that the grower can hope to do is to select the varieties which combine the best range of useful characteristics for his farm and production system. Rapid developments in plant breeding mean that new and improved varieties are marketed frequently and the grower should review his choice of varieties annually.

REFERENCES AND FURTHER READING

Allard, R.W. (1960)  Principles of Plant Breeding.
    London: Wiley.
Harris, P.M. (1980)  'Agronomic research and potato pro-
    duction practice'.  In Opportunities for Increasing
    Crop Yield, eds. Hurd, R.G., Biscoe, P.V. and Dennis,
    C.  London: Pitman, 205-217.
Lawrence, W.J.C. (1971)  Plant Breeding.  Institute of
    Biology's Studies in Biology No.12.  London: Edward
    Arnold.
National Institute of Agricultural Botany (1981)  Farmers
    Leaflets Nos. 3,5,7,8,9 and 15.  Cambridge: NIAB.
National Seed Development Organisation (1980)  Potatoes.
    Cambridge: NSDO.
Scottish Agricultural Colleges (1982)  Cereal Variety
    Trials 1981.  Technical Note No.49.  Edinburgh: SAC.
Simmonds, N.W. (1979)  Principles of Crop Improvement.
    London: Longman.

Sylvey, V. (1978)   'The contribution of new varieties to increasing cereal yield in England and Wales'. Journal of the National Institute of Agricultural Botany, 14, No.3, 367-384.

# 6  Crop Establishment

Seeds are the units of propagation of most temperate crops, with the exception of the potato, and successful crop production relies on establishing an adequate population of vigorous plants. A knowledge of the structure and factors affecting the germination of seeds can help in achieving this objective. It is important to sow seed of good quality and in many countries this is achieved by ensuring that it has been subjected to the requirements of a certification scheme. Certification schemes involve two procedures. Firstly, the crop producing the seed is inspected to determine the levels of impurities (varietal and from other crops) and, in some cases, the population of weeds, the seeds of which are difficult to separate after harvest and control. This procedure effectively controls the purity of the sample in the field. Secondly, the seed, after harvest, is subjected to analysis and a germination test. To satisfy the germination test, the sample must exceed the minimum standard for the crop under defined testing conditions. Laboratory analysis of a seed sample assesses the levels of impurities and debris, against agreed standards. As a result of certification the grower is assured of high standards of crop and varietal purity and germination. The standards for certification for each crop differ, but in all cases they result in the sale of high quality seed to the grower.

A knowledge of seed structure can be helpful in understanding the requirements for successful establishment in
the field.  Seeds all have a similar structure in that
they consist of an embryo (the young shoot and root) and
food reserves to sustain growth until the emerged seedling
starts to photosynthesise.  Figure 6.1 shows the structure
of three crop seeds, to illustrate the range which exists.
Wheat is typical of all the monocotyledonous cereals and
has a large endosperm reserve (80-86 per cent by weight)
which consists largely of starch.  The embryo and scutel-
lum comprise only 3-4 per cent of the total weight.  The
rest of the seed consists of the protective outer layers.

The *Phaseolus* bean provides an example of a typical
dicotyledonous seed.  The embryo, consisting of the young
plumule and radicle, occupies a small proportion of the
total seed weight.  Other examples of crops with this seed
structure are field beans, peas and oilseed rape.  The
sugar beet is also a dicotyledon but the structure is

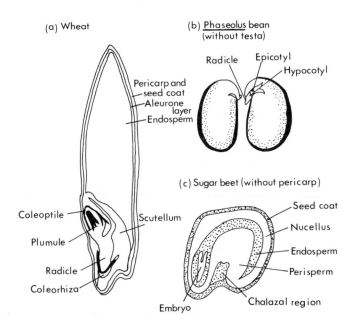

*Figure 6.1  The structure of crop seeds (not to scale)*

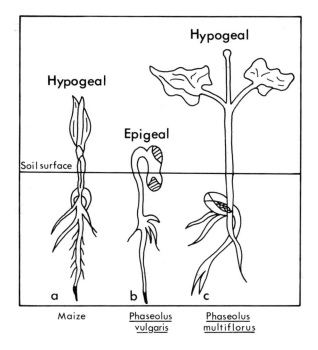

*Figure 6.2  Seedling morphology*

different from the *Phaseolus* example.  In sugar beet, the
food reserves are mainly stored in the perisperm and endosperm rather than in the cotyledons alone.  The whole
structure is surrounded by a thin testa.  The seed is en-
cased in the lignified pericarp which may contain germination inhibitors.  The radicle emerges during germination
by lifting off a seed cap.  The tightness of the seed cap
varies with genotype and can present a barrier to the
emerging radicle.

The type of development of the seedling varies after
germination with different crops (Figure 6.2).  In maize
and other cereals the remnants of the seed remain below
ground while the first leaf emerges from the coleoptile.
This pattern of seedling growth is called hypogeal.  Some
dicotyledonous plants also exhibit this pattern of growth

139

and the cotyledons stay below ground as the first true leaves expand above. Field beans, peas, and the *Phaseolus multiflorus* (see Figure 6.2) behave in this way. Other dicotyledonous seedlings behave differently and the cotyledons emerge above ground, expand and develop chlorophyll. The first true leaf develops after cotlyedon emergence in these cases. The example shows this emergence pattern (epigeal) for *Phaseolus vulgaris*, but oilseed rape and sugar beet show similar early growth.

In the period between the initiation of germination and the emergence of the expanded cotyledons or first true leaf, the seedling is dependent on the reserves stored in the seed. In some seeds, e.g. oilseed rape and sugar beet, these reserves are small and sowing depth must be carefully controlled to ensure that the emergence period is short. In these cases, the sowing depth should not exceed 2-3 cm unless the surface layer of the soil is dry. Large-seeded crops such as maize and field beans have greater food reserves and can be sown deeper at 5 cm or more. Sowing seed deeper than the optimum may be necessary where some soil-acting herbicides are used, to protect them from damage, e.g. tri-allate for wild oat control in cereals and simazine with field beans. Seeds and seedlings are vulnerable to damage from various sources until they start to photosynthesise. Care must be taken to protect the plants in these very early stages of growth.

STORAGE AND SEED TREATMENT

The seed for establishing crops can come from two sources: the seed merchant or from seed grown on the farm. In both cases it is stored on the farm for a period of time before sowing. The storage environment affects the viability of the seed and should be controlled where possible. Seeds can be stored for many years in the correct environment without serious loss of viability. The main environmental factors affecting the viability of seeds during storage

are temperature and moisture. Deterioration of viability
is slowest when seeds are stored at low temperatures and
with a low moisture content. Cereal seeds are normally
dried to moisture content of less than 15 per cent whereas
the smaller oilseed rape seeds are dried to below 9 per
cent. The humidity of the storage environment is also important and should be kept as low as possible. In addition to preventing loss of viability, the storage of dry
seeds in a dry atmosphere prevents the development of fungal organisms, mites and insects which can damage them.
Light is not an important factor in the seed storage environment.

Seeds in store should also be protected from damage
from rodents and birds.

Seeds are often treated in some way before they are
stored and/or sown. The main methods of seed treatment
are summarised below.

(i) Physical. Seed lots after harvesting are often
    graded for size to eliminate the largest and small-
    est seeds. The purpose of this is to remove small
    and unviable seeds and to produce a uniform sample
    which will give a high percentage and uniformity of
    emergence in the field. In addition, the uniformity
    of size after grading makes the seed more suitable
    for use in precision drills. Grading is often pre-
    ceded by a cleaning process to eliminate weed seeds,
    crop debris, stones, soil and other crop seeds.
    Cleaning increases the purity of the seed lot.

    Sugar beet fruits are subjected to a rubbing
    process which removes the outer layers of the peri-
    carp and the remains of the perianth. Rubbing makes
    the fruits more regular in shape and removes a pro-
    portion of the germination inhibitors. After
    rubbing, the fruits are regraded before pelleting.
    Pelleting is the process of coating the fruits in a
    mixture of clay minerals to produce spherical units.

The pellets are more suitable for precision sowing
than the rubbed seed. The pellet must be sufficiently robust to withstand mechanical damage in
handling and in the drill but it must break down
quickly when it comes into contact with soil
moisture.

(ii) Chemical. Various chemical treatments are applied
to seeds. In its simplest form chemical treatment
involves soaking the seeds in water to remove germination inhibitors, e.g. sugar beet. However chemical treatment is more commonly identified with the
application of insecticides and fungicides. Insecticides are applied to protect the seed or young
seedling from damage from soil-borne or aerial
insect pests. A good example of this is wheat seed
which is often treated against wheat bulb fly and
wireworm attack. Brassica seeds are protected from
flea beetle attack by a seed dressing. Fungicides
are also widely used as seed dressings. Fungicidal
seed dressings can either be applied to protect the
seed and seedling from soil- or seed-borne pathogens
or the more mature plant from foliar pathogens.

A good example of both of these objectives is
found with barley. In addition to a fungicide to
protect the seed and seedling, spring barley can be
treated with ethirimol to protect the young plants
against powdery mildew.

Seed treatments with crop protection chemicals
can adversely affect germination and seedling growth.
It is important to ensure that the correct treatment
method is used with the correct quantities of chemical. Excessive amounts of chemicals can reduce the
viability of the seed and result in abnormal seedling growth. Treated seed often has a limited
storage life and its ability to germinate should be
tested after lots have been stored for long periods.
Furthermore the chemicals used may be toxic to the

person applying them, and to other forms of life,
and appropriate safety precautions should be taken.

(iii) *Rhizobium* inoculation.   One of the benefits of
growing legumes is their ability to fix atmospheric
nitrogen in the root nodules, by the action of
*Rhizobium* bacteria.   In soils which have not grown
the selected legume in the past, the appropriate
strains of *Rhizobium* may not be present and good
nodulation does not occur.   In these situations the
seed can be inoculated before sowing with a *Rhizo-*
*bium* preparation.   Inoculation can be achieved by
mixing the seeds with a dry preparation or a slurry,
or by incorporating the *Rhizobium* in pelleting
materials.   The bacteria do not survive for very
long and the seeds must be sown soon after the
treatment.   Inoculation is not necessary with field
beans and peas in most arable soils of temperate
regions.   However, it can be beneficial to soya
beans and lucerne in soils which have no previous
history of growing them.

## FACTORS AFFECTING GERMINATION

In the absence of specific dormancy problems in seeds
(described later) the main factors which affect germination are environmental.   Temperature is very important in
controlling both the percentage and the speed of germination.   In temperate climates most crops are sown in the
spring or autumn when temperatures in the seedbed are
below optimum.   This often results in a slow and low percentage germination.   Most temperate crop plants will
germinate at temperatures as low as 3-5°C but the optimum
range is much higher at 15-37°C (Table 6.1).   Adverse
effects on seed germination due to high temperatures are
not likely to be encountered in temperate regions.   Wheat
seeds will germinate over a wide range of temperatures,
but the optimum is in the range  15-31°C.   In contrast,
maize requires a minimum of 8-10°C for germination and the

*Table 6.1  Temperature ranges in which germination occurs for differ-ent crop seeds (after Mayer and Poljakoff-Mayer, 1975)*

| Crop | Temperature (°C) | | |
| --- | --- | --- | --- |
| | Minimum | Optimum | Maximum |
| Maize | 8–10 | 32–35 | 40–44 |
| Rice | 10–12 | 30–37 | 40–42 |
| Wheat | 3–5 | 15–31 | 30–43 |
| Barley | 3–5 | 19–27 | 30–40 |
| Rye | 3–5 | 25–31 | 30–40 |
| Oats | 3–5 | 25–31 | 30–40 |

optimum range is 32–35°C. It is important with sensitive crops to sow the seeds when the temperature of the seedbed is above the minimum.

The effects of temperature on the germination patterns

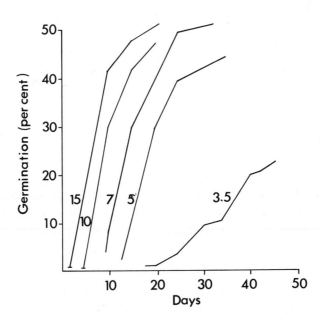

*Figure 6.3  The effect of temperature (°C) on the germination patterns of sugar beet cv. Sharpe's Klein 'E' (after Scott, English, Wood and Unsworth, 1973)*

of sugar beet seeds are shown in Figure 6.3. At 3.5°C
the onset of germination is delayed until almost 20 days
after the beginning of the treatment and then proceeds
slowly to reach a maximum of 25 per cent after 45 days.
In contrast, at 15°C germination starts after 2 days and
proceeds more rapidly to reach a maximum of over 50 per
cent after 20 days.

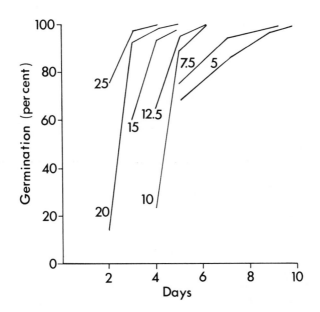

*Figure 6.4   The effect of temperature (°C) on the germination pat-
terns of sunflower cv. Fransol (Harper and Ferguson, 1979)*

The sunflower example in Figure 6.4 shows that the
final germination percentage is not affected by temperature over the range 5-25°C and in all cases reaches
almost 100 per cent. Germination is complete after 6 days
with temperatures above 10°C and after 10 days at 5°C.
These two examples illustrate the different effects of
temperature on the rate of germination and the numbers
which eventually produce emerged radicles.

Water is essential for germination and is taken up by
the dry seed from the seedbed by imbibition. The extent
and rate of water uptake is determined by the composition

of the seed, the permeability of the seedcoat and the availability of water in liquid or gaseous form in the environment. The amount of water taken up by the seed during imbibition is approximately 150 per cent of the original seed weight in wheat, sunflower and maize. It is therefore important to have adequate moisture in the seed-bed at sowing. The availability of water is increased where there is good contact between soil and seed and the seedbed should be consolidated after sowing. In dry seed-beds, large seeds can be sown deeper to ensure adequate moisture supply, although this practice can delay emergence.

Oxygen is also essential for germination and sowing into very wet seedbeds should be avoided. The oxygen supply to the seed depends on the permeability of the seedcoat and the air pore space in the soil. Good drainage can prevent waterlogging of seedbeds and the lack of oxygen supply.

Light is not a limiting factor to the germination of most cultivated plants.

DORMANCY

Dormancy is a period of rest in the life cycle of plants when growth is suspended. Many crop seeds exhibit dormancy which can cause problems with establishment and some processing operations which require the germination of seeds. Viable seeds are said to be dormant when they fail to germinate in favourable environmental conditions. A good example of this is found with freshly-harvested barley seed which may fail to germinate in optimum temperature and water supply conditions. If the seeds are stored for a period of time, which may need to be several months, in a dry state, they will germinate readily when placed in the same environmental conditions. This has serious implications for malting varieties of barley where a rapid and high level of germination is essential. Barley varieties which exhibit dormancy, but which are

suitable for malting in other respects, require to be
stored before being subjected to the malting process.

The causes of seed dormancy are usually related to
their morphology and physiology.  In some members of the
family Leguminosae the seed coat or testa is hard and
impermeable to water.  A good example of this is found
with white clover seeds which will not germinate to their
full capacity unless the seed coat is broken in some way.
This can be achieved by abrasion or the use of concentrated acids.  This source of dormancy is not a problem
with the grain legumes in temperate climates.

Premature harvesting of seeds can lead to immaturity
of the embryo and cause dormancy in this way.  Poor germination of a proportion of sugar beet seeds in a seed bulk
can be attributed to this cause.

Dormancy in some seeds is attributable to the presence
of germination inhibitors in the testa or pericarp.  These
inhibitors are water soluble and can be removed by washing
or soaking the seeds in water for a short period.  In
sugar beet, the inhibitors are concentrated in the pericarp of the fruit and are mainly organic acids, e.g.
gallic, vanillic and p-hydroxy benzoic.  This is one of
the causes of poor germination in sugar beet.

The temporary dormancy in barley grains is attributable to a need for 'after-ripening' in storage.  Wheat
and oats also exhibit this kind of dormancy but to a
lesser extent.  This may lead to problems of establishment
of autumn-sown crops sown after harvest of the seed crop,
unless a suitable period of storage has elapsed.  In contrast, this phenomenon of dormancy can be a useful attri-
bute in preventing seed from germinating in the ear in
periods of high rainfall before harvest.

Some seeds are light-sensitive and will not germinate
unless they are exposed to light when they are imbibed.
This cause of dormancy is not a problem in crop plants
(except for lettuce) but it is a common feature in weeds,
e.g. dock (*Rumex crispus*).  Other seeds require a period

147

of exposure to low temperatures (chilling) when imbibed
before germination will occur. Again this is not a feature of the important crop plants in temperate regions and
is more common in woody species.

Problems from seed dormancy, caused by various factors,
are not of great importance in the major arable crop
plants; the one exception being barley for malting.

Dormancy is not a phenomenon restricted to seeds; it
also occurs in buds. Bud dormancy is important in
potatoes where subsequent growth depends on the development of buds in the eyes of the seed tuber. During the
development of a tuber on the mother plant there is no
true dormancy in the buds, although they only develop very
slowly. After harvest, true bud dormancy is evident and
this may last for 18-33 weeks, depending on the variety.
The normal range for most varieties is 20-23 weeks. The
phenomenon of bud dormancy is useful during the storage
phase when shoot growth is undesirable. Tubers which are
stored for a long period will start to produce shoots
after dormancy has passed if temperatures are high enough.
Sprout growth can be inhibited by storage at low temperature (below 4°C) or by the use of a chemical sprout suppressant, such as chlorpropham with propham or tecnazene.
This is an important factor in the storage of ware
potatoes into the late winter and early spring to achieve
the higher prices which prevail then.

In seed tubers, the breaking of dormancy is necessary
to initiate sprout growth prior to planting. Storage at
low temperature (3-4°C) breaks dormancy and permits
sprout development when the temperature is increased. Bud
dormancy can be broken by chemical treatment also. As
with seeds which require a period of low temperature to
break dormancy, the dormant buds of potato tubers contain
low levels of gibberellic acid and high levels of the
inhibitor, abscisic acid. The treatment of seed tubers
with gibberellins can break dormancy. Dipping the tubers
into a solution of thiourea is also effective in this

respect but removes apical dominance resulting in a multi-sprouted tuber. Exposure of tubers to high temperatures shortens the dormant period.

Once bud dormancy in tubers has been broken the type and rate of sprout growth can be manipulated by varying the temperature, light and humidity of the storage environment. The bulk of the maincrop ware area is planted mechanically and in order to avoid damage in the planter, storage conditions are designed to produce short and sturdy sprouts or to maintain tubers in an unsprouted state. The choice of storage temperature regimes can have large effects on the subsequent growth through altering the physiological age.

## THE CHOICE OF SEED RATE

The seed rate selected for a particular crop determines, in large part, the final plant population density. Aspects of plant population will be considered in chapter 7. However the seed rate has to be selected with the germination and establishment potential of the crop in mind. Laboratory germination standards ensure the viability of the seed, but these are determined under favourable and controlled conditions, and may not be a good indicator of the performance in the seedbed. As a result seed rates are selected with an insurance factor in mind to account for losses during the establishment phase. Establishment is usually high in cereals (80 per cent) but under adverse seedbed conditions it may be less than 50 per cent. The sugar beet seed is very small and, although germination is above 80 per cent, establishment in the field may be as low as 20 per cent. The example of sugar beet illustrates the major sources of poor germination and establishment in crop plants. Some of the points mentioned below are specific to sugar beet but others apply to a wider range of crops.

Sources of poor germination:
   (i) small fruits and seeds
   (ii) water-soluble inhibitors in the pericarp and testa
   (iii) under-developed seeds
   (iv) tight fruit caps
   (v) empty fruits
   (vi) seed-borne pathogens
   (vii) immaturity of the embryo.

Sources of establishment losses:
   (i) bird damage
   (ii) rodent damage
   (iii) poor seedbed tilth
   (iv) compacted seedbed
   (v) sowing too deep
   (vi) low moisture supply
   (vii) fertiliser damage.

Establishment losses are very important in sugar beet which is sown to a stand at a relatively low density. Low establishment can lead to plant populations which are below the optimum. The irregularity of plant distribution which is associated with poor establishment can also depress sugar yields.

Traditionally crops were sown at a specified weight of seed per unit area irrespective of the size of the seed. Examination of seed samples shows that seed size can vary considerably and thus the number of seeds per unit weight varies (Table 6.2). The deficiencies of the traditional system are overcome by adopting an approach based on the numbers of seeds sown per unit area. This requires a knowledge of the thousand seed weight and an adjustment of the seed weight sown accordingly. Table 6.3 illustrates the effect of different thousand seed weights on the seed rates (kg ha$^{-1}$) required to sow different seed numbers per unit area. As an example, one variety of wheat may have a thousand seed weight of 40 g and another 50 g. In order to sow 350 seed m$^{-2}$ the seed rates (kg ha$^{-1}$) need to be 140 and 175 respectively. This approach to calculating

Table 6.2 Aspects of seed rate in the major temperate crops

| Crop | Thousand seed weight (g) | Normal range of seed rates (kg ha⁻¹) | | Seeds m⁻² |
|---|---|---|---|---|
| Oilseed rape – winter | 2.0-2.2 | 6-8 | | 270-400 |
| – spring | 2.3-2.4 | 6-8 | | 250-350 |
| Monogerm sugar beet | | | | |
| – rubbed fruits | 5-15 | – | | |
| – true seeds | 1-3 | – | | |
| – pellets | 50-75 | 8-13 | in 50 cm wide rows at 10 cm spacing | 10-26 |
| Winter wheat | 40-50 | 130-200 | | 260-480 |
| Winter barley | 30-45 | 110-190 | | 240-630 |
| Winter oats | 30-40 | 150-200 | | 370-670 |
| Spring barley | 35-45 | 120-180 | | 260-520 |
| Spring oats | 30-40 | 200-250 | | 500-830 |
| Field beans – winter | 670-710 | 170-230 | | 25-32 |
| – spring | 400-650 | 200-250 | | 30-50 |
| Maize | 600-900 | 60-120 | | 11-14 |

*Table 6.3  The effect of thousand seed weight and target seed numbers per $m^2$ on seed rate (kg $ha^{-1}$) of cereals*

| Seed numbers $m^{-2}$ | Thousand seed weight (g) | | |
| --- | --- | --- | --- |
| | 30 | 40 | 50 |
| 150 | 45 | 60 | 75 |
| 200 | 60 | 80 | 100 |
| 250 | 75 | 100 | 125 |
| 300 | 90 | 120 | 150 |
| 350 | 105 | 140 | 175 |
| 400 | 120 | 160 | 200 |

seed rate gives greater precision to the procedure and more economic use of valuable seed.

The range of thousand seed weights normally encountered in the major temperate crops is shown in Table 6.2. In oilseed rape, the seeds are very small and the range is narrow. The seed rates used are normally in the range 6-8 kg $ha^{-1}$ and these result in a seed density range of 250-440 $m^{-2}$. The target plant population with this crop is approximately 200 $m^{-2}$ and the seed rates allow for establishment losses.

The situation with monogerm sugar beet is not so simple. The true seeds are very small but the fruit weights (after rubbing) are approximately five times heavier. The irregular shape of the monogerm beet fruit does not lend itself to precision sowings with conventional drill mechanisms. The fruits are therefore pelleted, by coating them in a mixture of clay minerals. Pelleting produces a further increase in 'seed' weight. In this case, it is necessary to consider the weight of pelleted seed sown. Sugar beet is drilled to a stand and the number and weight of seed sown will depend on the spacing selected. The example given in the table is applicable to a crop grown in 50 cm wide rows with 10 cm spacing between the 'seeds'. In favourable conditions the spacing may be increased to 12.5 cm or wider with a subsequent reduction in the weight of seed sown per unit area.

Thousand seed weights in cereals are normally within the range 30–50 g. The seed rates vary considerably and may span the range 100–250 kg ha$^{-1}$ depending on the crop, thousand seed weight and the site conditions. The target seed densities in this range are between 240 and 850. The choice of seed rate in cereals need not be as precise as in other crops because of the ability of the plants to compensate for low plant numbers by tillering. Intensive winter wheat systems may only use 100 kg ha$^{-1}$, or less, of seed and subsequently achieve the desired ear population through stimulating tillering by the application of nitrogen fertiliser at the appropriate development stage. Other systems use high seed rates of over 200 kg ha$^{-1}$ and use less nitrogen during tillering. This ability to compensate for low plant numbers in cereals is useful and makes the choice of seed rate less critical.

The winter and horse field bean varieties have larger seeds than tic beans sown in spring but both are large compared with other crops. The required plant densities for beans are much lower than in cereals and they display some ability to compensate by tillering. Consequently seed weights sown are not exceptionally high, but with the largest seeded types may exceed 250 kg ha$^{-1}$.

Maize has relatively heavy seeds and, like sugar beet, is precision sown. The target plant population is approximately 100,000 – 120,000 ha$^{-1}$ and seed rates are adjusted to achieve this, on the assumption that 20 per cent of the seeds may not produce seedlings. Seed numbers should be calculated on the basis of thousand seed weights of each variety.

The choice of seed rate depends on different factors in different crops. In cereals, seed rate is not so crucial as in sugar beet, because of the different establishment and growth characteristics of the two crops. In all

153

cases, losses during establishment must be taken into consideration. The seed rate should be high enough to
achieve the minimum acceptable plant population to ensure
adequate yields. Recommended seed rates have been delib-
erately avoided in this text because some degree of flexibility should be exercised in the choice according to the
conditions of the site and objectives of the production
system. Particular attention to seed rates is required
under adverse establishment conditions. Conditions where
higher than normal seed rates should be used include:

   (i) late sowings
  (ii) soils with poor drainage
 (iii) rough seedbeds
  (iv) sites with trash present from the previous crop
   (v) after late-ploughed grass
  (vi) with seeds of a high thousand seed weight
 (vii) with seed of low germination
(viii) where there is a known serious weed problem
  (ix) where pest and disease problems are anticipated
   (x) light-textured soils prone to drought.

    In favourable site conditions seed rates can be
reduced.

    The calculation of the most appropriate 'seed' rate
for potatoes is more complex. In practice the planting
density of potatoes is manipulated through the number and
size of seed tubers. However, there are several ways of
examining the units of density in potatoes:

   (i) the number of 'eyes'
  (ii) the number of sprouts
 (iii) the number of seed tubers
  (iv) the surface area of the seed tuber
   (v) the weight of seed planted
  (vi) the number of stems per unit area and their distri-
      bution.

The easiest method for the grower to understand is the weight of seed planted as this is the way in which he buys it. The total yield of tubers increases with increasing weight of seed planted over the range 1-3 t ha$^{-1}$. It is evident from this that larger weights of 'seed' are involved with potatoes and seed costs form a large proportion of growing costs. In practice the seed rate used is approximately 3 t ha$^{-1}$ for maincrop ware and up to 4 t ha$^{-1}$ for seed crops. The higher rate for seed crops encourages the production of a higher proportion of small tubers suitable for seed.

If seed weight is taken as the measure of seed rate, then the intra-row spacing may have to be adjusted according to the size of individual tubers. There are more small tubers per tonne than large, and seed spacing must be adjusted to accommodate the different sizes of tubers. In general, total tuber yield, and the yield over small riddle sizes, increases with increasing seed tuber size. All the market outlets require tubers of a particular size, and adjustment of seed tuber numbers and size can occur to meet the market requirements. If stem density is increased by planting more tubers, the number of tubers per plant and per stem decreases. This can lead to an increase in total tuber numbers per unit area and, if the total yield remains constant, the proportion of small tubers increases. In summary, the choice of seed rate in potatoes depends on a combination of total seed weight, tuber size and number.

## TIME OF SOWING OR PLANTING

The decision on when to sow or plant a crop is an important one. Time of sowing experiments have been widely carried out and reported in the literature and the optimum periods for temperate arable crops have been defined. However the definition of the precise optimum sowing date is not always of great practical use. Unfavourable weather conditions and the fact that large areas have to be sown on some farms mean that precise sowing dates cannot be adhered to.  Nevertheless, it is important to know the best time to sow various crops so that work programmes can be organised accordingly and high yields achieved.

The primary consideration in the choice of sowing date is its effect on the yield of the economic product.  The effects on yields will be considered for spring- and autumn-sown crops.  In a temperate climate the choice of sowing date is important because of the need to make the maximum use of resources in a short growing season.  A short period is available in the spring when crops should be sown to maximise yields.  Early sowing into cool seedbeds can result in poor establishment and the risk of frost damage or bolting in biennials.  A delay in sowing results in a shorter growing season and the risk of dry seedbeds.  Figure 6.5 shows the response of spring barley and sugar beet to sowing date.  The data for barley show that the yield is highest when sown in March (February sowings may be advantageous in southern areas).  Delaying sowing until after mid-April results in a large decrease in yield.  The rate of yield decline is very rapid from late-April into early-May.  The difference between the yields of the earliest and latest-sown crops is approximately 1 tonne (over a 20 per cent reduction).

Sugar beet crops should not be sown too early because establishment is poor in seedbeds where the temperature is below 5°C and the risk of bolting is greater.  On the other hand the main limitation to increasing yields of sugar is the slow leaf development in the spring and early-summer resulting in inefficient radiation interception.  Thus the choice of sowing date for sugar beet is a compromise between risking poor establishment and bolting and the need to establish a leaf cover early.  In the main beet growing areas of the United Kingdom the target sowing date period should be between 20 March and 10 April.  Lower yields may be achieved by sowing too early and too late.  Where very early sowing is practised bolting-

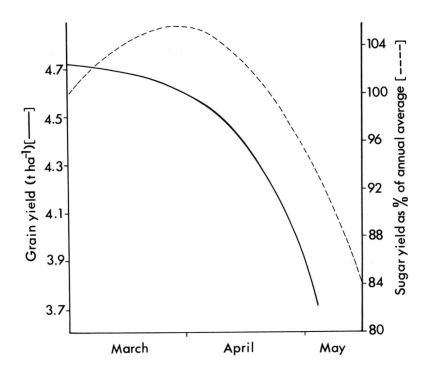

*Figure 6.5 The effect of sowing date on the grain yield of barley in Scotland, (1960-1977) (Blackett, 1981) and sugar from sugar beet in Suffolk, England (12-year average) (Sugar Beet Research and Education Committee, 1982)*

resistant varieties should be used. Delaying sowing until after 10 April reduces the yield of sugar and if sown in May the rate of yield loss is about 0.6 per cent for each day's delay. The rate of sugar accumulation in the autumn is similar from a wide range of sowing dates.

Surveys on the effects of planting date on the yield of maincrop ware potatoes in England and Wales have shown that yields decline if planting is delayed until after the second and third week in April. There is no great value in planting maincrop potatoes in March and, in fact, yields may be lower if the earlier emergence results in frost damage. The rate of yield decline from planting after mid-April has been calculated at about 0.75 t ha$^{-1}$

per week until mid-May. After mid-May the rate of decline is accelerated. A delay in planting results in later tuber initiation and a shorter period of tuber bulking which, because of similar bulking rates from all sowing dates, results in a lower yield. However as with sugar beet, the yield of tuber dry matter is correlated with the amount of light interception over the season and it is important to establish a leaf cover early and sustain it into the autumn. Sprouting the tubers before planting can partly compensate for the effects of late sowing.

The examples of barley, sugar beet and potatoes illustrate the critical importance of the choice of sowing date for spring-sown crops. Delaying sowing beyond the optimum period can result in large yield losses, but sowing too early into cold seedbeds must also be avoided. Other spring-sown cereals and oilseed rape respond in a similar way to the examples quoted. The importance of soil temperature on the establishment of maize has already been stressed and sowing should not occur until the soil temperature (5 cm) is above 10°C. This normally occurs in late-April in southern and central England. Late-sown maize is also lower yielding because of the high demand for Ontario Heat Units.

Field beans respond to very early sowing and the optimum period is mid-February to mid-March.

With autumn-sown crops, the objective is to get the crop well-established before growth is restricted by declining temperatures in the autumn. Latitude is an important consideration here as temperatures decline earlier in northerly regions.

One of the most sensitive temperate crops to variation in autumn sowing date is oilseed rape. Seed and oil yields are related to the size of the plant at flower initiation, which occurs in the winter, and thus are determined by the period available for late-summer and early-autumn growth. Consequently the crop should be sown in the second half of August or the first week of

September. Delaying sowing after mid-September results in small plants entering the winter and increases the risk from pigeon damage and reduces yields. In contrast, crops sown very early flower early in the spring and yield losses may occur from spring frosts.

Winter barley also responds to early sowing. This crop should be sown from mid-September to mid-October to obtain maximum yields. Delaying sowing of winter barley until mid-November can produce acceptable yields in southern areas. Small plants from late sowing are more likely to be damaged by frost-heaving. Similar arguments relating to sowing date apply to winter oats. Winter wheat is generally more tolerant of a wider range of sowing dates than barley or oats, however it should not be sown too early, especially on heavy-textured soils, and early- to mid-October is the optimum period. Delaying the sowing of wheat into November and early-December results in reduced yields.

Early sowing of autumn cereals in September and early-October increases the risk of disease infection. Crops sown this early are more susceptible to mildew, eyespot, yellow rust and barley yellow dwarf virus. The risk of barley yellow dwarf virus is associated with the activity of the aphid vectors in the warmer early autumn. Consideration of the increased use of fungicides and insecticides should be given where early sowing occurs. The disease risk is increased in continuous cereal systems where trash and volunteer plants from the previous crop can support the pathogens.

Field beans should be sown before the end of October so that the plants have three or four leaves before the onset of winter frosts.

In many autumn-sown crops it is very important to sow early to get the crop well established before low temperatures restrict growth. However, with wheat and barley there is a three-month period when they can be sown (September to November) without large differences in

159

yields occurring. This degree of flexibility is not available with spring-sown crops.

Other considerations of choice of sowing date are considered briefly.

(i) <u>Quality</u>. In addition to reduced seed yield from late-sown oilseed rape and sunflowers, the oil content is lower in late-sown crops. The grains from late-sown spring barley have a higher nitrogen content and are less suitable for malting. Late-sown spring cereals produce a higher proportion of small and shrivelled grains.

(ii) <u>Establishment</u>. Low temperatures can reduce the establishment of early-sown spring and late-sown autumn crops. Low seedbed moisture content reduces the establishment of late-sown spring and early-sown autumn crops.

(iii) <u>Harvest dates</u>. Late sowing of spring cereals can delay maturity resulting in higher drying costs and difficult harvesting.

(iv) <u>Weed control</u>. Later sowing allows more time for seedbed cultivations to kill weeds. However, early-sowing results in a higher competitive ability of the crop with late-germinating weeds.

(v) <u>Pests</u>. Manipulation of sowing dates can help to avoid the periods of greatest risk from pests (see chapter 4). Examples of this are wheat bulb fly and frit fly in autumn-sown cereals.

CULTIVATIONS AND METHODS OF ESTABLISHMENT

The soil conditions into which seeds are sown influence the subsequent establishment and performance of the crop. An understanding of the effects of mechanical cultivators on seedbed conditions requires a knowledge of the principles of soil management. This subject has been covered in other texts (Davies, Eagle and Finney, 1982) and only the basic principles will be considered here. The type of

cultivation system used depends primarily on the requirements of the crop and the structural and drainage characteristics of the soil. Traditionally ploughing was the
first step in the preparation of a seedbed, but since 1970
there has been a pronounced departure from this approach,
with some crops, towards reduced cultivations and direct
drilling.

The major objective of cultivations is to prepare a
suitable tilth for the crop although this clearly does not
apply with direct drilling. Other objectives of cultivations include the correction of soil structural problems,
as with subsoiling, and the control of certain weeds.
Furthermore cultivations can be done to produce a levelling of the seedbed to allow more uniform drilling to
occur.

The use of the mouldboard plough is essential where
deep rooting crops are grown, such as sugar beet and
potatoes. Ploughing provides the basis for secondary
cultivations to produce a good deep tilth which allows
ease of root penetration. With cereals and oilseed rape,
ploughing may not be necessary on medium- and light-
textured soils. Ploughing is a time- and energy-consuming
operation and is not an attractive method of primary
cultivation in many intensive arable systems. The emphasis
on autumn-sowing of cereals and oilseed rape in many areas
of western Europe means that there is no time to plough
all of the land before sowing and it is thus impractical.

The depth of ploughing can be varied and this may have
implications for subsequent crop growth. A ploughing
depth of 20-25 cm is adequate for most crops, but cereals
may not need such a depth of tilth. Ploughing deeper than
30 cm is not necessary in most situations but it can help
in breaking soil pans created by previous years of shallow
cultivations. However, this could also be achieved by
subsoiling before ploughing.

Two other aspects of ploughing should be mentioned.
The time of ploughing is important and it can be done in

the autumn, winter or early-spring. Autumn ploughing is valuable on heavy land where frost action helps to produce a finer tilth for small-seeded crops such as sugar beet. In contrast, spring ploughing is adequate for most cereals. The other aspect of ploughing is the condition of the soil when it is done; ploughing should not be done in very wet soils where smearing of the soil can create a barrier to subsequent root growth. A further point relating to both the timing and conditions of ploughing is the risk of erosion which may follow with wind and rain action. Sloping fields are most at risk from water erosion whereas sandy and peaty soils may be prone to wind blowing.

Secondary cultivations are necessary after ploughing to create a seedbed tilth and a number of implements are available for this purpose. Implements with discs arranged at an angle to the direction of travel provide a good tilth after ploughing. In addition discs are useful for primary cultivations on some soils. A range of tine cultivators are also available for preparing a seedbed. The strongest form of tine cultivator is the chisel plough which can substitute for conventional ploughing. Chisel ploughing in dry conditions produces a shattering effect on the soil and also keeps the organic matter on the sur-face, which can help to prevent capping. However the smearing effects of chisel ploughs in wet soils can be harmful to crop growth and create drainage problems. Powered rotary cultivators are useful for producing a good shallow tilth in a single operation but can be damaging to soil structure and create 'loose' seedbeds. With all methods of cultivation it is important to prepare a seed-bed which gives good contact of the seed with the soil aggregates to ensure adequate moisture supply. Consolid-ation of seedbeds by rolling before or after sowing is necessary to achieve this. In contrast, soil compaction arising from too much heavy traffic on the field must be avoided.

The type of cultivation and the number of operations

used depends on the degree of fineness of seedbed required. In small-seeded crops, a seedbed of small and stable aggregates is necessary in the drilling depth range, with good structure beneath. Crops with larger seeds are not so demanding of fine seedbed conditions and cereals will establish adequately where the aggregate size is up to 5 cm in diameter. Very poor tilths consisting of big dense clods are unsuitable for most crops. Field beans and peas are tolerant of rough seedbeds.

The method of seedbed preparation is often designed to create good conditions for the establishment of a crop but in potatoes harvesting conditions are also important. Potato tubers are difficult to separate mechanically from large clods of soil and stones at harvest. In this case it is crucial to prepare a clod-free soil for planting. Stones are a problem in some soils and separation, crushing or removal is necessary to simplify harvesting and reduce the risk of tuber damage.

Weather conditions affect the ability of the farmer to carry out cultivations and their effectiveness. Where large areas of crops need to be sown during the optimum period, it can be difficult to carry out the cultivations quickly enough and under the right conditions. Estimates have been made of the number of days available in each month for machine work on medium-textured soils (Table 6.4). In the spring, only half, or less, of the total days in a month may be suitable for cultivations. The number of days suitable in the autumn declines progressively from August into December. These estimates are based on rainfall data and drainage characteristics of the soil. The estimates are only approximate and will vary from area to area. Also wind is an important factor determining the rate of drying of soils. Soil texture is important and the number of days suitable for cultivations will be lower on heavy and poorly-drained soils and higher on lighter soils.

Table 6.4 also shows the effect of soil texture and

Table 6.4  Estimates of (a) available machine work days for medium-textured soils and (b) the number of days of drainage after heavy rainfall needed for soil to become suitable for working.  (Source: ADAS, 1974)

a)

| Month | Jan | Feb | Mar | Apr | May | Jun | Jul | Aug | Sep | Oct | Nov | Dec |
|---|---|---|---|---|---|---|---|---|---|---|---|---|
| No. of days | 12 | 12 | 13 | 17 | – | – | – | 26 | 22 | 19 | 14 | 12 |

b)

| | Depth to water table (cm) | | | | |
|---|---|---|---|---|---|
| | 150 | 100 | 60 | 20 | |
| Soil type | | | | | |
| Clay | 3 | 6 | 10 | 25 | |
| Loam | 1 | 3 | 5 | 13 | |
| Silt | 3 | 9 | 33 | 69 | |

the depth of the water table on the number of days of
drainage required after heavy rainfall before the soil is
suitable for working again.  Silt soils are a particular
problem in this case, especially where the water table is
close to the surface.  Loam soils, with deep water tables,
provide the quickest return of the soil to working conditions after heavy rainfall.  Damage can be done to the
soil if it is cultivated too early after rain and the
temptation to carry out operations on wet soil should be
resisted.  The effects of working the land under unsuitable conditions are likely to be more damaging to yield
than waiting for better conditions and sowing after the
optimum period.

Direct drilling offers a number of advantages in
arable farming including the possibility of sowing in
wetter conditions than would be suitable for cultivations
because of the reduced level of soil disturbance involved.
This means that crops can be sown at or nearer to the
optimum date compared with a system involving cultivations.
Reduced cultivations, i.e. non-ploughing, are also helpful in achieving this objective.  Direct drilling requires the use of special drills and is only appropriate
for certain crops on some soil types.  Cereals and oilseed
rape are well-suited to direct drilling but sugar beet is
not.  The benefits of direct drilling, from better timeliness of sowing, are greatest on heavy soils where cultivations are more difficult.  However, yield reductions
from direct drilling cereals on heavy soils are greater
than on light ones.  Direct drilling is well-suited to the
medium- and light-textured soils where the low level of
soil disturbance helps to conserve moisture.

Yield reductions are often observed in cereal crops
which are direct drilled as opposed to those established
after conventional cultivations.  An example of the
effects of different cultivations and direct drilling on
the yield of spring barley is shown in Table 6.5.  The
depression in yield from direct drilling is greatest at

Table 6.5  The effects of cultivations on the yield of spring barley
(eight-year means in t ha$^{-1}$ at 15 per cent moisture)

| Nitrogen fertiliser applied (kg ha$^{-1}$) | Plough depth 33 cm | Plough depth 20 cm | Tined cultivation 3 passes | No tillage Direct drill |
|---|---|---|---|---|
| 0 | 2.38 | 2.36 | 2.05 | 1.89 |
| 50 | 3.76 | 3.86 | 3.61 | 3.13 |
| 100 | 4.25 | 4.47 | 4.25 | 3.90 |
| 150 | 4.59 | 4.60 | 4.42 | 4.38 |

(Experiments carried out with the variety Zephyr on a
loam and sand clay loam soil; Holmes, 1976)

low nitrogen fertiliser inputs and, provided that nitrogen supply is high, yield differences are small between
all treatments.  The effects of ploughing to different
depths are small in this example and the yield from the
tined cultivation treatment is intermediate between
ploughing and direct drilling.

Direct drilling has the attraction of being simple
and it permits the sowing of a crop nearer to the ideal
time.  However several factors have restricted its widespread adoption in arable systems:

(i) it is not suitable for all soil types
(ii) surface soil wheel compaction restricts early root
growth
(iii) the adequate disposal of crop residues is a problem
(iv) specialised drills are required
(v) problems arise with certain weeds which would be
killed or reduced by cultivation
(vi) insufficient management skills to operate the
system efficiently
(vii) it is unsuitable for fields which have deep ruts,

e.g. after sugar beet harvesting
(viii) the increased nitrogen requirement increases the
energy and production costs.

There is a wide range of equipment available for
establishing crops. Cereal drills employ a metering mechanism which delivers the seeds into the 'furrows' which
are created by coulters or discs. This mechanism gives
no control over the precision of spacing within the row.
In contrast sugar beet and maize are sown with a precision
drill with an adjustable mechanism to control the intra-
row spacing. Precision drills are normally used with
crops where a low number of seeds per unit area are sown
in wide rows. Precision sowing of cereals is possible and
results in increased yields through a more uniform arrangement of plants. In the early 1970s, drills were developed
for sowing pre-germinated seeds suspended in a gel. This
method is mainly employed with vegetable crops and ensures
more rapid and uniform emergence of a higher number of
plants.

Planting machines for potatoes also employ a mechanism
to space the tubers uniformly in the 'drill'. Damage to
tubers, especially those with sprouts developed, must be
minimised in the planter to avoid delayed and reduced
emergence.

The type of establishment implement varies from crop
to crop. In all methods care must be taken to avoid
damage to the seeds and to sow them at the correct depth
for the prevailing soil conditions.

Some crops are raised in seedbeds and transplanted
into the field. This method is most widely used for field
vegetable brassica crops, e.g. Brussels sprouts. Trans-
planting gives considerable control over the spacing and
survival of plants in the field and eliminates the seedbed losses associated with other crops.

REFERENCES AND FURTHER READING

Agricultural Development and Advisory Service (1974)
    'Cereals without ploughing'. ADAS Profitable Farm
    Enterprises, Booklet 6. Ministry of Agriculture,
    Fisheries and Food: Pinner, Middlesex.

Agricultural Development and Advisory Service (1978)
    'Sowing cereals'. ADAS Short-term Leaflet 94.
    Ministry of Agriculture, Fisheries and Food: Pinner,
    Middlesex.

Allen, E.J. (1978)  'Plant Density', In The Potato Crop,
    ed. Harris, P.M.  London: Chapman and Hall.

Blackett, G.A. (1981) 'Optimising spring barley yield'.
    College Digest 1981.  Aberdeen: North of Scotland
    College of Agriculture.

Cannell, R.Q. (1981)  'Potentials and problems of simpli-
    fied cultivation and conservation tillage',  Outlook
    on Agriculture, 10 (8), 379-384.

Davies, D.B., Eagle, D.J. and Finney, J.B. (1982)  Soil
    Management.  Ipswich: Farming Press.

Davies, D.B., Vaidyanathan, L.V., Rule, J.S. and Jarvis,
    R.H. (1979)  'Effect of sowing date and timing and
    level of nitrogen application to direct drilled winter
    wheat'.  Experimental Husbandry, 35, 122-131.

Francis, A.L. (1974)  'Time of sowing spring barley and
    spring wheat'.  Experimental Husbandry, 26, 76-89.

Harper, F. and Ferguson, R.C. (1979)  'The effects of
    bitumen mulch and sowing date on the establishment and
    yield of oilseed sunflower (*Helianthus annuus* L.).
    Journal of agricultural Science, Cambridge, 93, 171-
    180.

Holmes, J.C. (1976)  'Effect of tillage, direct drilling
    and nitrogen in a long-term barley monoculture system'.
    Report of the Edinburgh School of Agriculture for
    1976.

Imperial Chemical Industries Limited (1975)  Outlook on
    Agriculture, 8, (Special number on reduced cultivation

and direct drilling.)

Jeffs, K.A. (ed.) (1978)  Seed Treatment.  Harpenden:
CIPAC Monograph No.2.

Longden, P.C. (1975)  'Seed pelleting'.  ADAS Quarterly
Review, 18, 73-80.

Mayer, A.M. and Poljakoff-Mayer, A. (1975)  The Germination of Seeds (2nd edn).  Oxford: Pergamon Press.

Moorby, J. (1978)  'The physiology of growth and tuber
yield'.  In The Potato Crop, ed. Harris, P.M.  London:
Chapman and Hall.

Radley, R.W. (1964)  'The effect of season on growth and
development of the potato'.  In The Growth of the
Potato, eds. Ivins, J.D. and Milthorpe, F.L.  London:
Butterworth.

Roberts, E.H. (ed.) (1972)  The Viability of Seeds.
London: Chapman and Hall.

Scott, R.K., English, S.D., Wood, D.W. and Unsworth, M.H.
(1973)  'The yield of sugar beet in relation to
weather and length of growing season'.  Journal of
agricultural Science, Cambridge, 81, 339-347.

Scott, R.K., Ogunremi, E.A., Ivins, J.D. and Mendham, N.J.
(1973)  'The effect of sowing date and season on
growth and yield of oilseed rape (*Brassica napus*)'.
Journal of agricultural Science, Cambridge, 81, 277-
285.

Smith, L.P. (1972)  'The effect of weather, drainage
efficiency and duration of spring cultivations on
barley yields in England'.  Outlook on Agriculture,
7 (2), 79-83.

Sugar Beet Research and Education Committee (1982)  Sugar
Beet - a Grower's Guide.  London: Ministry of Agriculture, Fisheries and Food.

Thomson, J.R. (1979)  An Introduction to Seed Technology.
Glasgow: Blackie.

# 7 Competition
# 1. Intra-specific Competition

THE CONCEPT OF COMPETITION

Crop plants are not grown in isolation but in closely-spaced populations. In the establishment and early-seedling phases of growth, individual plants are usually sufficiently widely-spaced not to interfere with each other. At some point, as the seedlings grow, they start to interfere with their neighbours and competition for resources begins. Competition can be defined as the struggle between individuals within a population for available resources, when the level of resources is below the combined needs of the members of the population. The resources involved in crop growth are primarily light, water and nutrients.

In populations of plants of similar genotypes, in the absence of weeds, the competition is intra-specific, i.e. within a species. Where different species of crops are grown in mixtures and where weeds are present, the competition is inter-specific, i.e. between species. This chapter is concerned with aspects of intra-specific competition and the discussion assumes a pure stand of the crop with no weeds present. Chapter 8 deals with mixed cropping and competition from weeds.

In essence, the examination of intra-specific competition in crop plants is the study of the effects of plant population. The agronomist is concerned with the efficient use of resources by his crops and his interest in plant population arises from the effects on crop yields. Seed, and other propagating material, form a significant proportion of the growing costs of most crops and more efficient use can be made of them if the optimum plant population is known. It is therefore important to quantify the optimum plant population for each crop in a range of circumstances.

Plant populations are usually quantified in terms of the number of plants per unit area of land. The arrangement of the plants within a given population is also important. Plant arrangement, or plant rectangularity can be varied by changing the row width and the spacing between plants in the row. Comparisons of the effects of plant populations should be made at standard row widths to remove any effects of plant arrangement. The assumption is made here that all crops are grown in rows, but it is recognised that some may be broadcast in practice.

Plants compete for the resources of the aerial and soil environment. As the leaf canopy develops, the leaves of individual neighbouring plants start to overlap and compete for light. This results in an inefficient leaf system where mutual shading occurs and the lowest leaves of the canopy operate at a reduced level of photosynthesis. In extreme cases, the lower leaves may be functioning below the compensation point where respiratory losses exceed photosynthetic gains. Competition for light is therefore an important consideration in selecting the plant population and arrangement for a crop.

Competition for gases in the aerial environment is less critical. Carbon dioxide levels with crop canopies can be temporarily depleted, but are usually quickly replenished by diffusion and wind movement from the atmosphere above the crop.

Competition for the resources of the soil is important. Root systems of neighbouring plants compete for the essential mineral elements in the soil. Where plants are grown

171

at high populations, the root system of individual plants
is small and has a small reservoir from which to extract
nutrients. High plant populations may therefore require
higher fertiliser inputs to sustain growth and maintain
yield. Similar points are relevant to the competition for
soil water. The less extensive nature of the root systems
of plants grown at high populations results in a greater
susceptibility to drought and more frequent irrigation may
be necessary where crops are grown at high densities in
dry areas.

The definition of the unit of expression of plant
population is not straightforward. In crops such as maize
and sugar beet, the unit is a plant and populations can be
expressed as plants per hectare or per square metre. In
cereals, the plant is not the most appropriate unit because of their ability to tiller. In this case, a more
appropriate unit is the number of fertile tillers, or ears,
per hectare. Similarly, for potatoes, the definition of
the population unit is not simple (see chapter 6). The
number of seed tubers planted per unit area is a convenient method of expressing plant population but it does not
take account of the fact that each tuber can produce a
number of stems from the buds, each of which can be considered as a unit. Stem numbers per hectare may be a more
appropriate method of expressing population in potatoes.
Comparisons of yield should be made in the best unit of
population for each crop.

THE EFFECTS OF PLANT POPULATION

The effect of varying the plant population on the yield of
crops is of the most importance to the grower. This
subject has been thoroughly examined by research and
development programmes and the objective of this section
is to review the effects of plant populations on the yield
of the major temperate crops. Two aspects of competition
are important in determining the effects on yield: the
amount, or intensity, and the time of onset. Figure 7.1

172

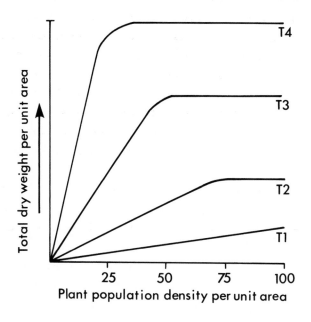

*Figure 7.1  The relationship between plant population density and yield on four occasions ($T_1 \rightarrow T_4$) (hypothetical)*

illustrates the general relationships between total dry weight and plant population density at four periods in the life of a crop.  In the early stages of growth ($T_1$), yield is linearly related to plant population throughout the whole range.  At a later date ($T_2$), yield is proportional to density over the range 0-75.  At the higher densities (75-100), similar yields are produced.  This signifies the earlier onset of competition and reduced growth rate of plants grown at higher populations.  As time progresses, yields are similar over a wider range of densities.  At $T_3$, similar total dry weights are obtained over the density range 50-100.  At the end of the period ($T_4$) yields are similar over most of the density range (25-100).  Yields are only proportional to population for densities below 25, where the development of the leaf canopy is insufficient to utilise all of the incident radiation.

    This hypothetical example illustrates the point that

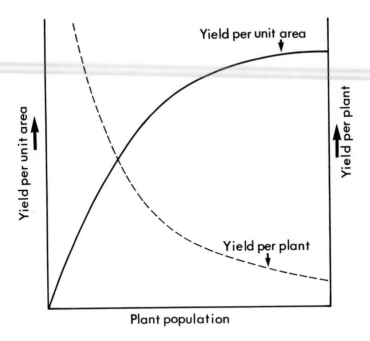

*Figure 7.2 The effect of plant population on yield per unit area (Y) and per plant where the relationship with Y is asymptotic, e.g. forage maize, (hypothetical)*

competition occurs early at high plant populations. This results in an earlier reduction in the relative growth rate, and plants at the lower populations catch up. As a result of the lower numbers per unit area at low populations, the plants grow on longer before competition causes a decline in growth rate. At very low densities, with most crop plants, competition may not occur at all and resources are not efficiently used. The selection of the plant population for a crop must avoid the inefficient use of resources at low levels and the excessive competition at high ones.

The time of onset of competition is affected by the arrangement of the leaves; the leaf area of rosette plants, e.g. sugar beet, is less effectively distributed than that of a cereal or potato crop.

The relationship between the final yield of a crop and

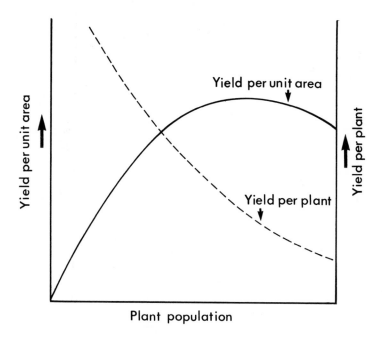

*Figure 7.3 The effect of plant population on yield per unit area (Y) and per plant where the relationship with Y is parabolic, e.g. grain yield of maize, (hypothetical)*

plant population is either asymptotic or parabolic (Figures 7.2 and 7.3). Figure 7.2 shows an example of an asymptotic relationship. The yield per unit area increases linearly with increasing population over the lower range but thereafter the rate of increase declines until a maximum value is reached. Further increases in plant population above this maximum do not produce further increases in yield. The yield of individual plants declines rapidly over the lower range of populations, but the rate is slower at the higher densities. In the example of a parabolic relationship (Figure 7.3), the total yield declines at higher populations and there is an identifiable optimum value.

Several temperate crops display an asymptotic yield response to increasing plant population, especially those

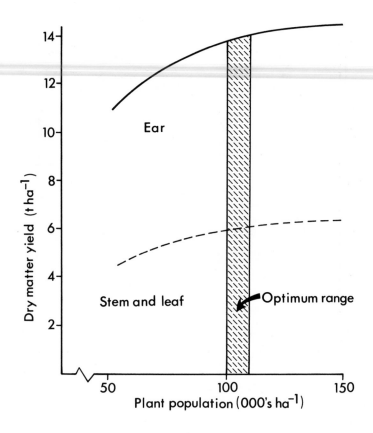

*Figure 7.4 The effect of plant population on the dry matter yield of forage maize (Milbourn, 1975)*

grown for their products of vegetative growth. Forage maize is grown in suitable areas of the United Kingdom and the effect of plant population on total dry matter yield is shown in Figure 7.4. Total yield increases from 50,000 to 100,000 plants per hectare beyond which only small increases in yield are obtained from higher plant populations (up to 150,000). The partition of the dry matter is also affected by plant population and the proportion of ear declines with increasing density. The optimum plant population for forage maize is 100,000 to 110,000 and for grain 90,000 to 100,000, in south-east England. Establishing plant populations above these optima is wasteful of

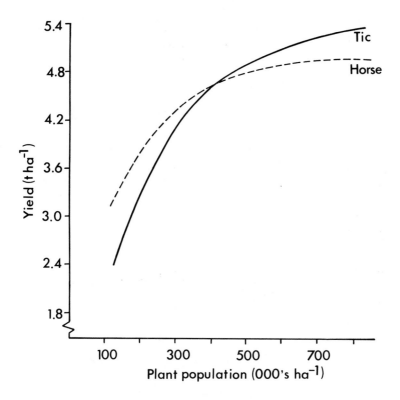

*Figure 7.5   The effect of plant population on the yield of tic and horse spring beans sown in the spring (Ingram and Hebblethwaite, 1976)*

seed and reduces the quality of the product.

Spring-sown tic and horse field beans also show an asymptotic relationship over a range of 100,000 to 850,000 plants per hectare. Tic beans are more sensitive to changes in plant population than horse beans (Figure 7.5) and respond throughout most of the range. Horse beans show only small increases in grain yield at populations above 500,000 ha$^{-1}$. In field beans, the seed rates necessary to achieve the highest populations are large because of the high thousand seed weights (chapter 6) and may not be economic. Ingram and Hebblethwaite (1976) argued that, for tic beans, seed rates up to 235 kg ha$^{-1}$ may be

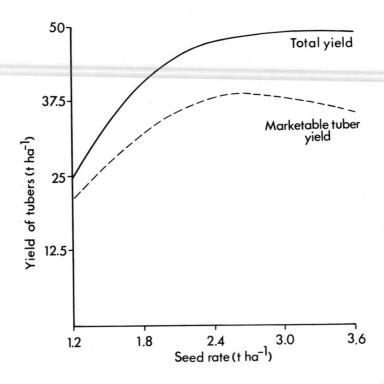

*Figure 7.6 Effect of seed rate (total tuber weight) on the yield of maincrop potatoes, variety King Edward (after Eddowes, 1967)*

economic. However the seed rate required to achieve the highest yield may be as large as 450 kg ha$^{-1}$ and the additional 215 kg ha$^{-1}$ of seed only produce an extra 330 kg ha$^{-1}$ of yield.

Further arguments for avoiding the use of high plant populations are the increased risk of lodging and, in winter beans, chocolate spot disease.

The difficulty of defining the unit of population in potatoes has been discussed. The relationship between seed tuber weight sown and the yield of maincrop ware potatoes is shown in Figure 7.6. The response, in total tuber yield, to changes in seed rate is also asymptotic. In this example, only small yield increases are apparent with seed rates above 2.4 t ha$^{-1}$. Between the seed rates of 1.2 and 2.4 t ha$^{-1}$, total tuber yield increases more sharply. Total tuber yield does not reflect the economic value of the potato crop and it is more appropriate to consider the effects on the yield of marketable tubers, i.e. those within the ware size range. This relationship is not asymptotic but parabolic. At the low seed rates, the yield of marketable tubers is similar to that of total tubers. However as the seed rate increases, the proportion of the total yield which is marketable decreases due to the increased numbers of small tubers resulting from greater competition. Maximum yield of marketable tubers is obtained at a seed rate of approximately 2.5 t ha$^{-1}$ in this example. At higher seed rates, yields of marketable tubers decrease and the proportion of the total yield becomes even smaller. This example illustrates the effect of increasing plant population on the changes in the size grade distribution of the marketable product.

Increasing the seed tuber weight can either be achieved by increasing the number of small tubers or increasing the size of individual tubers. The net result of an increase in seed tuber weight is an increase in the number of eyes planted and consequently the number of mainstems produced. Total tuber yield is proportional to the number of stems in the early part of the season. The size of set used to achieve a given density does not influence greatly the total or marketable yield (Bleasdale, 1965).

The increase in the numbers of small tubers produced at higher seed rates can be commercially exploited in seed crops. Seed rates for seed production may be as high as 4 t ha$^{-1}$ compared with 2.5 to 3 t ha$^{-1}$ for maincrop ware production. Higher seed rates may be beneficial in early crops where the growing season is shorter and in this case, 3.5 t ha$^{-1}$ is suitable.

In potatoes, the seed rate, and hence the stem population, can be varied to meet more efficiently the size grade requirements of different market outlets and to compensate for differences in the length of the available

growing season.  Seed tubers form approximately 25 per
cent of the variable costs of maincrop production and this
emphasises the need to select the most economic seed rate
for the system.

The control of size of individual plants by manipulating plant population is important in root vegetable
crops.  Close spacing of carrots results in a higher proportion of the roots in the canning size range and this is
achieved at plant populations of approximately 350 $m^{-2}$.
Root size can also be controlled by varying the length of
the growing season.

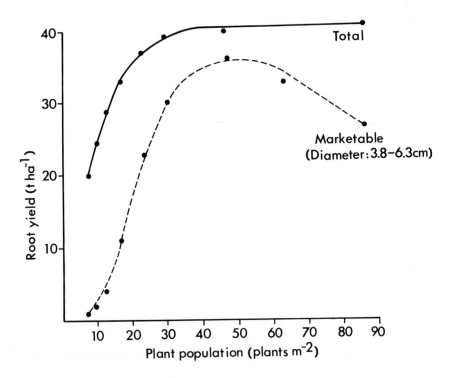

*Figure 7.7  The effect of plant population on the total and market-
able yield of parsnips cv. Avonresistor (redrawn from Bleasdale and
Thompson, 1966)*

The example of parsnips (Figure 7.7) shows that there
is an asymptotic relationship between total root yield and
plant population over the range 7-86 plants per square
metre.  Maximum yields are reached at 40 plants per square

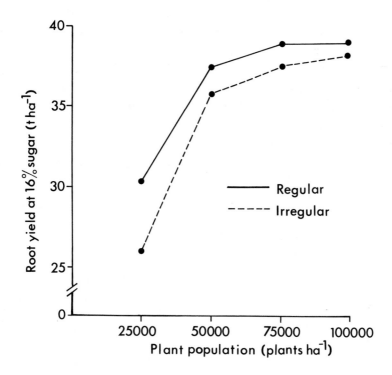

*Figure 7.8  The effect of plant population on the root yield of sugar beet (hand-harvested) where the plant arrangement is regular and irregular (after Sugar Beet Research and Education Committee, 1982)*

metre.  However, as with potato tubers, the relationship with marketable yield is parabolic.  Similar total root yields are achieved over a density range of 30-85 $m^{-2}$, but the yield of marketable roots is maximal in the range 40-50.  The proportion of the crop which is marketable is small at low populations because of the large number of large roots and at high populations because of the large number of small ones.  In crops of this kind, plant population is a critical factor which determines the proportion of the yield which is marketable.

Plant population also has a pronounced effect on the root yield of sugar beet (Figure 7.8).  Individual root size is not an important criterion determining the marketable proportion of this crop and total root yield is the

main interest of the grower. Root yields increase sharply
when the plant population is increased from 25,000 to 50,000
ha$^{-1}$. Smaller yield increases are evident from increasing
the population to 75,000 ha$^{-1}$, but further increases up to
100,000 ha$^{-1}$ do not result in extra yields. The optimum
plant population for sugar beet is considered to be 75,000
ha$^{-1}$.

Most of the beet crop is drilled to a stand and this
results in irregular plant spacing within the row.
Irregular spacing reduces the yields of roots compared to
regularly-spaced plants at the same plant population. The
reduction due to irregular plant spacing is greatest at
the lowest populations. At plant populations of 75,000 to
100,000 ha$^{-1}$ irregular plant spacing causes only small
yield reductions. Widely-spaced plants, at low populations, never completely cover the ground with their leaves
and radiation interception is less efficient than at high
populations. Irregular plant spacing accentuates this
problem.

The smaller roots produced at high populations are
more likely to be lost in mechanical harvesting and in
practice there may be a yield penalty from spacing the
plants too closely. In reality, it is difficult to predict final plant populations when crops are drilled to a
stand because of the uncertainty associated with the
establishment (see chapter 6). Field establishment may
be less than 50 per cent and growers tend to sow the seeds
more closely as an insurance policy against losses. In
the event of establishment being high, the final plant
population may be above the optimum.

A further disadvantage of high plant populations in
sugar beet, and other root crops, is that the shoot to
root ratio is increased. The increased competition for
light at high densities results in excessive leaf growth
at the expense of the roots. Total yield (root and shoot)
may be increased at high populations but root yields are
not changed and the risk of harvesting losses is greater.

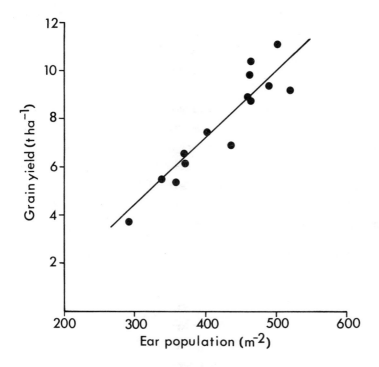

.*Figure 7.9   The relationship between grain yield and ear numbers per square metre for crops of Maris Huntsman wheat grown in England (after Biscoe, 1979)*

The sugar content of the smaller roots from high plant populations is generally higher.

The question of the most appropriate plant population for cereals is an interesting one.  All of the temperate cereals show the ability to compensate for low plant populations by producing more tillers.  Consequently grain yields may be unaffected by seed rates over a wide range. Very low plant numbers are undesirable because of the excessive tillering required to compensate.  Late-formed fertile tillers are lower yielding and mature later, resulting in more difficult harvesting.  There is therefore a limit to the lowest populations which are practical. Reference has already been made to the potential for manipulating tillering patterns by nitrogen fertiliser and, provided that there is a reasonable number of plants present at the tillering stage, yields can be maintained over a wide range of plant populations. Plant population in cereals is therefore not such an important consideration as it is in other crops.

Surveys of commercial crops of winter cereals have demonstrated that grain yields are correlated with the ear populations. This is clear from Figure 7.9, where the grain yield of Maris Huntsman winter wheat is strongly correlated with ear numbers at harvest. In high-yielding systems, it is essential to have high ear populations. Yields of grain in excess of 7 t ha$^{-1}$ are only achieved if the ear populations are above 400 m$^{-2}$. High ear populations can be achieved in two ways. In the Laloux system of winter wheat production developed in Belgium, low seed rates are used (220 seeds m$^{-2}$ or 120 kg ha$^{-1}$) and the high ear populations are achieved by promoting tillering by nitrogen application. In the Schleswig-Holstein system of winter wheat production, developed in West Germany, the high ear populations are achieved by using relatively high seed rates (400 seeds m$^{-2}$ or 220 kg ha$^{-1}$) and the use of high levels of nitrogen at the tillering stage. Excessive tiller production from the nitrogen is prevented by the increased competition resulting from higher plant numbers. Both systems aim to produce ear populations of 500-600 m$^{-2}$. The plants each have 1.5 - 3 fertile tillers, the exact number depends on the system involved.

Further evidence of the importance of high ear populations to the attainment of high grain yields comes from surveys of winter wheat and barley crops on commercial farms in the United Kingdom. The survey of winter wheat crops on 899 farms in 1980 showed that the average yield of the highest 25 per cent was 9.1 t ha$^{-1}$, and of the lowest, 5.9 t ha$^{-1}$ (Table 7.1). Plant numbers established at the time of the spring top dressing of nitrogen showed little variation (235 to 266 m$^{-2}$), but ear numbers at harvest displayed a greater range (464 to 542 m$^{-2}$). The

Table 7.1 Effects of plant and ear populations on the yield of winter wheat and winter barley (from ICI Surveys 1980 and 1981)

| | Yield (t ha$^{-1}$) | Plants m$^{-2}$ in spring | Ears m$^{-2}$ at harvest | Grains per ear | 1000 grain weight (g) |
|---|---|---|---|---|---|
| **Winter wheat** | | | | | |
| Highest 25 per cent | 9.1 | 266 | 542 | 44 | 50 |
| | 7.7 | 259 | 529 | 42 | 47 |
| | 6.9 | 250 | 511 | 42 | 47 |
| Lowest 25 per cent | 5.9 | 235 | 464 | 39 | 45 |
| **Winter barley** | | | | | |
| Highest 25 per cent | 6.9 | 265 | 882 | 25 | 45 |
| | 5.8 | 261 | 831 | 24 | 44 |
| | 5.1 | 251 | 794 | 25 | 42 |
| Lowest 25 per cent | 4.1 | 242 | 705 | 24 | 40 |

(Based on surveys of 899 fields of wheat and 610 fields of barley)

185

highest grain yields were associated with the highest ear populations. Similarly, with a winter barley survey in 1981, grain yields were highest from the crops with the highest ear populations at harvest. The yield range in barley was 4.1 to 6.9 which corresponded to ear populations of 705 and 882 $m^{-2}$ respectively, for the lowest and highest 25 per cent of the sample.

In the winter wheat survey, the highest yields were also a result of higher grain numbers per ear and thousand grain weights. Thus all the major components of grain yield in wheat are high where the highest yields are obtained. However the differences in the grain numbers and weights were smaller than those in ear numbers. In winter barley, high yields were associated with high thousand seed weights but grain numbers per ear were similar over the whole yield spectrum.

It is clear from data of this kind that the ear population is the major factor controlling the grain yield of winter cereals. Plant populations are of less importance provided that they exceed a minimum of 200 $m^{-2}$.

The effects of seed rate on spring barley are illustrated by an example (Table 7.2). These data are for a single variety, Golden Promise, grown in two years in south-east Scotland. Plant population was closely related to seed rate over the range 83 to 218 kg $ha^{-1}$. Over the same seed rate range, the ear numbers per plant declined progressively from 2.96 to 1.34. Ear populations increased up to a seed rate of 183 kg $ha^{-1}$ but increasing the seed rate to 218 kg $ha^{-1}$ did not result in further ear numbers. Grain yield increased up to a seed rate of 146 kg $ha^{-1}$ and then showed no further increase. Within this range grain yield is asymptotically related to seed rate, plant population and ear populations. In this example of a relatively low-yielding crop there is no evidence of the linear relationship of yield with ear populations.

The components of yield were also affected by seed rate. The number of grains per ear decreased with

*Table 7.2  The effects of seed rate on yield and components of yield*
*of spring barley, variety Golden Promise (means of 4 trials in 1973*
*and 1974) (from Rodger, 1975)*

| | Seed rate (kg ha$^{-1}$) | | | | |
|---|---|---|---|---|---|
| | 83 | 118 | 146 | 183 | 218 |
| Grain yield (t ha$^{-1}$) | 3.86 | 4.02 | 4.15 | 4.18 | 4.20 |
| Plant population (millions ha$^{-1}$) | 1.99 | 2.74 | 3.29 | 4.35 | 5.21 |
| Ears per plant | 2.96 | 2.26 | 1.99 | 1.60 | 1.34 |
| Ear population (millions ha$^{-1}$) | 5.89 | 6.19 | 6.55 | 6.98 | 6.97 |
| Grains per ear | 23.8 | 23.2 | 22.8 | 22.0 | 21.7 |
| 1000 grain weight (g) | 36.9 | 35.7 | 36.6 | 35.7 | 35.2 |

increasing seed rate.  A small decrease in thousand seed
rate was apparent at high seed rates.

Spring barley is more prolific in tiller production
than spring wheat and higher seed rates are required with
spring wheat to compensate for this and to achieve high
yields.

The examples described here, selected from a range of
crops, illustrate the importance to successful crop production of knowing the yield response to changes in plant
populations.  Yield is not the only factor to be considered.  Quality is also affected by plant population.
The proportion of potato tubers and vegetable roots in the
marketable range is significantly affected by plant population.  Similarly grain size is reduced in spring
cereals grown at high seed rates and this can affect their
suitability for malting or selling into Intervention.  A
further example of the effects of plant population on
quality is the reduction in the proportion of the ear in
forage maize crops at high densities with the consequent
reduction in feeding value.

In cereals, field beans and maize, the risk of lodging
is greater at high plant populations.  The thinner and
weaker stems, resulting from greater competition for light

in dense stands of plants, renders them more prone to
damage from adverse weather conditions.

The risk of increased disease infection is also
greater at higher plant populations with some crops. The
example of chocolate spot in field beans has been
mentioned. The higher humidity, within dense canopies of
plants growing at high plant populations, provides a more
favourable environment for the germination of fungal
spores and increases the risk of infection.

A further important aspect of plant population in
crop production is the effect on the competitive ability
with weed plants. Crops which are sown at high densities
have a greater potential for competing successfully with
weeds than those which are widely spaced. Cereals are a
good example of this competitive ability associated with
high densities. Sugar beet on the other hand, grown at
relatively low plant populations, exhibit slow early
growth and are not very competitive with weeds. This
indirect effect of plant population influences the choice
of the weed control system in different crops.

ROW WIDTH AND PLANT ARRANGEMENT

The discussion so far has been concerned with the effects
of numbers of plants per unit area and has made little
reference to the effects of the arrangement of plants
within populations. The majority of arable crops are
sown in rows and, at the populations which are considered
to be optimal for each crop, the row width is usually
greater than the distance between plants within the row.
It is however possible to change the plant arrangement at
a given population by varying the row width and plant
spacing. The effects of different plant arrangement
patterns on crop yields have been extensively studied and
some examples are referred to in the following section.

In practice, the row width is determined by non-
biological factors. Traditionally, crops were grown in
wide rows to allow weed control by inter-row cultivations.

The development of herbicides largely eliminated this reason for using wide rows. In root crops, such as potatoes and sugar beet, relatively wide rows are still needed to allow the efficient use of harvesting equipment, with a minimum of damage to the crop. Some sugar beet harvesting systems are capable of topping and lifting five or six rows at once and, where these are used, wide rows are not essential.

The problems of stones and clods are serious in the potato crop because of the difficulty of separating them from the tubers at harvest. Furthermore tuber damage is increased if a high proportion of clods and stones are concentrated in the ridges. Compaction of the soil is increased by tractor traffic through the crop to apply crop protection chemicals and this increases the risk of clods at harvest. The use of wide rows allows traffic through the crop without compacting the soil in the ridge and reduces the problem of clods. Stones can be separated from the soil before planting the tubers and deposited between the ridges. Unless wide rows are used this process cannot be done effectively.

Access to most crops is required throughout their life to apply fertiliser, herbicides, growth regulators, insecticides and fungicides. This can only be done with a minimum of damage to the crop, if the rows are wide enough. In cereals, where narrower rows are used, some damage is inevitable and this can cause yield losses and late-tillering from damaged plants. This problem has been overcome in cereals by using tramlines, where selected rows are left unsown, with the sole purpose of allowing machinery to get into the crop throughout the season.

Theoretically more efficient use of resources and a delay in the time of onset of intra-specific competition would result from adopting narrow rows and increasing the spacing within the rows. At a given population this would produce a square rather than a rectangular arrangement (Figure 7.10). The example shows the effect on the

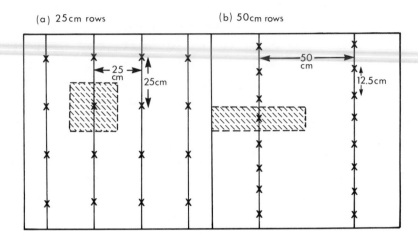

*Figure 7.10  The effect of different row widths (25 cm and 50 cm) on the arrangement of regularly-spaced plants at the same population density (160,000 ha⁻¹).  In (a), the area available to an individual plant (shaded area) is square, and in (b), rectangular.  The area available to each plant in both cases is 625 cm²*

distribution of space available to individual plants of varying the row width and spacing at a population of 160,000 ha⁻¹.  In 25 cm wide rows, the spacing required to achieve the population is 25 cm and the space available is a square.  In 50 cm rows, 12.5 cm spacing is required to achieve the same population and this results in a rectangular arrangement of plants.  The closer spacing of plants in wide rows results in inefficient light interception early in the season and the earlier onset of leaf competition within the row.  Similarly, competition for soil resources is greater with the more crowded root systems in wide rows.  In theory, plants arranged in a square should make more efficient use of resources than those in a rectangle.

Potatoes are traditionally grown in rows 60-76 cm apart although early crops may be planted in narrower rows.  Row widths up to 90 cm may be necessary to permit the use of harvesting equipment.  When comparisons are made at similar plant densities, the effects of changes in row width, within the range 60-90 cm, do not have large effects on the yield of marketable tubers. Maincrop potatoes can compensate for the disadvantages resulting from wide rows and the crop is very tolerant of changes in plant arrangement. Extending the row width to 137 cm does however result in reduced yields. Planting potatoes in a square arrangement in bed systems does not significantly affect yields and may result in excessive greening of tubers due to the difficulty of achieving adequate soil cover. Lodging of the stems of potatoes is reduced in wide rows and this can have important effects on light interception. The evidence for potatoes is that narrow rows are not beneficial and extreme rectangularities have only a small depressing effect on yield.

In sugar beet, the optimum plant population is approximately 75,000 ha$^{-1}$ which is achieved by spacing plants 25 cm apart in rows 51 cm wide. Within this relatively low population, there is less scope for manipulating the arrangement. However, extending the row width beyond 51 cm results in lower sugar yields. Narrower rows of 46 cm produce consistently higher yields, especially in monogerm crops which are drilled to a stand, as the more favourable distribution of the foliage helps to compensate for poor and irregular establishment. Bed systems have been considered for sugar beet but have not been widely adopted commercially. Harvesting losses, with conventional equipment, are greater at narrow row widths.

The effects of row widths on the yield of cereals were extensively reviewed by Holliday (1963). The general conclusion for cereals, at that time, was that decreasing the row width below 17-20 cm had a small effect on yields of all crops grown at the same seed rates. The magnitude of the increase in grain yield from using narrow rows was, on average, 5-7 per cent. Increasing row widths above 20 cm (up to 40 cm) produced a small yield decrease. The ability of cereals to compensate by tillering accounts for

these small differences. This survey also concluded that
there was no evidence of more efficient use of fertiliser
by plants in narrow rows.

In the period 1960 - 1980, in the United Kingdom, there
has been a trend towards growing cereals in narrower rows
(8-10 cm) and this has been possible through improved
drill designs. In addition, precision drilling of cereals
has been considered. In trials (Roebuck and Trenerry,
1978) with higher yielding spring barley and winter wheat
crops, the effects of row width and precision sowing have
been examined. The yield of the spring barley variety
Julia was increased by 8 per cent by using precision-sown
seeds in 10 cm rows, compared with conventionally sown
crops. The best arrangement in these trials was obtained
from seeds spaced at 2.5 cm intervals in 10 cm rows, which
resulted in a 14 per cent increase in yield over conventionally drilled crops in 18 cm rows. Precision-sowing of
winter wheat in 10 cm rows (2.5 cm spacing) increased
yields by 17 per cent compared with conventional drilling
in 18 cm rows. These experiments support the earlier
evidence that narrow rows result in larger grain yields in
cereals. There is additional evidence that precision sowing results in further benefits, through a more favourable
arrangement of plants, but this is a difficult and slow
operation in practice. In conclusion, the effects of
plant arrangement in cereals are small because of the
ability of the plants to compensate by tillering.

Small increases in yields of peas and maize grains are
produced from using narrower rows. In vegetable root
crops, similar yield advantages have been found from
adopting a squarer plant arrangement in narrow rows. A
further benefit of narrow rows in carrots is that the size
and uniformity of the roots can be controlled more effectively, which is desirable for canning crops. This has
resulted in the widespread use of the bed systems of
carrot production for canning.

The effects of plant arrangement on crop yields,

within the populations normally used in practice, are
small.  This is contrary to the theory that more efficient use of resources occurs when plants are arranged in
a square rather than a rectangular pattern.  Most crops
display sufficient compensatory growth when grown in wider
rows to offset any effects of earlier and increased competition.

## THE EFFECTS OF REGULARITY OF PLANT DISTRIBUTION

The major arable crops are established by mechanical
drills or planters.  As a result of the inadequacies of
these machines and incomplete establishment, variation in
the intra-row spacing occurs.  With crops like cereals,
which are sown at high seed populations and establish a
high proportion of plants, irregular spacing may not have
a damaging effect on yield.  However, where crops are
grown at low seed populations and establishment is low
(e.g. sugar beet), large gaps may appear in the rows.
Irregular plant distribution is potentially more damaging
to yield in these crops.

   Evidence has already been cited of the yield benefits
obtained from precision sowing of cereals.  The more
regular spacing of plants which results from this technique, where establishment is high, produces small
increases in yield.

   The effects of irregular spacing on the root yield of
sugar beet over a range of plant populations are shown in
Figure 7.8.  At low plant populations irregular spacing
causes a large reduction in yield (17 per cent), but at
the optimum population of 75,000 plants per hectare the
difference is much smaller (4 per cent).  However these
figures relate to hand-harvested trials and losses from
machine-harvesting are likely to be greater with irregular
spacing as a result of the greater variation in root size.

   Commercial potato planters can produce extremely
irregular spacings.  Tuber yields however are relatively
unaffected by irregular planting of sets by conventional

planters. Extensive experiments in Scotland examined the
effects of irregular tuber spacing on the yield of
potatoes of different seed tuber weights and mean spacings
(Pascal, Robertson and Langley, 1977). The results indi-
cated that irregular spacing had no significant depressing
effects on potato yield. The mean spacings used in these
experiments were from 30 cm to 46 cm and the coefficients
of variation of these means ranged from 43 to 80 per cent
using commercial planters.

Except for crops grown at low plant populations, the
effects of irregular compared with regular plant distribution patterns are small.

## ACHIEVING THE PLANT POPULATION AND ARRANGEMENT

There is sufficient information available for the grower
to select the most appropriate plant population and
arrangement for each crop. The importance of these factors to yield, quality and other aspects of crop production has been emphasised in this chapter. Once the
appropriate population and arrangement have been selected,
the grower has to decide on the best methods of achieving
them in practice. Mechanised methods of crop establishment are available for all crops and the grower must
familiarise himself with the equipment. Drills and
planters must be carefully calibrated to give the desired
spacing. In addition, the machine must be operated efficiently. The forward speed of the machine often affects
the sowing pattern and the temptation to sow faster than
the recommended rates should be avoided to ensure good
seed or tuber distribution. Machines should also be set
and operated in a way which reduces to a minimum the
physical damage to the propagating material. This is
particularly important with potato tubers which have been
sprouted.

Seed rates should be selected which include an allowance for losses in establishment. This is an important
insurance factor which should be considered. In cereals,

precision in the choice of seed rate is not crucial because establishment is usually high and ear populations
can be manipulated by nitrogen fertiliser application.
However, in sugar beet, sown to a stand, a judgement has to
be made regarding the likely level of establishment. The
use of certified seed, of high germination and vigour,
which has been treated with the appropriate crop protection chemicals, helps to ensure successful establishment.
Adequate preparation of the seedbed is a further vital
factor in ensuring good establishment.

Post-establishment treatments, to ensure the survival
of plants, may be necessary to maintain optimum populations. These include the use of an adequate weed control programme and the application of pesticides to protect seedlings.

The establishment of the optimum plant population of
healthy plants, in the most suitable arrangement pattern,
is the foundation of a successful crop production system.
Every effort should be made in this early phase of crop
growth to ensure that there are sufficient plant numbers
established to achieve good yields.

REFERENCES AND FURTHER READING

Allen, E.J. (1978) 'Plant density' In The Potato Crop,
    ed. Harris, P.M. London: Chapman and Hall, 279-326.
Biscoe, P.C. (1979) 'Gembloux's consistent wheat yields'.
    Big Farm Management, November 1979, 8-15.
Bleasdale, J.K.A. (1965) 'Relationship between set
    characteristics and yield in maincrop potatoes'.
    Journal of agricultural Science, Cambridge, 64, 361-
    366.
Bleasdale, J.K.A. (1966) 'Plant growth and crop yield'.
    Annals of Applied Biology, 57, 173-182.
Bleasdale, J.K.A. and Thompson, R. (1966) 'The effects of
    plant density and the pattern of plant arrangement on
    the yield of parsnips'. Journal of Horticultural
    Science, 41, 371-378.

Donald, C.M. (1963) 'Competition among crop and pasture plants'. Advances in Agronomy, 15, 1-118.

Eddowes, M. (1967) Maincrop Potato Production. Technical Bulletin of Harper Adams Agricultural College, Shropshire.

Harper, J.L. (1961) 'Approaches to the study of plant competition'. In Mechanisms in Biological Competition. Symposium of the Society for Experimental Biology No. 15. Cambridge: University Press, 1-39.

Holliday, R. (1960) 'Plant population and crop yield: Part I'. Field Crop Abstracts, 13 (3), 159-167.

Holliday, R. (1960) 'Plant population and crop yield: Part II'. Field Crop Abstracts, 13 (4), 247-254.

Holliday, R. (1963) 'The effect of row width on the yield of cereals'. Field Crop Abstracts, 16, 71-81.

Imperial Chemical Industries (1980) Pointers to Profitable Wheat. A survey of winter wheat growing in 899 fields in England in 1980. Billingham: ICI.

Imperial Chemical Industries (1981) Pointers to Profitable Winter Barley. A survey of 610 fields in England in 1981. Billingham: ICI.

Ingram, J. and Hebblethwaite, P.D. (1976) 'Optimum economic seed rates in spring- and autumn-sown field beans'. Agricultural Progress, 51, 27-32.

Milbourn, G.M. (ed.) (1975) Maize Growers' Handbook (3rd edn). London: Home Grown Cereals Authority.

Pascal, J.A., Robertson, T.P. and Langley, A. (1977) 'Yield effects of regularly and irregularly spaced potato tubers'. Experimental Husbandry, 32, 25-33.

Rodger, J.B.A. (1975) 'Barley seed rates'. ESCA Technical Note No. 105C. Edinburgh: East of Scotland College of Agriculture.

Roebuck, J.F. and Trenerry, J. (1978) 'Precision drilling of cereals'. Experimental Husbandry, 34. 1-11.

Sugar Beet Research and Education Committee (1982) Sugar Beet — a Grower's Guide. London: Ministry of Agriculture, Fisheries and Food.

Willey, R.W. and Heath, S.B. (1969)  'The quantitative relationships between plant population and crop yield'. Advances in Agronomy, 21, 281-321.

# 8 Competition –
# 2. Inter-specific Competition

MIXED CROPPING

The subject of inter-specific competition concerns the effects of growing different crops in mixtures and the effects of weeds on crop yields. In temperate climates mixed cropping is not widely practised and it is more important in tropical agriculture. The objective of growing a mixture of crops is to improve the efficiency of resource use during the available growing season. The resources involved are light, nutrients and water. The effects of mixed cropping, or intercropping, in tropical crops, have been comprehensively reviewed by Willey (1979).

Mixtures of different cereals have been grown in the United Kingdom and are referred to as mixed corn. This crop was mainly grown for animal feed purposes and has declined in importance. Examples of mixed cropping exist in grassland and forage crops in temperate areas. In most situations, grassland consists of a mixture of grass species and an accompanying legume. This results in competition between individual species within the sward and the botanical composition varies throughout the season and from year to year, depending on the system of management imposed. Annual forage crops can also be grown in mixtures. Whole-crop arable silages are useful to produce high yields of good quality forage for ensilage. The mixture in this case usually consists of barley, oats and a legume which is usually a forage pea or vetch.

Studies on the competition between two species have utilised a replacement series. This involves generating a range of mixtures by starting with a monoculture of one species to progressively replacing plants of that species with plants of another until a monoculture of the latter is produced. The effects, on the total yield of the crops, of such a replacement series are shown in Figure 8.1. The Figure shows two types of responses. The broken lines represent the yield of the mixture and of the component species (A and B) where each one is of equal competitive ability. The total yield represents the sum of the yield of the two species. The monoculture of crop A is the highest yielding treatment and the relationship shows a straightforward replacement effect.

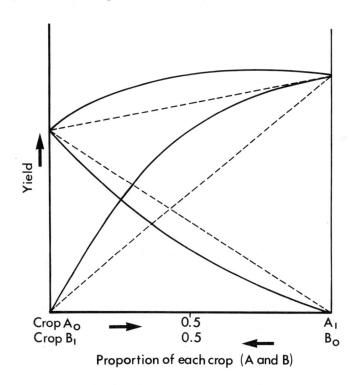

Figure 8.1 The effect of mixing two crops on the yield per unit area where crops A and B are of equal competitive ability (----) and where crop A is the stronger competitor (——)

The second example (continuous lines) represents a mixture where crop A is the stronger competitor. In this case, except where monocultures are grown, the yield of crop A in the mixture is higher than would be expected from a straightforward replacement series because of its stronger competitive ability. Consequently the yield of the mixture is higher throughout the series.

The establishment of relationships of this kind is difficult. The major problem involved is the accurate expression of the density units which should be used where more than one species is involved. Different species require different amounts of space in which to grow and the choice of components for the mixture must take account of this. A common method of mixed cropping involves maize and *Phaseolus* beans. One maize plant requires the same amount of space as two *Phaseolus* beans and thus the proportion of seeds of the two species in the mixture should be balanced accordingly. One obvious advantage of such a mixture is the nitrogen-fixing ability of the legume component which benefits the maize plants.

A further point to be considered in the choice of species for a mixture is the similarity of growth periods. If a crop, which is slow to establish, is grown with one which has rapid early growth, the competitive balance will be strongly in favour of the latter. Similarly the crop which is rapid to establish may mature sooner and harvesting periods may not synchronise.

COMPETITION FROM WEEDS

Arable soils inevitably carry a burden of weed seeds (or rhizomes and stolons) which may germinate or grow at a similar time to crop seeds, resulting in inter-specific competition between the two. The effect of competing weeds on the growth and yield of crops depends on a number of factors which will be discussed in this chapter. The main reasons for reductions in crop yields from weeds are their competitive abilities for the resources of light,

200

water and nutrients needed by the crop. Light is necessary for photosynthesis and growth and vigorously growing
weeds can shade the crop plants and reduce their growth
rate. The extent of the competition for light depends on
rate of growth of the weeds, their growth habit, their
density and the time at which they start to grow relative
to the crop. Some annual weeds have rapid early growth
rates and can start to compete with the crop for light
early. This is often aggravated by the ability of the
weed to grow faster than the crop at low temperatures. An
example of this is found with cleavers and common chickweed in autumn-sown cereals. Serious competition with the
crop can occur in these cases in the autumn and necessitate some control measures. Similarly in spring-sown
crops many weed species show faster initial growth and
compete early with the crop for light.

The growth habit of the weed relative to the crop is
also important. Weeds with a prostrate growth habit, e.g.
knotgrass, in an erect growing crop may not pose a serious
competitive threat for light. However weed plants with an
erect habit of growth in slow-growing prostrate crops provide serious competition for light. The slow early growth
of sugar beet, with its rosette of leaves, makes it very
susceptible to competition for light from the erect-
growing fathen and mayweeds. Therefore the growth characteristics of the weed, relative to the crop, markedly
affect the degree of competition for light. This aspect
cannot be considered in isolation and the degree of effect
will be influenced by the density of the weeds and their
time of emergence relative to that of the crop.

The density of weeds, relative to that of the crop,
will clearly have an influence on the degree and time of
onset of competition for light. Dense populations of
weeds are more likely to compete earlier with the crop for
light and, in extreme cases, may smother the plants.
Early development of the weed population leads to an
earlier onset of competition. At some point, when the

weed density is high, and competition develops early, inter-specific competition between different weed species and the crop and intra-specific competition between crop plants and individual weeds of the same species occurs. Thus where high densities of mixed weeds occur in a crop the aspects of competition become complex.

Competition for water is a further aspect to be considered where weeds are present. Water is an essential factor for the satisfactory growth of plants and deficiencies can cause yield and quality reductions. The ability of a plant to successfully compete for water depends on the rate and efficiency with which it utilises the soil supply. This is mainly dependent on the relative growth rate and rate of root extension. The early development of a deep and extensive tap root system of many dicotyledonous weeds results in early competition for water with crops which have shallow and fibrous root systems. In periods of moisture shortage, such weeds are better adapted to survive and compete for other resources than crops. Competition for water is closely linked with competition for nutrients as the rate of uptake of nutrients is dependent on the flow of water to the root surface.

A number of experiments (Zimdahl, 1980) have emphasised the fact that some weeds usually absorb fertilisers faster and in relatively larger amounts than crops. The effect of this is to reduce the amount available to the crop. However the weeds also respond to the nutrients and this gives them a further competitive advantage. Increasing the level of fertiliser supply to the crop may not therefore provide a benefit except where the weed populations are low. Competition studies with black bindweed (*Polygonum convolvulus*) in wheat have shown that a greater grain yield reduction was evident where higher fertiliser levels were used. Other studies with wild oat (*Avena fatua*) in wheat have shown that both plants responded similarly to fertiliser application and no additional yield reduction was evident where higher fertiliser was used. The growth habit of the weed is also important in competition for nutrients. Prostrate weeds are generally considered to be more serious competitors for nitrogen than erect types which are more important competitors for light.

Weeds compete for phosphorus and potassium as well as nitrogen. They are generally less sensitive to low soil potassium levels than crops although they respond to amounts applied additionally. Studies with fathen have shown that it accumulates nitrogen and potassium at the expense of crops. Although the subject of competition for nutrients is a complex one, it is clear that in many situations weeds provide a serious threat to crop plants in this respect.

There is a considerable amount of evidence that many weed plants are serious competitors with crops for the major resources of light, water and nutrients. The magnitude of crop yield depression depends on the extent and duration of the competition.

THE EFFECTS OF WEEDS ON CROP YIELDS

Competition from weeds can lead to reductions in yield of the economic product of growth. Ideally it would be helpful to the grower if the yield reductions could be predicted so that the benefits of weed control methods could be assessed. However it is not a straightforward matter to specify yield reductions for different populations of weeds in different crops. A number of factors will affect the level of yield reduction and these will be discussed here.

The *density* of weeds in the crop is a major factor controlling the extent of the yield reduction. Initially the weed density depends on the burden of weed seeds in the soil. This factor is extremely variable and will change from one field to another. The number of weed seeds present in a soil reflects its previous history;

the number of seeds shed on or disseminated into it in the current year and dormant seeds from preceding years. Estimates for very weedy fields in the United Kingdom suggest that populations of over 250 million seeds ha$^{-1}$ may be present. Most arable fields probably have more than 20 million ha$^{-1}$. If no further additions of weed seeds occur then the population can be expected to decline by between 20 and 50 per cent per year. The seeds of many weed species exhibit dormancy which means that control of all the weeds in one year will not guarantee a clean field in subsequent years. Individual species vary in their dormancy characteristics. Common chickweed seeds may display 95 per cent germination within a year of shedding but a proportion of the remainder can survive for sixty years when buried deeply. Cultivations change the position of the seeds in the soil profile and can stimulate germination. Most weed seeds can only emerge from depths of less than 3 cm and their survival depends on being placed in this zone of the profile by cultivations. Large seeds of the winter wild oat can emerge from depths up to 20 cm. The maximum depth from which seedlings can emerge is related to the size of the seeds. Unless the seeds are returned to the appropriate zone for establishment they will eventually disappear. Seeds of the spring wild oat do not normally survive for more than nine or ten years.

It is clear, from the evidence on soil populations of weed seeds and a knowledge of the factors affecting their establishment, that the density of weeds in a crop is unpredictable. Experience of the weed populations of individual fields can help in deciding on appropriate control measures. Experiments on the effect of weed density are difficult to carry out because of the interactions which occur with the type of weeds and the time of onset and duration of the competition. In general, the relationship of weed density with crop yield is non-linear and follows a sigmoidal pattern (Figure 8.2). Yield reduction is small over a range of densities at the low end of the

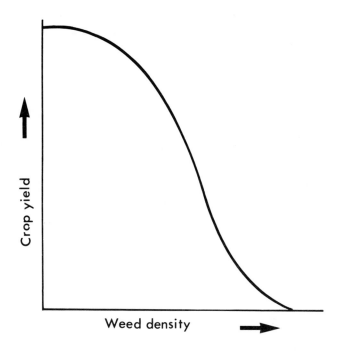

*Figure 8.2  The relationship between crop yield and weed density*

spectrum and then falls rapidly before levelling out at
high densities.  Studies with a range of crops confirm
this relationship.  The implication of this is that low
weed densities can be tolerated without serious loss of
yield and completely 'clean' crops are not necessary.

Some of the most comprehensive studies on weed density
effects have been carried out with sugar beet (Scott and
Wilcockson, 1976).  The results in Figure 8.3 summarise
the effects of establishing fathen (*Chenopodium album*) and
scentless mayweed (*Tripleurospermum inodorum*) at different
densities of sowing and one week after emergence.  When
sown with the crop, fathen is very competitive and large
yield reductions occur at densities of less than 20 plants
$m^{-2}$.  Mayweed is less effective in reducing crop yields
at similar densities.   Delaying the competition
from fathen until after crop emergence reduces the

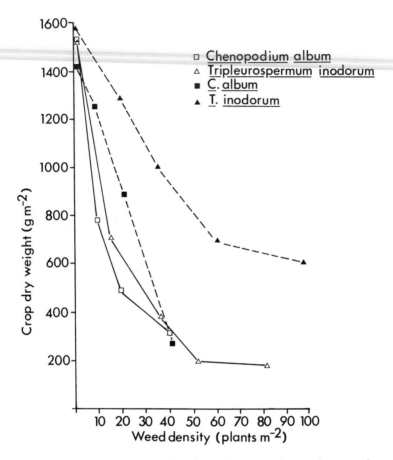

*Figure 8.3  The effect of density of two weed species on the crop yield of sugar beet when sown with the crop (open symbols) and one week after emergence (closed symbols) (after Scott and Wilcockson, 1976)*

severity of yield depression but it is still substantial. Late competition from mayweed produces a much smaller yield reduction.  In all cases the crop yield was closely correlated with the dry weight of weeds produced.  In addition, at high weed densities, a higher shoot to root ratio occurred, indicative of competition for light.  This study emphasises the fact that the reduction in crop yield is dependent on weed density.  However it is clear that the extent of the yield depression is affected by the growth habit of the weed and the time of onset of the competition.

Weed density effects in other crops are not so well studied. Zimdahl (1980) summarises data for soyabean and reports yield reductions of 30-50 per cent over a wide range of densities of *Brassica kaber*. Yield loss in cereals is considerable where populations of wild oat exceed 10-20 m$^{-2}$. Similarly, where blackgrass (*Alopecurus myosuroides*) populations exceed 30 plants m$^{-2}$ in the early spring, the grain yield of winter wheat can be reduced by over 1 tonne ha$^{-1}$. Weed density therefore has a marked effect on the yield of cereals.

A further important aspect of weed competition is the *duration*. It may not be necessary to keep the crop free from weeds throughout its life and the concept of a

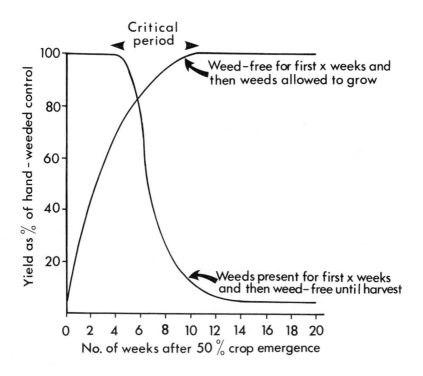

*Figure 8.4 The concept of a critical period for weed competition (drawn from Nieto, Brends and Gonzalez (1968) and based on an example for onions (Hewson and Roberts, 1971))*

critical period for weed competition has been evolved.
The effects of different periods of weed competition with
the crop are summarised in Figure 8.4. Where weeds are
present only in the early stages of crop growth there is
no effect on yield. In the example, based on onions, this
period is from 0 to 4 weeks. Allowing weeds to be present
in the crop for longer than 4 weeks results in a rapid
decline in crop yield. After 12 weeks of weed competition
crop yields are only 5 per cent of those from weed-free
controls.

If weeds are prevented from growing in the crops for
the early stages of growth and then they are allowed to
become weedy, a time occurs when yield reductions are
negligible. In the example, weeds allowed to grow after
10 weeks of the growing period do not cause a yield reduction. However, if the crop is kept weed-free for only
2 weeks, and then weeds allowed to grow, the yield reduction is substantial. A critical period therefore exists
when crops are vulnerable to weed competition. In the
example this period extends from 4 to 10 weeks after 50
per cent crop emergence. Weeds must be controlled during
this period if yields are to be maintained.

Individual crops differ in their critical period for
weed competition (Table 8.1). The examples in the table
reflect times from sowing and emergence. The period of
weed competition tolerated by maize varies from 2 to 8
weeks after emergence. Similarly the length of time in
which the crop needs to be kept weed-free after sowing or
emergence varies from 4 to 9 weeks. The examples on the
left and right-hand sections of the table do not always
come from the same experiments and comparisons are difficult. However, most crops have similar ranges of tolerance to early weed competition and lengths of period in
which they are required to be weed-free.

In sugar beet (Scott, Wilcockson and Moisey, 1979) the
latest date of starting weed removal, necessary to prevent
yield loss, was 6 weeks after emergence for crops sown in

Table 8.1 Tolerance of crops to weed competition

| Crop | Period of competition tolerated (weeks) after: | | Length of period required weed-free to prevent crop yield reduction (weeks) after: | |
|------|--------|-----------|--------|-----------|
|      | Sowing | Emergence | Sowing | Emergence |
| Maize | 3–6 | 2–8 | 3–5 | 4–9 |
| Potato | 4–6 | – | 9 | – |
| Soyabean | 4–9 | 2–8 | 2–6 | 4–6 |
| Sugar beet | 12 | 4 | 4–10 | 6 |
| Sunflower | 4 | – | 4–6 | – |
| Winter wheat | – | – | 4–6 | – |

Based on survey of literature by Zimdahl (1980) from experiments in N. America and Europe involving mixed annual weeds

late-March to early-April. For later sowing in late-April to early-May, the equivalent period was shorter, at 4 weeks. The time of emergence and hence the growth rates of the weeds and crop have an effect on the period of early weed competition which can be tolerated. The crop had reached the four to six true-leaf stage when the time for weeding to occur started. Delaying weeding after this time resulted in a 1.5 per cent yield reduction for each day that weeds were allowed to remain. In these studies the erect fathen weed caused greater yield reductions than common chickweed or scentless mayweed.

In some crop situations, there is no distinct critical period for weed control and yields could be maintained by a single weeding where the two lines overlap (see Figure 8.4).

The examples quoted here illustrate the importance of considering the duration of weed competition to the effect on yield. In most crops, weeds are tolerated in the first 0-6 weeks of growth without serious loss of yield. Thereafter the presence of weeds results in yield reductions. Furthermore, allowing weeds to grow in the crop after a period of approximately 8-10 weeks, having been previously kept weed-free, does not seriously affect yield.

The effect of *growth habit* of the weed in relation to the crop on the degree of competition has already been mentioned but it is clearly an important factor.

The *time of onset of competition* is also an important consideration and is partly covered in the discussion on duration. However the time at which competition occurs with the crop is affected by the time of emergence of the weeds. Weed seeds differ in their periodicity of germination and examples are illustrated in Figure 8.5. Information of this kind can be useful in predicting the periods of greatest risk from weeds. The examples of shepherd's purse, annual meadow grass and common chickweed show that seed germination occurs throughout the year and there is

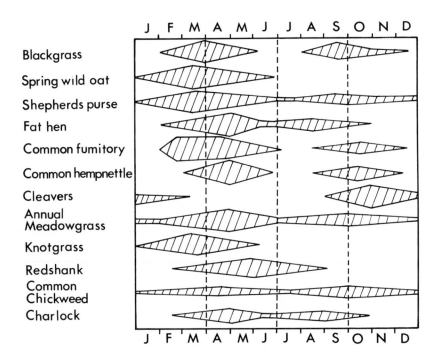

*Figure 8.5 The main germination periods of some common weeds of temperate crops (drawn from Fryer and Makepeace (eds.), 1977)*

always a competition risk irrespective of when the crops are sown. However these weeds are more likely to be a serious threat to crops in spring and autumn when conditions for seedling growth are optimal. Charlock is also in this category although there is a distinct increase in germination in April and May. Other weeds germinate over a shorter period of time. Knotgrass germinates in late-winter and early-spring with a peak period of activity in March. Spring-sown crops, especially early-sown cereals, are at greatest risk from this weed. Spring wild oat shows a similar pattern of seed germination to knotgrass. Redshank also shows a single period of seed germination but the peak is much later in May and early-June. Late-sown cereals and sugar beet are most at risk from weeds of this kind. Cleavers show a peak of germination activity from October to November and autumn-sown cereals and oil-seed rape are vulnerable to competition at this time.

A further category of weeds shows two main periods of germination. Blackgrass, common fumitory and hempnettle all exhibit this pattern with seeds germinating in late-spring and again in early-autumn. Autumn- and spring-sown crops are at risk from all of these weeds. Fathen also shows two main periods of germination but the first peak occurs much later (April to early-May) with a later one in August. Emerging sugar beet crops are vulnerable to fathen competition in the spring when the seeds germinate after pre-emergence herbicides are no longer effective.

Effective weed control, in part, relies on predicting the likely weed populations and species. A knowledge of the periodicity of weed seed germination relative to the emergence time of the crop is a useful aid to planning a weed control schedule.

The *spatial arrangement* of the crop plants and the weeds also has an effect on the intensity of competition. Crops which are grown at low densities in relatively wide rows, and which display slow early growth, are most at risk from weeds. The sugar beet crop is a good example of this, and where early competition occurs the yield reductions can be as great as 90 per cent. Cereals are grown in narrow rows at high seed rates and compete more effectively with early-germinating weeds. Potatoes, which are grown in wide rows, are slow to emerge and vulnerable to early weed competition. However, after emergence, the crop grows rapidly and weed control measures are only necessary before a full crop leaf cover is achieved. Increasing the seed rate of the crop increases its competitive ability with weeds and may be used as an insurance factor in marginal weed competition situations. Thurston (1962) reported that wild oats in winter and spring cereals were controlled by a dense crop. The effectiveness of the suppression of wild oats by the crop depends on the density when the wild oats germinate in the spring. There is therefore evidence in some crops that the intensity of weed competition can be reduced by manipulating the seed rate and row width.

A further factor influencing the competitive ability of a weed relative to the crop is its ability to withstand adverse conditions. In stress conditions, crop growth may be retarded more than that of the weeds. This is particularly so in drought situations where weeds with a deep tap root system, e.g. *Rumex* species, will grow faster than a cereal crop with a relatively shallow fibrous root system.

It is clear that a number of factors influence the competitive ability of weeds in crops. An understanding of these factors can help in the implementation of an efficient weed control system.

OTHER EFFECTS OF WEEDS

Weeds can have other adverse effects on crop production. The quality of cereals can be reduced by competition from weeds. The reduced supply of nutrients and water to cereals from weed competition can reduce grain size and the suitability of the product for a particular market.

Wheat grain may be less suitable for milling where grain size is reduced by weeds. Weed seeds which are of a similar size, shape and density to those of the crop are difficult to separate in cleaning processes. Contamination of seed samples with such weed seeds can result in their rejection for sale for these purposes. Furthermore the seeds of some weeds are poisonous and their presence in grain for milling and human consumption is dangerous, e.g. corncockle (*Agrostemma githago*).

Weeds can also interfere with field operations in crops. The presence of a mat of rhizomes of perennial grass weeds impedes cultivation and drilling operations. The main effect here is to slow down the operation by blockage of tines and coulters. In addition, harvesting of grain and root crops is slower where high densities of weeds are present. The tough stems of knotgrass and fathen prevent efficient harvesting of *Phaseolus* beans and can block the sieves of machines in sugar beet factories.

Weeds can also have adverse effects by providing alternative hosts for crop pests and diseases. Several cruciferous weeds, such as charlock and shepherd's purse, are infected by the club root organism and provide a means of perpetuating the disease in the absence of a brassica crop host. In cereals, the grass *Agropyron repens* (couch) can support populations of the take-all fungus which is a major disease of wheat and barley. Blackgrass, and other grass weeds, can be affected by ergot and provide a risk of this disease to cereal crops. A further example of the importance of weeds as sources of disease is provided by volunteer cereals, growing from seeds shed by the previous crop, which can carry foliar diseases through the winter and provide a source of inoculum for infecting crops in the following spring.

Several weeds also act as alternative hosts to crop pests. The beet cyst nematode infects a wide range of weeds and can survive satisfactorily by these means in the absence of a suitable host crop. Weeds such as thistles,

docks and fathen provide alternative hosts for aphids
(especially the black bean aphid) which then migrate to
susceptible host crops. The case against weeds as alternative hosts of crop pests and diseases is strong and
should be considered as a serious reason for their control.

In rare situations, weeds can be considered as beneficial. In soils prone to erosion, their root systems
provide a binding matrix to reduce this problem. In addition, seedbed weeds may have some value as a green manure
when they are ploughed in. However, on balance, weeds
have a number of detrimental effects on crop yield, quality and health and are generally undesirable.

## FACTORS AFFECTING WEED COMMUNITIES

The density of weeds and the variety of species encountered
in any crop situation are of interest to the grower. It is
possible to predict to some extent the nature of the weed
community by a knowledge of the biology of weeds. One of
the main factors affecting the weed community is the weed
seed population. The magnitude of this encountered in
arable soils has already been referred to and is substantial. One factor influencing the seed population is the
number of seeds produced by each weed plant. This varies
greatly from species to species and does not take account
of those weeds which are propagated vegetatively. Seed
numbers produced by a single plant of ivy-leaved speedwell
can be as low as 50 but the common poppy can produce up to
17,000 from a single plant. The number of seeds produced
by a wild oat plant may be between 50 and 100 but plants
growing free from competition may produce as many as 2000.
The numbers of seeds produced by a wild oat plant depend
on the crop it is growing with. In spring barley the
range is 40-50 whereas in winter wheat it may be only
10-30 (Cussans, 1976). Even if it were possible to predict weed seed production accurately it might not be useful
information in predicting future weed problems because of

the dormancy factors involved.

Knowledge of the method of propagation of the weed can be useful. Most weeds are propagated by seed and the periodicity of germination can be predicted. However some of the most difficult weeds to control are propagated by vegetative means. Couch grass and creeping bent are a serious threat to cereals and they are propagated from rhizomes and stolons respectively in the soil. This type of weed requires a different approach to control from that used on weeds growing from seeds. Control methods which are aimed at killing the rhizomes and stolons may be more effective with these types of weed. Dicotyledonous plants which reproduce vegetatively can also be a problem. Creeping thistle and field bindweed provide good examples of weeds in this category.

Some weeds are a problem because they shed their seeds before the crop is harvested. Where this occurs, problems in the next crop can be expected. Annuals, such as shepherd's purse and groundsel, may flower within six weeks of emergence and subsequently shed their seeds. In this case several generations of seeds can occur in a single growing season and lead to a build-up of seeds. One of the reasons why blackgrass has become a problem in cereal crops is that, by the time the crop is ready to combine, the seeds have already been shed and germinate in the succeeding crop. When cereals were cut by binder, earlier harvesting was possible, which partially eliminated this problem. Wild oats also shed their seeds in cereal crops before harvest. To some extent the risk of seed shedding in a crop is a reflection of the flowering requirements of the weed. Chickweed and annual meadow grass are insensitive to day-length and flower and produce seed throughout the year, when temperatures permit. Wild oats are long-day plants and flower and produce their seeds in the early summer period.

Other factors which affect the nature of the weed community are the dormancy characteristics of the seed and

the depth in the soil profile at which the seeds are
situated. Both of these aspects have been discussed
earlier.

WEED CONTROL METHODS

The range of weed control methods available to the grower
is wide and will not be dealt with in detail here. The
major approaches to weed control and the factors affecting
their success are summarised.

   (i) Roguing. Where weeds are present at low populations in valuable crops their removal by hand may be
the most appropriate method. Hand roguing of wild
oats in cereal crops for seed reduces their competitive influence and increases the chances of the
crop being suitable for seed purposes. In this example, the plant should be removed from the field
and disposed of because seed maturation may continue
after the plants have been pulled up. Hand roguing
is of limited use in a wider context in temperate
cropping systems.

 (ii) Rotations. The importance of crop rotations in
cropping sequences has been referred to in chapter 4.
One of the benefits of a sequence of crops as
opposed to a monoculture is that it offers an opportunity to use a wider range of weed control measures.
The increase in cereal monoculture with reduced
cultivations has led to the build-up of some weeds
which are not easily controlled. The introduction
of another crop provides an opportunity for using a
different range of herbicides and cultivations for
weed control. The more rigid rotations of the nineteenth and early twentieth centuries involved the
use of row crops which allowed inter-row cultivations to be used. To some extent this is still
practised with sugar beet and potatoes in cereal
systems. However the wider range of herbicides

available has led to a further decline in this
practice. The different times of cultivations and
sowing dates of different crops in a rotation stimulate changes in the weed flora and never allow one
weed to become dominant. The use of rotations ensures that individual weeds, although always present,
never become a serious problem.

The use of rotations is unlikely to be an effective means of total weed control in itself but when
used in conjunction with herbicides is likely to
produce a more effective control programme. The
introduction of potatoes into a cereal system is a
good example of this. Grass weeds which develop in
the cereal can be dealt with in the potato crop in
a number of ways. The more extensive system of
cultivations used for potatoes helps to control
weeds by burying rhizomes and stolons and desiccating them by bringing them to the surface. Potatoes
are planted later than spring cereals allowing more
time for seedbed weed control measures in the spring.
The period between planting and emergence of
potatoes is lengthy and this allows the use of pre-
emergence non-selective herbicides, e.g. paraquat,
to control weeds. During the early life of the
crop, weeds between the rows can be controlled by
cultivation. In addition, the dense canopy of the
potato crop which eventually develops, effectively
smothers late developing weeds. All of these factors help to provide a cleaning effect on the land
which could not be achieved with cereals and illustrates the benefits of rotational measures in weed
control. These benefits still have a role to play
even where a wide range of herbicides are available.

(iii) <u>Cultivations</u>. The trend towards reduced cultivations and direct drilling has increased the problem with some weeds. A good example of this is
where blackgrass seeds are shed on the soil surface

and the subsequent crop is direct drilled. Blackgrass seeds then develop without any soil impedance
to germination and pose problems in the next crop.
Cultivations are an effective means of reducing
problems of this kind. One benefit of cultivations
is in the burial of seeds and underground organs of
propagation. In addition, weed seeds and rhizomes
near the surface which are inverted to the bottom of
the plough layer are unlikely to emerge until
returned to the surface by subsequent cultivations.

Cultivations also serve to fragment plant organs
by cutting which can result in death. However, with
weeds such as couch grass, the cutting of the
rhizomes merely serves to increase the number of
units of propagation and spread them, unless additional control measures are taken. Cultivations in
the preparation of a seedbed can bring roots, seedlings and rhizomes to the surface and result in
their death from desiccation if environmental conditions are favourable. Tined cultivators and
harrows are effective in this respect. Repeated
cultivations and stimulation of weed growth can lead
to the death of weeds through depletion of their
carbohydrate reserves. Cultivations also stimulate
weed seed germination through the provision of
favourable soil conditions.

*Table 8.2 The effect of site and cultivation
method on the blackgrass content (plants $m^{-2}$)
of winter wheat crops (after Moss, 1979)*

|  | Site | | |
| --- | --- | --- | --- |
|  | 1 | 2 | 3 |
| Ploughing | 4 | 28 | 8 |
| Tine cultivation | 78 | 130 | 88 |
| Direct drill | 177 | 159 | 91 |

The relative effectiveness of different cultivations in controlling blackgrass in the south Midlands of England is demonstrated in Table 8.2.  The
number of blackgrass plants in a winter wheat crop
at three sites is very much lower where the land was
ploughed after the previous crop compared to direct
drilling.  The reduction by ploughing is great and
illustrates the benefits of this method of seedbed
preparation.  Tined cultivations result in the
burial of a proportion of the seeds but the numbers
establishing are still substantial.  The effect of
tined cultivations is dependent on the site; at
Site 1 the numbers are less than half those in
direct drilled treatments but at Site 3 the reduction is negligible.

Cultivations are unlikely to result in total
weed control *per se* but when used in conjunction
with rotations and herbicides they can make a
valuable contribution to a control programme.

Where no cultivations are used, the efficient
disposal of crop residues can help to reduce the
weed burden especially in cereals.  Weed seeds are
returned to the soil in the straw after combine
harvesting and provide a reservoir for development
in the next crop.  Removal of the straw helps to
reduce this problem.  Where no straw removal occurs
and the succeeding crop is direct drilled good controlled burning can destroy weeds on the surface.
Effective straw-burning can destroy up to 70 per
cent of freshly shed blackgrass seeds and stimulate
germination in a proportion of the rest.  Similarly
straw-burning can destroy up to 70 per cent of wild
oat seeds and break the dormancy of some of those
which survive.

(iv) <u>Prevention of spread</u>.  Weed seeds are disseminated
by a variety of means and the prevention of spread
can help to reduce the problem of weed competition.

219

Prevention of seed dispersal by natural agents such
as wind, water and animals cannot be influenced by
the grower. However, seeds can be spread in and on
machines and through sowing contaminated crop seeds.
Statutory regulations minimise the weed seed content of seed sold in most countries and the risk of
spread by this means is small if certified seed is
used. Weed seeds can be spread in drills and harvesters, and efforts should be made to minimise this
source through regular cleaning of machines. Weed
seeds are also spread in soil adhering to machinery
but control of this method is difficult. Some seeds
survive the passage through the digestive tracts of
farm animals, and farmyard manure may provide a
source of weeds on land receiving it.

(v) <u>Chemical means</u>. The use of chemicals for weed control first occurred with the use of copper sulphate
in cereals in France in 1896. Developments in
herbicide technology were slow until 1950 when a
large number of chemicals were introduced. The
advances in herbicide technology accelerated in the
1960s and 1970s until in 1980 almost 100 chemicals
were available in over 500 different commercial
formulations. The obvious conclusion from these
facts is that the choice of herbicide for a particular crop situation is a complex matter and profes-
sional advice should be sought for each situation.
However there are a number of principles of the use
of herbicides which are well established and will be
discussed here. The first point relating to the
efficient use of herbicides is the identification of
the nature of the weed problem and an assessment of
the numbers and species of weeds present in the crop.
It is often necessary to anticipate the weed problem
in advance in order to use herbicides before the
crop and weeds emerge. A knowledge of the previous
cropping and history of the field is a useful aid

with this problem. Regular and accurate field records can provide useful information of this kind.

Once the nature of the weed problem is known the selection of the herbicide programme can take place. This is more efficiently done if the grower has a knowledge of the characteristics of herbicides. Herbicides are classified in a number of ways. The simplest classification is to consider their action as *non-selective* or *selective*. Non-selective chemicals will kill the crop and the weeds and must be applied before the crop emerges, e.g. paraquat on potato ridges. Selective herbicides kill the weeds but not the crop. The basis of this selectivity depends on the differential effect of the chemical on the physiology and metabolism of the crop and weed plants. MCPA and 2,4-D are selective herbicides which can be used to control dicotyledonous weeds in cereals. The entry of the chemical into the plant is usually through the leaves but it may be taken up by the roots when applied to the soil. An example of a soil-applied selective herbicide is atrazine for use in maize crops.

Herbicides can also be classified by their method of application and mode of action. The method of application of the chemical may be *foliar* or *soil*. Foliage treatments are widespread and can be further sub-divided according to whether they are *contact* or *translocated* in the method of effect. Contact chemicals only affect the part of the plant receiving the chemical. In the case of translocated types, the chemical is transported around the plant in the vascular system and affects other parts of the plants including the roots.

Soil treatments by herbicides can also be considered in a sub-classification according to the time in the life of the crop at which they are applied. In this case the classes are termed

*pre-sowing, pre-emergence* and *post-emergence*. The
sugar beet crop provides examples for all of these
categories. TCA (trichloracetic acid) is used pre-
sowing as a soil-incorporated herbicide to control
perennial grass weeds. Lenacil can be applied pre-
emergence, but after sowing, as a band or overall
spray, and phenmedipham can be used as post-
emergence selective treatment for late-germinating
weeds. In many situations all three approaches may
be necessary to control weeds effectively.

Thus herbicides can be grouped and described
according to the following scheme:

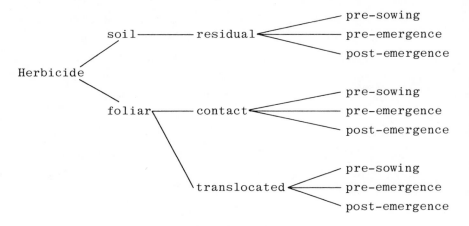

A further classification of herbicides can be
made on their chemical structure and groups (Table
8.3). There are eighteen chemical groups which contain compounds with herbicidal activity and a few
others which do not fit into any of the major groups.
Examples of commonly used herbicides in each group
are given but the list is not comprehensive. It is
a complex matter to select the most appropriate
chemical(s) for a particular crop and field. The
situation is further confused by the practice of
marketing the same chemical, or mixture of chemicals,
under different trade names. Great care and caution
must be taken to select the right ones for each crop.

Table 8.3 *Groups of herbicides according to their chemical structure*

| Group | Examples |
|---|---|
| 1. Inorganic salts | Sodium chlorate |
| 2. Halo-alkanoic acids | TCA-sodium and Dalapon-sodium |
| 3. Phenoxyalkanoic acids | 2,4-D and Mecoprop |
| 4. Aromatic acids | 2,3,6-TBA and Dicamba |
| 5. Amides and nitriles | Propyzamide and Bromoxynil |
| 6. Anilides | Propachlor and Propanil |
| 7. Nitrophenols | Dinoseb |
| 8. Nitrophenyl ethers | Nitrofen and Bromofenoxim |
| 9. Nitroanilines | Trifluralin and Dinitramine |
| 10. Carbamates | Propham and Barban |
| 11. Thiocarbamates | EPTC and Di-allate |
| 12. Ureas | Linuron and Metoxuron |
| 13. Triazines | Simazine and Atrazine |
| 14. Pyridines | Paraquat and Diquat |
| 15. Pyridazines | Pyrazone and Norflurazon |
| 16. Uracils | Bromacil and Lenacil |
| 17. Unclassified hetero-<br>cyclic compounds | Aminotriazole and Ethofumesate |
| 18. Organo-arsenic<br>compounds | Cacodylic acid |
| 19. Unclassified | Dimexan and Glyphosate |

(Compiled from Fryer and Makepeace, 1977)

Further discussion on the mode of action of individual groups of chemicals will not be made here.

A number of factors affect the efficiency and safety of use of chemicals for weed control. These are:

<u>Choice of chemical</u>. It is usually important to select the right chemical for use in the crop which will control the spectrum of weeds present. This applies particularly to selective herbicides. An example of this is shown in Table 8.4 regarding the choice of selective herbicides for controlling

Table 8.4 The choice of herbicide for cereals

| Weed | MCPA | Mecoprop | Dichlorprop | 2,3,6-TBA + Dicamba + MCPA + Mecoprop | Bentazone + Dichlorprop |
|---|---|---|---|---|---|
| Charlock | ** | * | * | * | * |
| Fathen | ** | * | * | * | * |
| Common chickweed | + | ** | * | * | * |
| Cleavers | R | ** | * | * | * |
| Knotgrass | R | R | + | * | MS |
| Mayweeds | R | * | + | ** | * |
| Corn marigold | R | R | R | R | ** |

(Compiled from ADAS, 1980)

Key:  * Satisfactory control of weed
 ** The most suitable weedkiller
 R Resistant to the weedkiller
 MS Moderately susceptible to the weedkiller
 + Useful control in ideal conditions

annual dicotyledonous weeds in cereals. MCPA gives good control of charlock and fathen and some control of common chickweed. However the other four weeds are resistant to MCPA and will not be controlled. Mecoprop offers a wide spectrum of control but does not control knotgrass and corn marigold. Dichlor-prop gives satisfactory control of most weeds except corn marigold. Mixing MCPA, mecoprop, 2,3,6-TBA and dicamba gives satisfactory control of most weeds again with the exception of corn marigold. The mixture of bentazone and dichlorprop gives good control of corn marigold and satisfactory control of the others except for knotgrass which is only moderately susceptible to this mixture. This example illustrates the importance of choosing the herbicide or mixture of herbicides to control the whole range of weeds present. Most selective herbicides have a limited spectrum of activity. Where mixtures are used and where herbicides are applied with other crop protection chemicals care must be taken to ensure that the mixtures are compatible.

Method of application. In addition to selecting the right chemicals, consideration must be given to the most appropriate method of applying them. The method depends on the mode of action of the chemical and the two main methods are as foliar sprays or by soil application. The manufacturer's instructions should be carefully followed to ensure maximum effectiveness. Some soil applied herbicides are volatile (trifluralin) and have to be incorporated into the soil within a short time after application.

Rate of application. Care must be taken to apply the chemical at the recommended rate in order to obtain maximum effectiveness. Application of the chemical at sub-optimal rates results in a reduced effectiveness of control. The use of rates higher than the recommended levels may cause damage to the

225

crop through scorching or deformation of growth and
development. Where herbicides are applied as
liquids the volume of water in which they are
sprayed can be important and recommendations must
be adhered to.

Calibration of machinery. The efficiency of herbicide use depends on accurate application. Machines
must therefore be well-maintained and accurately
calibrated before crops are sprayed.

Stage of growth. With selective foliar-applied
herbicides the stage of growth of the crop and weed
at the time of application is important. The
majority of broadleaved weeds are most susceptible
at the seedling stage and should be sprayed then.
However the crop must also be at the correct stage
of growth for application. Damage to cereals, in
the form of deformed ears, can result from applying
some herbicides too early in their growth. Crop
variety susceptibility also has to be considered
especially with wild oat herbicides for cereals.
With some translocated foliar herbicides the weed
must be actively growing before control is effective, e.g. glyphosate for couch grass control.

Environmental influences. Foliar-applied herbicides take time to penetrate the leaves and are
vulnerable to rain soon after spraying. Spraying
should therefore only be done in fine weather. The
effectiveness of some soil-applied residual herbicides is reduced at low temperatures and this aspect
should be considered. Furthermore the soil type may
influence the effectiveness of the herbicide. Some
soil-applied herbicides are absorbed onto the
surface of organic matter particles and are rendered
ineffective. This is a particular problem in soils
in the Fenlands of England which are high in organic
matter. An example of this is provided by the
herbicide chlorthal-dimethyl which is used to

control germinating weeds in onion crops. The herbicide linuron with monolinuron should not be used on sands, very light soils or soils with a high organic matter content. Soil texture can therefore influence the safe and effective use of some herbicides.

Safety aspects. The majority of herbicides are toxic to plants and various types of animals and safety is an important aspect of their use. Avoidance of spraying in windy conditions will reduce the risk of drift to other susceptible crops. Machine operators should wear appropriate protective clothing and dispose of containers safely to avoid pollution and risk to other forms of life. Herbicides are a valuable component of weed control systems and they should be used wisely and with awareness of the risks associated with them.

This chapter has mainly been concerned with aspects of inter-specific competition between weeds and crops. Weeds are detrimental to crop growth in many ways and should be controlled in an effective, safe and economic manner. Developed agricultural systems rely heavily on the use of herbicides for weed control. However it is evident that there are limitations to their use and the other methods available should be employed. In many situations, the best control can be obtained by employing a combination of methods which usually involves the use of herbicides.

REFERENCES AND FURTHER READING

Agricultural Development and Advisory Service (1980) Weed Control in Cereals 1981. Booklet 2253(81). London: Ministry of Agriculture, Fisheries and Food.

Chancellor, R.J. (1966) The Identification of Weed Seedlings of Farm and Garden, (2nd edn). Oxford: Blackwell Scientific Publications.

Chancellor, R.J. and Peters, N.C.B. (1974) 'The time of

onset of competition between wild oats (*Avena fatua* L.) and spring cereals'. Weed Research, 14, 197–202.

Cussans, G.W. (1976) 'Population dynamics of wild oats in relation to systematic control'. 6th Report of the Weed Research Organisation, 1974–1975, 47–56.

Elliot, J.G. (1980) 'Weed control: past and present — a historical perspective'. In Opportunities for Increasing Crop Yields, eds. Hurd, R.G., Biscoe, P.V. and Dennis, C. London: Pitman Publishing, 285–296.

Fryer, J.D. and Makepeace, R.J. (eds.) (1977) Weed Control Handbook. Volume II. Recommendations (8th edn). Oxford: Blackwell Scientific Publications.

Hewson, R.T. and Roberts, H.A. (1971) 'The effect of weed removal at different times on the yield of bulb onions'. Journal of Horticultural Science, 46, 471–483.

Klingman, G.C. and Ashton, F.M. (1975) Weed Science. New York: John Wiley and Sons, Inc.

Makepeace, R.J. and Holroyd, J. (1978) 'Weed control'. In The Potato Crop, ed. Harris, P.M. London: Chapman and Hall, 376–406.

Ministry of Agriculture, Fisheries and Food (1982) Approved Products 1982. London: HMSO.

Moss, S.R. (1979) 'The influence of tillage and method of straw disposal on the survival and growth of black-grass, *Alopecurus myosuroides*, and its control by chlortoluron and isoproturon'. Annals of Applied Biology, 91, 91–100.

Nieto, J.H., Brends, M.A. and Gonzalez, J.D. (1968) 'Critical periods of the crop growth cycle for weed competition'. Pesticide Articles and News Summaries (C), 14, 159–166.

Peters, N.C.B. and Wilson, B.J. (1980) Dormancy in Wild-oat Seed and its Agricultural Significance. 8th Report of the Weed Research Organisation, 1978–1979, 52–58.

Roberts, E.H. (ed.) (1972) Viability of Seeds. London:

Chapman and Hall.

Scott, R.K. and Wilcockson, S.J. (1976) 'Weed biology and the growth of sugar beet'. Annals of Applied Biology, 83, 331-335.

Scott, R.K., Wilcockson, S.J. and Moisey, F.R. (1979) 'The effects of time of weed removal on growth and yield of sugar beet'. Journal of agricultural Science, Cambridge, 93, 693-709.

Spitters, C.J.T. (1980) 'Competition effects within mixed stands'. In Opportunities for Increasing Crop Yields, eds. Hurd, R.G., Biscoe, P.V. and Dennis, C. London: Pitman Publishing, 219-232.

Thurston, J.M. (1962) 'The effect of competition from cereal crops on the germination and growth of *Avena fatua* in a naturally-infested field'. Weed Research, 2, 192-207.

Willey, R.W. (1979) 'Intercropping − its importance and research needs. Part 1. Competition and yield advantages'. Field Crop Abstracts, 32, 1-10.

Willey, R.W. (1979) 'Intercropping − its importance and research needs. Part 2. Agronomy and research approaches'. Field Crop Abstracts, 32, 73-85.

Zimdahl, R.L. (1980) Weed-Crop Competition. A Review. Oregon: International Plant Protection Center.

# 9 Principles of Crop Nutrition

## ELEMENTS REQUIRED FOR PLANT GROWTH AND DEVELOPMENT

Mineral elements are essential to sustain the physiological processes controlling growth and development.  The
grower can manipulate the supply of nutrients to crops to
control yield and quality through the application of
fertilisers of various types.  An understanding of the
principles involved in the nutrition of crop plants is
therefore an important part of crop production.

The three elements of nitrogen, phosphorus and potassium are the main ones controlling growth and development.
Other major elements such as calcium, magnesium, sodium,
sulphur and chlorine are also required by plants but are
not so widely applied as fertilisers.  A number of other
elements are required in small quantities and are known as
trace elements.  These include iron, manganese, zinc,
copper, boron, molybdenum and cobalt.  Deficiencies of
these elements can cause abnormal growth and development
and may give rise to animal health problems in farm livestock feeding on plant material deficient in one or more
of them.

Of the three major nutrients required, nitrogen has
the major controlling influence on growth.  Nitrogen is a
constituent of amino acids, proteins and nucleic acids and
plays a major role in the physiology of the plant.  Nitrogen is taken up in the form of ammonium and nitrate ions

and is subsequently converted to other nitrogenous compounds. In particular the growth of leaves is controlled by nitrogen. The size of the leaf canopy and its duration are both increased by increasing the amounts of nitrogen applied and hence the yield of most crops is affected by the supply of nitrogen. The chlorophyll content of the leaves is affected by nitrogen and deficient plants exhibit a pale green or yellow colouration. High levels of applied nitrogen can influence the protein content of specific organs of the plant, e.g. wheat or barley grains, and thus affect the quality.

The supply of nitrogen to the plant is affected by a number of factors. It exists in the soil in organic and inorganic forms and the activity of the soil bacteria in the nitrogen cycle creates a constantly changing situation. Some nitrogen is lost to the atmosphere in gaseous form and some is lost through leaching in drainage water. The inorganic forms are usually available to the plant whereas the organic forms are unavailable until mineralised by bacteria. The picture is further complicated where legumes are grown, because of their ability to fix atmospheric nitrogen through the activity of *Rhizobium* bacteria in the root nodules. These nodules have a limited life and eventually decay and release nitrogen to the soil. It is therefore difficult to predict what reserves of soil nitrogen are available to plants.

Phosphorus plays a fundamental role in plants in a large number of enzymic reactions which depend on phosphorylation. It is a constituent of the cell nucleus and essential for cell division. For this reason it is involved in the development of meristem tissue and is particularly required in the early rapid phase of growth. It is traditionally associated with root development in seedlings and adequate supplies of phosphorus in the seedbed are essential for most crops. Phosphorus deficiency is prevalent in some soils but in temperate arable systems annual insurance and maintenance applications reduce its occurrence. Phosphorus deficiency in cereals is exhibited by stunting and retardation of the development process. Severe stunting of root crops occurs in phosphorus-deficient soils. Plants take up phosphorus in the inorganic form, principally as the $H_2PO_4^-$ ion.

Potassium is not a constituent of the plant structural material but is essential in the synthesis of amino acids and proteins from ammonium ions. Adequate supplies of potassium are also essential for efficient photosynthesis and this element is involved in the transport mechanism of other nutrients across cell membranes. In many situations potassium supplies in the soil are adequate for crop growth, but where high nitrogen and phosphorus fertiliser levels are used, potassium may become a limiting factor to growth. Potassium deficiency is evident from chlorosis and necrosis of the margins of leaves and in the production of small fruits and seeds.

Calcium is essential for the normal development of meristems and is a major constituent of cell walls as calcium pectate. It is essential therefore to have adequate supplies of this element to sustain normal growth. Most soils have adequate quantities of calcium present but over a period of time leaching losses and removal in crop products can cause deficiencies.

In addition to being an essential element, calcium is the dominant base in soils and helps to keep the soil reaction neutral. Where high calcium leaching losses occur, positively charged hydrogen ions take its place and the soil reaction becomes acid, i.e. the pH declines. Crop growth is adversely affected at low pH values and when they fall to 5 most arable crops grow poorly or fail. Potatoes and oats are the most tolerant crops of low soil pH.

Where low pH occurs, liming should be done to restore the values to between 6 and 7 at which most crops grow well. Overliming should be avoided because at high pH values, above 7, some trace elements become unavailable.

232

Lime exists in a number of chemical forms but is commonly applied as calcium carbonate from ground limestone. Where magnesium is in short supply, dolomitic, or magnesian, limestone can be used.

In addition to calcium losses from leaching, ammonium fertilisers displace calcium ions from the surface of clay colloids and organic matter. Thus over a period of time the soil pH may fall and regular soil analysis should be done to determine the pH and lime requirement. Sugar beet and barley are the crops most sensitive to soil acidity.

Magnesium is a further essential element for crop growth. It is a major constituent of the chlorophyll molecule and a deficiency results in yellowing of the leaves and reduced photosynthetic efficiency. Magnesium deficiencies are most likely to occur on light textured soils in wet areas. Potatoes, sugar beet and brassicas are particularly sensitive to magnesium deficiency.

Sodium does not appear to be essential for achieving high crop yields. However some crops give better yields where sodium supplies are adequate. The sugar beet is a good example of this and produces higher yields from sodium even when there is adequate potassium available. This is associated with the fact that sugar beet is a halophyte and originated from a seashore environment where sodium is in adequate supply.

Sulphur is an important constituent of many plant proteins and is involved in oil synthesis in seeds. Certain areas may be deficient in sulphur but in general this element is not a limiting factor to crop yields. Sulphur is deposited in the soil in rainfall from the atmosphere and this source is usually adequate to supply the needs of most crops.

Chlorine is involved in the regulation of osmotic pressure and the cation balance in cell sap. Adequate quantities are usually present in soils and up to 50 kg ha$^{-1}$ per annum are deposited in rainfall.

The major elements required for normal plant growth and development have been described.  It is clear that they fulfil important roles and supplementation of soil reserves in the form of fertiliser may be necessary where deficiencies occur.

## CROP RESPONSES TO THE MAJOR ELEMENTS

It is important to establish the yield response of different crops to varying levels of fertiliser inputs so that appropriate quantities can be applied.  This subject has been extensively studied through experiments over many years and the types of responses are well known.  It is important in such experiments to take account of local variation in soil and weather conditions which may affect the degree of yield increment with increasing fertiliser input.

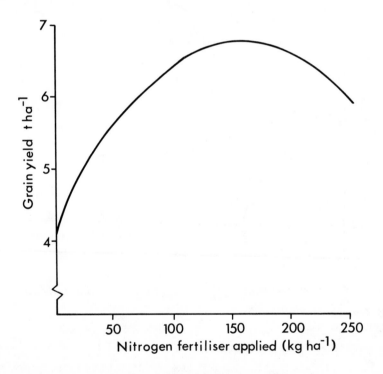

*Figure 9.1  The parabolic response of cereal grain yields to different amounts of fertiliser nitrogen (after Cooke, 1980)*

Nitrogen is the most widely used of all fertilisers and serves as a good example to illustrate crop responses. A typical response curve of the grain yield of cereals to increasing levels of nitrogen fertiliser is illustrated in Figure 9.1. The shape of the curve is parabolic. At the low end of the fertiliser range, large responses in grain yield are apparent. However as the levels of nitrogen (N) exceed 100 kg ha$^{-1}$ the response in grain yield is smaller per kilogram of nitrogen added. A maximum yield is achieved at approximately 150 kg ha$^{-1}$ in the example and at higher levels yields decline. This type of relationship is evident for many crops and enables recommendations to be made as to the most appropriate amount of nitrogen to apply. Sufficient data from a large number of experiments are necessary before confident recommendations can be made.

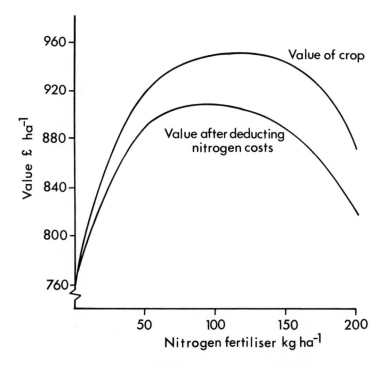

*Figure 9.2 Value of the sugar beet crop with different nitrogen fertiliser levels (from Sugar Beet Research and Education Committee, 1980)*

As the amount of fertiliser nitrogen is increased and yield increments become smaller the cost effectiveness of its use has to be considered. The value of the sugar beet crop with different nitrogen inputs is described graphically in Figure 9.2. In the case of the total value of the crop, the response curve is again parabolic and the maximum value is achieved with about 125 kg ha$^{-1}$ N. However if the cost of the fertiliser is deducted from the value of the crop the profitability declines after about 80 kg ha$^{-1}$. In this case, high levels of nitrogen encourage extra leaf growth with little effect on root and sugar yield. The maximum total value for the crop is achieved at the 125 kg ha$^{-1}$ level, but the optimum, in terms of profitability, is achieved at the lower level. Financial considerations are important in determining the levels of fertiliser for crops.

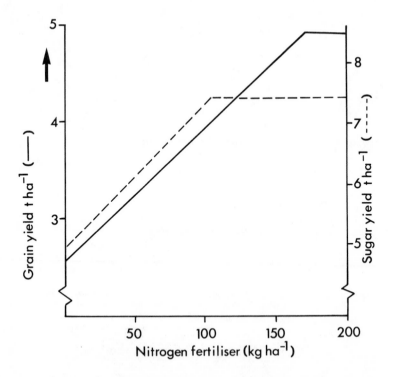

Figure 9.3  The linear relationship between grain yield and sugar yield and nitrogen fertiliser input (from Cooke, 1980)

The parabolic response of crop yields to nitrogen fertiliser is widely accepted. The data can however be interpreted in a different way which assumes that the response is not a curve. Two linear relationships on either side of a point of inflexion may fit the results of field experiments better than a curve (Figure 9.3). Sugar yield increases up to a maximum value of 100 kg ha$^{-1}$ N and thereafter no further increase is apparent and two straight lines adequately describe the data. In cereals the yield increases linearly over a wide range of nitrogen levels and the maximum response may be achieved at 160 kg ha$^{-1}$ N or more in winter wheat. Further additions of nitrogen result in little change in grain yield and in fact may cause a decrease.

The linear response over low levels of nitrogen is similar and apparent with most crops (although the scale will change) and it is only after the point of inflexion that crops differ in their response (Figure 9.4). With

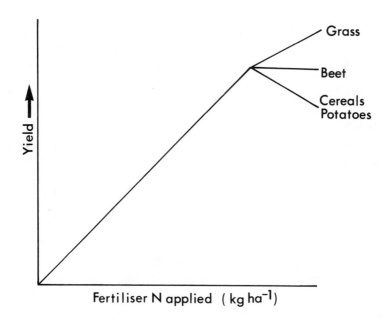

*Figure 9.4  The response relationships of different crops to applied nitrogen fertiliser (after Cooke, 1980)*

herbage grass, which is very responsive to nitrogen, yields continue to increase beyond the point of inflexion. Increasing nitrogen fertiliser beyond the point of inflexion for beet produces no further increase in yield. Thirdly with potatoes, and in some cases cereals, yields decrease markedly at very high levels of nitrogen. In this last case it is important to identify as accurately as possible the point beyond which decreases in yield are likely to occur.

Response relationships for phosphorus and potassium fertilisers have not been so clearly defined. In soils which are deficient in available forms of these elements, a linear response is evident over a small range of applied fertilisers. As a result phosphorus and potassium are usually applied in smaller quantities than nitrogen to maintain soil reserves. Crops differ in their requirements for these elements. Sugar beet has a high demand for potassium and potatoes require larger amounts of phosphorus than other crops. Therefore the fertiliser requirements for each crop should be carefully calculated. Legumes require little or no nitrogen, but have a relatively high requirement for phosphorus and potassium.

## THE INTERACTION OF FERTILISER ELEMENTS

The interaction of nutrients is important and in practice of course the crop requires quantities of all three major elements and possibly others. Figure 9.5 demonstrates an interaction between nitrogen and phosphorus in sugar beet. At low phosphorus levels root yields follow the normal parabolic response. Where high phosphorus levels are used, yields are higher throughout the nitrogen range 50-150 kg ha$^{-1}$. At the highest nitrogen level there is a proportionately greater response where high phosphorus levels are employed. This implies that low phosphorus levels are limiting the crop response to high nitrogen inputs. This kind of interaction is important where intensive systems of production are used which employ

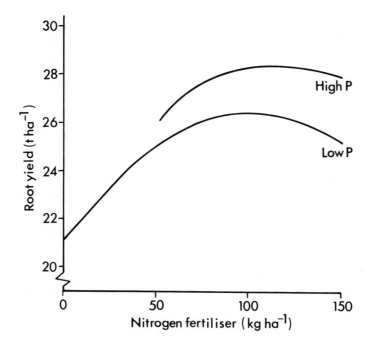

*Figure 9.5 The interaction between nitrogen and phosphorus fertil-
isers in sugar beet (after Cooke, 1980)*

high fertiliser levels. Similar interactions have been
observed in potatoes where high nitrogen levels can only
be justified where high phosphorus and potassium levels
are also used. Furthermore it is important to realise
that the response to the major elements may be limited by
shortage of another element such as magnesium or manganese.

Consideration of crop responses to individual elements
should be considered against a background of the level of
other elements required.

FACTORS AFFECTING THE RESPONSE TO FERTILISERS

The use of response relationships already described to
determine the optimum quantities of fertiliser required
must be considered with caution. At best, they represent
the average for a particular set of conditions. Allowance
must be made for differences in individual sites and the

239

optimum requirement will vary from field to field. A
number of factors affect the response of crops to fertilisers and only a brief treatment will be given here. For
a more detailed account the reader is referred to Cooke
(1982).

Soil characteristics have a major influence on the
response to fertilisers. Chemical analyses of soils can
be carried out to determine the status of available $P_2O_5$,
$K_2O$ and Mg. There are limitations to the value of these
analyses, but they provide a useful indicator of the soil
reserves and the likely response to applied fertilisers.
Soil analysis measures the amount of available elements
present and this can be represented by soil indices. The
scales vary for different countries, but in England and
Wales the range is from 0 (deficient) to 9 (excess). In
practice only the first 4 or 5 points on the scale are
relevant to arable soils.

Table 9.1 *The effect of soil index of available nutrients on the
recommended levels of $P_2O_5$ and $K_2O$ for selected crops (MAFF, 1981)*

| Index | Maincrop potatoes | | Sugar beet | | Cereals | |
|---|---|---|---|---|---|---|
| | $P_2O_5$ | $K_2O$ | $P_2O_5$ | $K_2O$ | $P_2O_5$ | $K_2O$ |
| 0 | 350 | 350 | 100 | 200 | 75 | 75 |
| 1 | 300 | 300 | 75 | 100 | 40 | 40 |
| 2 | 250 | 250 | 50 | 75 | 40 | 40 |
| 3 | 200 | 200 | 25 | 75 | 40 | 0 |
| over 3 | 100 | 100 | 0 | 75 | 0 | 0 |

Table 9.1 shows how the recommendations for different
crops of $P_2O_5$ and $K_2O$ are affected by soil indices. In
all cases the amount of the nutrients recommended
declines with increasing soil index values. Furthermore, it is evident from the table that crops differ
markedly in their requirements for the two nutrients.

Efficient use of fertilisers can be achieved by a knowledge of the soil reserves. Soil analysis is not a useful method of determining the available nitrogen reserves because of the dynamic nature of this element in the soil system.

Soil textural groups also have an effect on the recommended levels of fertiliser and this aspect is particularly relevant to nitrogen. Mineral soils require a higher nitrogen fertiliser input than the organic peat soils of the Fens and loamy peats. Chalky soils require more potassium than other textural groups and sands are usually low in phosphorus.

The residues left in the soil by previous crops can also affect the response to fertiliser. This is important for nitrogen and the soil index range for this element is based on previous cropping rather than soil analysis. The scale used is from 0-2. Where cereals were the previous crop, or where forage has been cut and removed, the soil N index is low at 0. After potatoes, peas, oilseed rape or grazed forage crops, considerable nitrogen residues are considered to be present and the index is valued at 1. Where large quantities of farmyard manure (FYM) have been applied or where the previous crop was lucerne, a long ley or good permanent pasture, even higher reserves are assumed and an index of 2 is applied. The effects of different soil N indices on N fertiliser recommendations are illustrated in Table 9.2.

*Table 9.2 The effect of soil nitrogen index on the fertiliser nitrogen (kg ha$^{-1}$) recommendations for different crops on mineral soils (MAFF, 1981)*

| N index | Maincrop potatoes | Sugar beet | Winter wheat |
|---------|-------------------|------------|--------------|
| 0       | 220               | 100        | 150          |
| 1       | 160               | 75         | 100          |
| 2       | 100               | 50         | 40           |

Recommended levels of $P_2O_5$ and $K_2O$ may also vary depending on the previous cropping. An example of this is found with spring cereals where higher levels of $P_2O_5$ and $K_2O$ are recommended after a third or more cereal crop in the rotation. However adjustments with these elements are smaller than with nitrogen.

Variation in the weather patterns may influence the response to fertiliser elements, especially nitrogen. Available forms of nitrogen are soluble in water and losses can occur over the winter period and in wet springs from leaching in drainage water. After such wet periods nitrogen fertiliser levels should be increased by about 25 kg ha$^{-1}$. Losses of $P_2O_5$ and $K_2O$ from leaching are insignificant and rainfall patterns do not influence the recommendations for these elements.

Where organic manures have been applied to the soil, appropriate adjustments to the chemical fertiliser recommendations should be made (see Table 9.3, page 246).

In dry areas, the efficiency of use of fertilisers can be low in the summer period. Recommendations should be adjusted downwards in these areas unless irrigation facilities are available.

TYPES OF FERTILISER

Fertilisers exist in two main types either as *straight* formulations, supplying one major nutrient, or as *compounds*, containing a combination of two or three elements. Formerly individual straight formulations were mixed on the farm but this practice has disappeared and compounds, containing different ratios of the major elements, are commercially available for most crops. The farmer has to decide on the type of fertiliser he will apply to a crop and choose between a straight or compound, or a combination of both. Phosphorus and potassium are commonly applied as compound fertilisers in the seedbed, with some nitrogen. Nitrogen is frequently applied straight, especially to cereals, after the crop has established, to control growth and development patterns.

Most formulations of fertiliser are sold in a solid form, either as crystals or granules. The production of granular or prilled forms has aided the efficiency of distribution in the field with conventional machines. The granules flow easily in distributors and are robust enough to withstand physical attrition. Liquid formulations also exist but they have not made a large impact in temperate systems. Anhydrous and aqueous forms of ammonia need to be injected into the soil and losses to the atmosphere can be high. Liquid compounds also exist but are not widely used and may result in leaf scorch when applied to growing crops.

In all fertiliser formulations, the container or bag, must display a statement regarding the quantity of the elements present. This is usually expressed as a percentage of the total contents and enables the grower to calculate the amounts of fertiliser needed to supply the required quantity of nutrients. The quantities of elements are expressed in different ways. (Nitrogen is expressed as N, phosphorus as $P_2O_5$, potassium as $K_2O$ and magnesium as Mg.) This method of expressing nutrient contents accords with fertiliser recommendations. An example of this for a compound fertiliser is as follows:

Compound supplied as 20:10:10, as stated on the bag. This refers to 20 per cent N, 10 per cent $P_2O_5$ and 10 per cent $K_2O$. In many cases, fertiliser is supplied in 50 kg bags and therefore each bag contains 10 kg N, 5 kg $P_2O_5$ and 5 kg $K_2O$. This is important to realise when calculating fertiliser needs.

The major elements required for plant growth are supplied in different chemical forms as fertilisers and a brief description of the main types follows.

Nitrogen fertilisers are mainly supplied as ammonium or nitrate compounds containing different amounts of N.

Ammonium nitrate contains 33.5 to 34.5 per cent N and is
the most widely used form of nitrogen fertiliser. It
occurs in granular form and provides a quick response in
most crops.

Ammonium nitrate lime fertilisers contain 25 to 26 per
cent N and the addition of lime offsets the acidifying
effect of the ammonium ions.

Sulphate of ammonia contains 21 per cent N but is not
widely used.

Anhydrous ammonia contains 82 per cent N and once in the
soil behaves as other ammonium fertilisers. It is applied
to the soil, under pressure and is hazardous to use.

Aqueous ammonia contains 21 to 29 per cent N and is
applied at lower pressure. It is not so hazardous as the
anhydrous form.

Urea contains 45 per cent N and is transformed in the soil
to ammonium salts. It is generally less effective than
other forms of N fertiliser and may cause damage to seedlings.

Aqueous N solutions contain 26 to 32 per cent N and are
usually mixtures of ammonium nitrate and urea.

Phosphate fertilisers also differ in chemical form and in
their efficiency. In many cases, only a proportion of the
$P_2O_5$ is water soluble and available to the plant. This is
usually specified on the container.

Superphosphate, known chemically as mono-calcium phosphate,
is one of the most effective forms of phosphorus fertiliser but its use has been curtailed by excessive manufacturing costs.

Ammonium phosphates are widely used in compounds and are
soluble in water and quick-acting.

Ground mineral phosphate is produced from mined rock phosphate. It usually contains about 28 per cent $P_2O_5$, most
of which is insoluble, and is only slow-acting and should
not be used for quick-growing crops.

Basic slags are a by-product of the steel-making process
and are no longer widely available.

Phosphated slags are a mixture of low grade basic slags
and ground mineral phosphate.

Nitrophosphates are a mixture of ammonium phosphate, di-
calcium phosphate and ground mineral forms and only a proportion of the $P_2O_5$ is soluble.

The main forms of potassium fertilisers are mined from
underground deposits of salts.

Muriate of potash is potassium chloride and contains 60
per cent $K_2O$. The production of a granular form has aided
application and storage.

Sulphate of potash contains 48-50 per cent $K_2O$ and is
manufactured from the muriate.

Kainit is a mixture of potassium and sodium salts and contains 14-30 per cent $K_2O$. This form of potassium fertiliser is particularly valuable for sugar beet. Some types
of Kainit contain substantial quantities of magnesium.

Magnesium can be supplied to crops in a number of
fertiliser forms including Kainit.

Magnesian limestone can be used for correcting low soil pH
and contains 3-12 per cent Mg.

Kieserite contains 16-17 per cent Mg and, chemically, it
is magnesium sulphate.

Calcined magnesite contains 48 per cent Mg.

It is clear that the major elements exist in a range of
chemical forms as fertilisers. In practice, where compounds are used, the farmer has no choice in the type of
chemical. However where elements are applied individually
there is a considerable choice. The benefits and disadvantages of each type in relation to efficiency and cost
should be considered before the choice is made.

A further source of nutrients on the mixed arable farm
is available as farmyard manure (FYM) or slurry. Both of
these sources are valuable and, in addition to providing
quantities of the major elements, they contain a range of
trace elements. The average contents of different types
of FYM and slurry are presented in Table 9.3. The most

Table 9.3  *The nutrient content of farmyard manure (FYM) and slurries (average values)*

| | Nutrient | | | |
| | N | $P_2O_5$ | $K_2O$ | Mg |
|---|---|---|---|---|
| Cow FYM (kg $t^{-1}$) | 1.5 | 2.0 | 4.0 | 0.8 |
| Cow slurry (kg $m^{-3}$) | 2.5 | 1.0 | 4.0 | 0.6 |
| Pig slurry (kg $m^{-3}$) | 4.0 | 2.0 | 2.7 | 0.4 |
| Poultry slurry (kg $m^{-3}$) | 9.0 | 5.5 | 5.5 | 1.3 |

abundant nutrient in these organic sources is potassium. Ruminant animals retain very little of the potassium ingested in herbage and it is excreted in the urine. Cow and pig slurry is low in phosphorus and nitrogen, but if sufficient quantities are applied, the benefits can be substantial. Poultry slurry contains relatively high levels of nitrogen, phosphorus and potassium. Magnesium is present in all types of slurry in small quantities.

These organic sources of nutrients should be applied to the soil and incorporated as they are generally unsuitable for top dressing on arable crops. In dry areas, the extra water-retaining capacity of soils receiving FYM indirectly increases yields and the efficiency of nutrient uptake.

## THE CHOICE OF TYPE, AMOUNT AND TIMING OF FERTILISER APPLICATION

A number of factors affect the type or form of fertiliser for a given crop, but in practice the choice is restricted. Ammonium nitrate is the main form of nitrogen used, potassium chloride dominates the potassium fertiliser market and ammonium phosphates are the major source of phosphorus.

The cost factor may influence the choice of type of fertiliser in a competitive market. Different fertiliser companies offer different ranges of fertiliser types and

prices may vary considerably.  As fertiliser costs make
up a high proportion of the variable costs of production
the wise grower will seek the cheapest source available,
without sacrificing quality.

The ease of application of fertilisers may also influence the choice.  Most farms are equipped with machines
to handle granular fertilisers and the choice will be
determined by this factor.  Anhydrous and aqueous ammonia
require specialised equipment and extra charges may be
involved through the use of contractors.  Liquid fertilisers can be applied with conventional spraying equipment
on farms.

Some fertilisers differ in their speed of response in
the crop.  Ammonium nitrate provides nitrogen in a readily
available form, but urea and some ammonium formulations
give slower responses because they have to be converted to
available forms in the soil.  Similarly different forms of
phosphate fertilisers produce different rates of response.
Ground mineral phosphates produce a slow response whereas
nitrophosphates, with a high water-soluble $P_2O_5$ content,
produce a more rapid response.

The type of crop also affects the choice.  Most crops
require quantities of all three major elements and a compound fertiliser is suitable for their needs.  The ratio
of elements in the compound will differ for individual
crops.  Spring cereals usually require a compound with a
ratio of 2:1:1 whereas potatoes demand a different ratio
such as $1:2\frac{1}{2}:2\frac{1}{2}$.  Legumes require no nitrogen and a 0:1:1
fertiliser would be suitable in this case.  It is often
difficult to match the ratio of nutrients in compounds
with recommendations but the nearest available type should
be selected.  Straight forms of nitrogen can be used to
adjust nitrogen supplies according to the demands of the
crop.

The amount of fertiliser applied is largely dependent
on the factors affecting the response already described.
Soil analysis, soil type, previous cropping, type of crop

and weather are all involved in this decision. Precise recommendations for each crop will not be given here because the requirements of individual crops should be calculated according to the prevailing local conditions. Local information from advisory services should be sought and a decision made against the background of the available information.

An important point to consider in the choice of amounts of fertiliser to be applied is the expected yield from the system. In extensive systems of production involving low inputs and low returns high expenditure on fertilisers cannot be justified. Increasingly in developed temperate cropping systems high yield targets are set. These cannot be achieved without high fertiliser inputs. Other aspects of the production system may also be important. Direct drilled crops of cereals require higher nitrogen inputs to maintain yields compared to crops established by conventional cultivations.

Flexibility is the key word in the choice of the amount of fertiliser to be applied. The grower should be prepared to adjust his fertiliser applications to take account of the wide range of factors affecting the response.

The timing of fertiliser application to crops is an important part of a cropping system. The fertiliser must be applied so that it is available to the developing root system to sustain and promote growth. Phosphorus and potassium fertilisers are not very mobile in the soil and leaching losses are small. These elements can therefore be applied before, or at sowing, or planting. Care must be taken to ensure uniform application and, except in the case of direct drilled crops, the fertiliser should be incorporated into the soil by ploughing or seedbed cultivations. There is no case for top-dressing established crops with $P_2O_5$ and $K_2O$ and these fertilisers should always be applied in the seedbed.

The timing of nitrogen application is more flexible.

In spring-sown crops most or all of the nitrogen should
be applied in the seedbed. This applies to spring cereals,
potatoes and sugar beet and there is no evidence to suggest that a split dressing is beneficial. In autumn-sown
crops, a decision has to be made on whether or not to
apply nitrogen in the seedbed. $P_2O_5$ and $K_2O$ are applied
in the seedbed in the autumn and, depending on the soil
nitrogen index, from zero up to 20 kg ha$^{-1}$ of nitrogen may
be applied. Winter cereals take up very little nitrogen
in the autumn and winter and additional applications are
wasteful. This principle applies to other autumn-sown
crops.

Spring nitrogen applications for winter cereals are
often applied as split dressings. Early spring application of nitrogen (late-February to early-March) is often
used to stimulate tiller production in winter cereals and
this can be useful in crops which have established badly
or have suffered winter damage. The most important time
for top dressing wheat is at the early-stem erection stage
of growth. In many situations, all of the spring nitrogen
can be usefully applied at this stage. A late application
of nitrogen at flag leaf emergence may produce small yield
benefits and increase the nitrogen content of the grain,
if there is adequate soil moisture available. Intensively
grown winter wheat crops may therefore receive three
spring applications of nitrogen as follows: 40 kg ha$^{-1}$ at
early tillering, 120 kg ha$^{-1}$ at early stem erection and
40 kg ha$^{-1}$ at flag leaf emergence. However many systems
of production apply a single application at the middle
stage.

In autumn-sown oilseed rape, all of the nitrogen in
the spring should be applied as a single dressing (150-
200 kg ha$^{-1}$).

It is clear that the timing of fertiliser application
is dependent on the needs of the individual crops. In
many crops, e.g. spring cereals, potatoes and sugar beet,
a single application at the appropriate time is sufficient.

In winter cereals, the timing of the nitrogen application can be manipulated to control specific aspects of growth and development.

A further aspect of fertiliser application to be considered is that of placement. In many situations the fertiliser is applied as an overall treatment to the soil and incorporated. It is apparent that some crops, e.g. potatoes and cereals, can benefit from having the $P_2O_5$ and $K_2O$ placed close to the 'seed' at planting. Combine drilling of cereals achieves this objective and results in more vigorous early growth and possibly higher yields. The response to placement of $P_2O_5$ and $K_2O$ in cereals is greatest in deficient soils in dry conditions. Potatoes are very sensitive to deficiencies of $P_2O_5$ and $K_2O$ and benefit from placement of these nutrients close to, but not in contact with, the tubers. Damage to the developing sprouts may occur if the fertiliser is placed too close to the tubers. Placement of $P_2O_5$ and $K_2O$ 5 cm to the side and 2.5 cm below the tuber gives the best response. Peas and beans also show yield benefits from placement of $P_2O_5$ and $K_2O$ fertilisers. Band application of nitrogen to sugar beet between the rows after sowing reduces the damage to young seedlings. Placement of fertilisers in some crops can have benefits over a broadcasting approach.

FORMULATION OF A FERTILISER POLICY

Earlier discussion has illustrated the complexity of the factors involved in the response of crops to applied fertilisers. However the grower has to make a decision at some point as to the specific quantities he is going to apply. The following list summarises the points which should be considered in this process:

(i) Consider the type of crop and its requirements.
(ii) Consider the yield response of the crop and the expected yield.
(iii) Take account of soil analysis.

(iv) Consider the effects of soil type and texture.

(v) Consider previous cropping and residues.

(vi) Consider rainfall patterns.

(vii) Consider the effects of irrigation.

(viii) Consider the interaction of nutrients.

(ix) Consult recommended data for the locality and seek advice if in doubt.

(x) Calculate the amounts required.

(xi) Choose the type of fertiliser to be used.

(xii) Choose the method of application.

(xiii) Select the time of application.

(xiv) Consider the cost of the fertiliser.

Attention to detail of this kind can help to improve the efficiency of fertiliser use and increase yields.

Fertiliser recommendations are expressed as kilograms per hectare (kg ha$^{-1}$) of nutrients required. This can cause confusion in calculating the requirements for a given crop. The following example indicates a process for calculating fertiliser needs.

Assume an area of 27 ha of spring barley for which the fertiliser recommendation is 100 kg N, 50 kg $P_2O_5$ and 50 kg $K_2O$ ha$^{-1}$.

(i) Choose a suitable compound to apply the ratio of nutrients recommended (2:1:1), e.g. 20:10:10.

(ii) Calculate the amounts of nutrient in each 50 kg bag, i.e. 10 kg N, 5 kg $P_2O_5$ and 5 kg $K_2O$.

(iii) Calculate the requirements for each hectare:
100 ÷ 10 for N = 10 bags = 500 kg of compound.

(iv) Calculate the requirement for the whole barley area:
27 x 500 kg = 13,500 kg = 13.5 tonnes of 20:10:10 compound.

(v) Order, store and eventually apply to the seedbed.

This procedure can be followed for any straight or compound fertiliser.

## THE IMPORTANCE OF TRACE ELEMENTS

In addition to the major nutrients required for normal crop growth, a number of other elements are required in small quantities. These are known as trace elements or micronutrients. Problems of trace element deficiencies are restricted to a few crops on certain soil types. Where the deficiencies occur they can have a devastating effect and render ineffective any applications of major nutrients as fertiliser.

Only a few trace elements are likely to cause problems in temperate systems. Boron is deficient in some soils and causes heart rot in beet and brown heart in swedes and turnips. The use of boronated compound fertilisers or an application of borax controls the deficiency. Overliming aggravates the problem of boron deficiency.

Copper deficiency can occur on peats, light sandy soils and thin organic soils over chalk and affects cereals and sugar beet. In severe cases, cereals fail to produce ears and complete crop loss can occur. Visible symptoms are rarely evident in sugar beet but yield increases have resulted from the application of copper sulphate. Various copper salts can be used as foliar sprays to remedy a deficiency.

Manganese deficiency is most frequently observed on peaty soils and sands at higher pH values. Spring cereals are badly affected and the leaves develop a characteristic brown speckling and yellowing. Sugar beet leaves develop a yellow speckling and yield losses occur through the loss of effective leaf area. Peas exhibit a different symptom and the seeds in the pods are spotted with brown decayed tissue which reduces their value for the human market. Manganese deficiency is aggravated by overliming and can be controlled by sprays of manganese sulphate.

Molybdenum deficiency causes abnormal leaf development in cauliflowers (whiptail) and this element is

unusual in that its availability is increased at high pH
values. Excessive molybdenum in herbage can depress
copper absorption by ruminants, inducing copper deficiency
in sheep and cattle.

Zinc and iron deficiencies are rarely a problem in
temperate climates but may occasionally appear on some
soil types.

An awareness of the effects of trace element problems
is important in considering crop nutrition. Where
deficiencies occur, serious losses of yield and quality
may result and remedial treatments should be applied as
soon as the problem is realised.

## FERTILISERS AND CROP QUALITY

The discussion so far has concentrated on the effects of
fertilisers on crop yields. However the quality of the
harvested product may also be affected and this should be
considered when formulating a policy. The classic example
of the effects of fertiliser on quality is the influence
of nitrogen, applied late in the season, on malting barley.
High levels of nitrogen fertiliser increase the nitrogen
content of the grain and render it unsuitable for malting
purposes. The nitrogen for spring barley for malting
should all be applied in the seedbed to avoid this problem. Early spring top dressings of nitrogen to winter
barley for malting are also necessary. In contrast wheat
grains for bread-making require a high nitrogen content
and late applications of nitrogen fertiliser are beneficial. The application of granular or liquid foliar
sources of nitrogen to wheat crops after flag leaf emergence is helpful in this respect.

High levels of nitrogen fertiliser applied to oilseed
rape depress the seed oil content. This is not usually
serious and recommendations are not adjusted to cater for
this effect.

Late applications of nitrogen can prolong the leaf
area duration of crops and delay maturity. This can

result in poor conditions at harvest and reduced quality of the product. Indirectly nitrogen can reduce grain quality in cereals by causing lodging.

In potatoes, increasing levels of nitrogen fertiliser decrease the dry matter content of the tubers which may affect their suitability for some processing outlets. In addition, fertilisers increase tuber size.

High fertiliser applications of nitrogen, potassium and sodium can increase the concentration of these elements in sugar beet roots and reduce the efficiency of sucrose extraction.

The examples quoted illustrate some of the ways in which fertilisers can influence crop quality. In many cases the effects are of sufficient magnitude to justify consideration when choosing a fertiliser policy.

REFERENCES AND FURTHER READING

Bowerman, P. and Harris, P.B. (1974) 'The rate and time of application of nitrogen on continuous spring barley'. Experimental Husbandry, 27, 45-49.

Boyd, D.A. and Lowsing, T.K.Y. (1976) 'Nitrogen requirements of cereals. 1. Response curves'. Journal of agricultural Science, Cambridge, 87, 149-162.

Burns, I.G. (1977) 'Nitrate movement in soils and its agricultural significance'. Outlook on Agriculture, 9 (3), 144-148.

Cooke, G.W. (1967) The Control of Soil Fertility. London: Crosby Lockwood and Son.

Cooke, G.W. (1980) 'Changes in fertiliser use in the UK from 1950-1980'. Proceedings of the Fertiliser Society, No.190.

Cooke, G.W. (1982) Fertilising for Maximum Yield (2nd edn). London: Granada Publishing.

Davies, D.B., Vaidyanathan, L.V., Rule, J.S. and Jarvis, R.H. (1979) 'Effect of sowing date and timing and level of nitrogen application to direct drilled winter wheat'. Experimental Husbandry, 35, 122-131.

Draycott, A.P. (1972)  Sugar Beet Nutrition.  London:
Applied Science Publishers.

East of Scotland College of Agriculture (1977)  Fertiliser
Recommendations. Bulletin No.18.  Edinburgh.

Harris, P.M. (1978)  'Mineral nutrition'.  In The Potato,
ed. Harris, P.M.  London: Chapman and Hall, 196-244.

Ministry of Agriculture, Fisheries and Food (MAFF) (1978)
Potassium and Sodium Fertilisers.  AL 443.  London:
MAFF.

MAFF (1979)  Phosphate Fertilisers.  Leaflet 442.  London:
MAFF.

MAFF (1981)  Lime and Fertiliser Recommendations No.1.
Arable Crops and Grassland.  Booklet 2191.  Alnwick:
MAFF.

MAFF (1981)  Magnesium Fertilisers.  Leaflet 596.
Alnwick: MAFF.

MAFF (1981)  Nitrogen Fertilisers.  Leaflet 441.  Alnwick:
MAFF.

Needham, P. and Boyd, D.A. (1976)  'Nitrogen requirements
of cereals. 2.  Multi-level nitrogen tests with spring
barley in south-western England'.  Journal of agricultural Science, Cambridge, 87, 163-170.

Needham, P. (1980)  'Matching nitrogen with cereal crop
needs'.  In Yield of Cereals.  Stoneleigh, Warwickshire: National Agricultural Centre, Cereal Unit,
56-65.

Russell, E.W. (1973)  Soil Conditions and Plant Growth
(10th edn).  London: Longman.

Sugar Beet Research and Education Committee (1980)  Sugar
Beet, A Grower's Guide.  London: Ministry of Agriculture, Fisheries and Food.

# 10 Chemical Control of Growth and Development

Growth and development in crop plants can be manipulated by changing the environment and the supply of nutrients. The potential for changing growth and development patterns by these external means has been discussed. Plants have their own internal control mechanisms based on the properties of chemical growth regulators. Growth regulators are present in small quantities in plants but their effects are dramatic. Knowledge of the presence and properties of growth regulators has accumulated since the isolation of indole-3-acetic acid in 1934. Several other naturally-occurring compounds have subsequently been discovered. The recognition of the potential of growth regulators stimulated the production of synthetic forms which simulated or counteracted their effects. The objective of this chapter is to consider the properties of growth regulators and review their potential for manipulating the growth and development of crop plants.

NATURALLY-OCCURRING GROWTH REGULATORS

Five main groups of growth regulators occur naturally in plants.
The groups are: auxins; gibberellins; cytokinins; ethylene; and abscisic acid (see Figure 10.1 for their basic chemical structures).

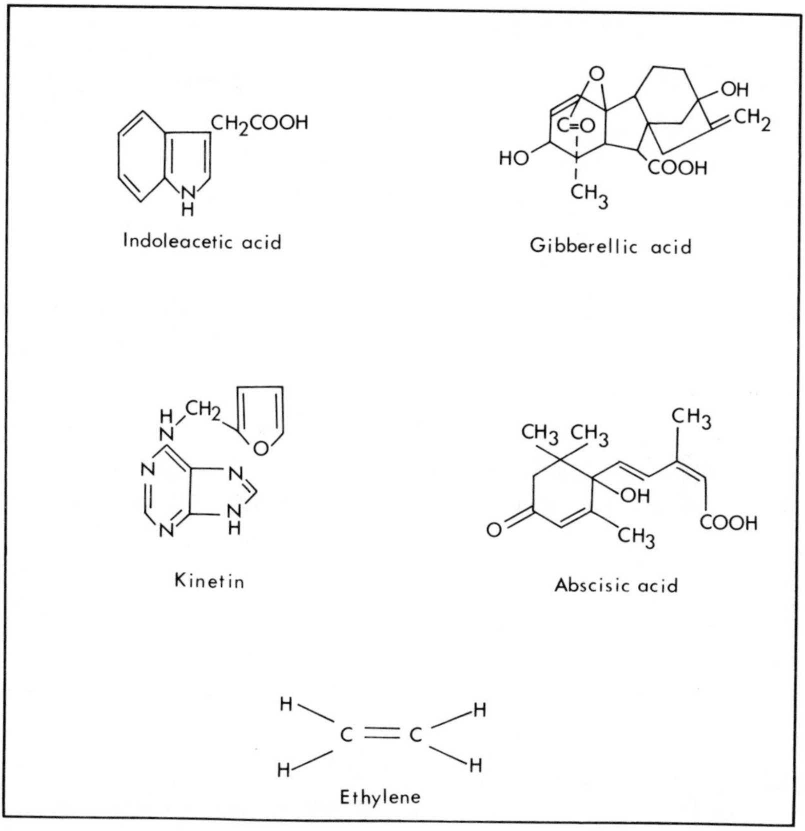

*Figure 10.1   The structure of naturally-occurring growth regulators*

Auxins

The auxins were the first growth regulators to be discovered in plants.  The naturally-occurring form, indole-
3-acetic acid (IAA), plays an important role in cell
enlargement of stems and coleoptiles.  This property is
potentially useful for promoting growth, but, at high concentrations, auxins have a retarding effect.  Auxins also
stimulate cell division and promote apical dominance.  One
of the first practical applications of auxins was in
stimulating rooting in stem cuttings of horticultural
plants.  Auxins can also initiate flowering in some plants,

e.g. pineapple, and induce fruit set.

## Gibberellins

Gibberellins were discovered in a fungus, which causes a disease in rice, in Japan in the 1930s. However, widespread interest in this group did not occur until the 1950s. Initially it was thought that there was a single gibberellin (GA) but further discoveries have demonstrated that over fifty such substances exist, each with a slightly differing structure. Structurally the gibberellins are more complex than auxins (Figure 10.1) and are more difficult to synthesise. Commercial products are isolated from a fungus.

The major role of gibberellins in plants is the stimulation of extension growth through the promotion of cell elongation. Stem growth is increased through the production of longer internodes. Gibberellins also accelerate leaf expansion, particularly in young plants. A further property of the gibberellins is the induction of flowering in plants which require vernalisation, e.g. carrot. Bolting occurs if rosette plants are sprayed with GA as a result of increased elongation and a greater number of cells. GA application to genetically dwarf plants promotes growth of the stems to normal heights.

GA can substitute for a chilling requirement in dormant seeds and enhance apical dominance. A further useful property of GA is the ability to stimulate pathenocarpic fruit development in grapes and pears. This property is valuable where the flowers or young fruits have been damaged by frost.

## Cytokinins

The cytokinins were discovered in the 1950s and the first compound to be isolated was called zeatin. Subsequently kinetin and benzyladenine have been produced. The major effect of the cytokinins is to stimulate cell division.

Growth is a result of cell division and elongation and the potential of cytokinins as growth promotors is obvious. The other important property of the cytokinins is the regulation of differentiation of cells from excised tissues, and in this respect they are useful in micro-propagation technology. The subsequent growth of the differentiated cells depends on the presence of auxin and this is an example of an interaction between growth regulators in modifying growth and development.

Cytokinins delay senescence in leaf tissue. The normal yellowing of old leaves, associated with loss of chlorophyll, is delayed if a cytokinin is applied. This is a potentially useful property in crop production which has not been exploited.

In contrast to IAA and GA, cytokinins overcome apical dominance and promote the growth of axillary buds. Furthermore cytokinins stimulate tuber formation on the stolons of potatoes.

The cytokinins are less mobile in plants than GA or IAA.

Ethylene

The three groups mentioned so far can all be isolated as solid compounds. Ethylene is a gas and behaves differently in plants. The recognition of the properties of ethylene as a natural growth regulator did not occur until the 1960s. However it is now well established that ethylene is produced in plant tissues, especially under stress conditions, e.g. waterlogging. Ethylene stimulates sprouting in potato tubers, following periods of brief exposure, and promotes the germination of seeds. The best-known property of ethylene is its ability to accelerate the ripening of fruits. This property has found practical application in apples and other fruit crops. Ethylene also induces premature abscission of leaves and young fruits.

## Abscisic acid

As its name implies, abscisic acid (ABA) promotes the
formation of abscission layers in plants. It is generally
recognised as being widespread in vascular plant as a
growth inhibitor. Associated with the promotion of
abscission is the ability of ABA to accelerate senescence
in leaf and fruit tissues. ABA is antagonistic to the
actions of GA and induces dormancy in some seeds and buds.
ABA accumulates rapidly in plant cells in stress conditions and is responsible for the closure of stomata
during droughts. This property is potentially useful and
has been exploited to some extent in practice where ABA
has been used as an antitranspirant.

This brief consideration of the main natural growth regulators emphasises their importance in controlling growth
and development. They therefore provide a potentially
useful means of manipulating growth and development to
maximise the production of the economic product.

## SYNTHETIC GROWTH REGULATORS

The discussion so far has concentrated only on those
chemical growth regulators which are found naturally in
plants. A range of other chemicals are known to modify
growth and development when applied externally to crops.
For the purposes of this discussion, this group are
collectively referred to as synthetic. Examples of this
group are listed in Table 10.1.

A number of compounds exhibit auxin-like activity and
are used commercially in horticulture and agriculture.
They do not all have the typical auxin structure (IAA in
Figure 10.1) but possess one or more of the properties of
the group. Carbaryl for example is used as a fruit
thinning agent in apples and exploits the property of
causing seed abortion. 2,4-D and 2,4,5-T are used mainly
as herbicides where, at relatively high levels of

CHEMICAL CONTROL OF GROWTH AND DEVELOPMENT

*Table 10.1   Examples of synthetic growth regulators used in crop production*

| Chemical name | Common name |
| --- | --- |
| **Auxin type** | |
| 1-naphthyl methyl carbamate | Carbaryl |
| 4-chlorophenoxyacetic acid | 4-CPA |
| 2,4-dichlorophenoxyacetic acid | 2,4-D |
| 4-(indol-3yl) butyric acid | IBA |
| 1-naphthalene-acetic acid | NAA |
| 2,4,5-trichlorophenoxyacetic acid | 2,4,5-T |
| **Cytokinin type** | |
| 6-benzylaminopurine | BAP |
| Methyl 1-(butylcarbamoyl) benzimidazol-2-yl carbamate | Benomyl |
| N,N$^1$-diphenylurea | DPU |
| **Ethylene-releasing or ethylene-generating type** | |
| 2-chloroethylphosphonic acid | Ethephon |
| **Growth retardants** | |
| α-cyclopropyl-4-methoxy-(pyridimin-5-yl)-benzylalcohol | Ancymidol |
| 2-chloroethyltrimethyl ammonium chloride | Chlormequat |
| N-dimethylaminosuccinamic acid | Daminozide |
| **Growth inhibitors** | |
| 6-hydroxy-3-(2H)-pyridazinone | Maleic hydrazide |
| Mixtures of methyl esters of fatty acids of chain length $C_6$ to $C_{12}$ | Fatty acid esters |
| **Herbicides** | |
| 1-1$^1$-ethylene-2-2$^1$-bipyridilium ion | Diquat |
| N-(phosphonomethyl) glycine | Glyphosate |

application, they selectively kill young dicotyledonous plants in cereals. IBA is used as a rooting compound and NAA as a sprout suppressant.

The gibberellins are all isolated from fungal tissues and cannot be classified as synthetic.

Cytokinins are not widely used commercially but benomyl,

used mainly as a systemic fungicide, has growth regulator properties.

Ethylene is a volatile gas and cannot be applied successfully to crops. The method of introducing ethylene into plants is to apply an ethylene-generating or ethylene-releasing compound which, when it contacts the cell sap, breaks down to produce the gas. Ethephon is the most widely-used chemical for this purpose. Its main use in agriculture is to control straw length and strength in cereals.

The growth retardants slow down cell division and elongation and are mainly used to control plant height. Their action prevents the expression of the properties of auxins and gibberellins in this respect. Chlormequat is also used in the pot plant industry but is more widely known for its ability to shorten and strengthen the straw of wheat and oats.

Growth inhibitors are designed to stop growth altogether rather than slow it down. Maleic hydrazide effectively prevents the shoot growth of onions and prolongs the useful storage period.

Some growth regulators, other than the auxin types, are used as herbicides, e.g. diquat. However diquat is useful as a desiccant in many crops where it accelerates senescence, e.g. in the haulms of potatoes. Glyphosate has similar properties but is mainly used for weed control.

The wide range of synthetic growth regulators presents the grower with a useful tool to manipulate growth and development. The full potential of growth regulators in agriculture has yet to be realised; they have found wider application in horticulture. The use of growth regulators as a means of controlling the growth of arable crops, with a few exceptions, has not been widely developed.

PRACTICAL APPLICATION

Germination and establishment

Growth regulators are involved in the physiological processes which are associated with germination.  During this
early phase of growth, cell division and expansion proceed
at a rapid rate in the young embryo.  It is conceivable
that sub-optimal levels of auxins, gibberellins and cytokinins are a limitation to germination and that seeds
would germinate better if treated with an appropriate
combination of them.  In practice, the benefits of soaking
seeds in solutions of growth regulators has produced only
small benefits.  The immaturity of the embryo of sugar
beet seeds has been referred to (chapter 6), and treatments of monogerm fruits with gibberellins and cytokinins,
as a soak, before sowing increases the percentage and the
speed of germination and the level of emergence in the
field.  This treatment is not done commercially.

Gibberellins will break dormancy, induced by a low
temperature requirement, in many seeds but few examples of
crop plants exist where this is important.  The problem of
dormancy in barley seeds is well established and this can
result in erratic and low levels of germination which is
a great disadvantage in the malting process.  Malting involves the conversion of starch in the endosperm to
simpler sugars during germination and it is the enzyme
$\alpha$-amylase that initiates this process.  $\alpha$-Amylase is concentrated in the aleurone layer of the seed and its production is stimulated by gibberellins.  Treatment of seeds
before malting speeds up the process and provides stricter
control.  This is one of the few examples where the
properties of naturally-occurring growth regulators have
been exploited in commercial practice.

Gibberellins can also be used to break dormancy and
manipulate sprout growth in potato tubers.

## Early growth and partition of the dry matter

Growth regulators are particularly effective in actively growing tissues. Early leaf growth is stimulated by the application of gibberellins to many crops. Gibberellic acid is used to increase the yield and length of the petioles of celery and rhubarb. Gibberellic acid treatment of winter wheat crops in the early spring changes the pattern of tiller development. Tiller production is inhibited initially after treatment but the remaining tillers develop earlier and survive through to harvest. In contrast chlormequat increases tiller production and retards the more advanced tillers. In both cases, the chemical treatment does not result in a consistent increase in yield.

In many crops the early development of a full leaf canopy is essential to achieve high yields. However, once this has been achieved, it is then desirable to prevent further leaf development so that the products of photosynthesis are diverted into the economic product of growth. Chlormequat and daminozide, when applied as foliar sprays, retard top growth and increase the root yields of carrots and other root vegetables. Similar effects have been demonstrated in sugar beet but the technique has not been adopted commercially. The application of daminozide to the foliage of potatoes results in a more favourable partition of the dry matter to the tubers. This type of manipulation of growth has considerable potential but has yet to be fully exploited.

## Stem growth

The elongation of the stems of crop plants is the result of cell expansion and division stimulated by auxins, cytokinins and especially gibberellic acid. Excessive stem growth can be undesirable in crops and can result in lodging in cereals. The control of stem growth of cereals by growth retardants is the best example of the application

*Table 10.2  Growth regulators for controlling stem growth in cereals*

| Chemical | Crop |
|---|---|
| Chlormequat | Winter and spring wheat |
| Chlormequat and additives* | Winter and spring wheat |
| | Winter and spring barley |
| | Winter and spring oats |
| Ethephon | Winter barley |
| Ethephon and mepiquat chloride | Winter barley |

*Several commercial formulations exist and the application rate and recommended stage of growth vary with formulation and crop

of growth regulators in agriculture. Chlormequat was the first chemical to be used for this purpose on wheat and oats. Ethephon and mepiquat chloride are also useful in this respect and are most effective on winter barley (Table 10.2). Stem growth in all of the major temperate cereals can be controlled by one or more of the growth retardants listed. The development of growth regulators for this purpose has reduced the risk of yield losses from lodging due to bad weather or the use of high levels of nitrogen fertiliser in intensive systems. This development also means that when the choice of crop variety is made, the straw strength and length characteristics do not need to be considered so carefully.

The chemicals are only effective in controlling straw length and strength if they are applied at the right concentration of active ingredient and at the correct stage of growth. The rates of application differ for each chemical and crop and the manufacturer's recommendations should be followed. With most chemicals it is important to apply them before the stem starts to elongate rapidly. Precise recommendations vary with the chemical formulation and crop, but with chlormequat the most effective stage is from early tillering to the beginning of stem elongation. Ethephon and mepiquat chloride formulations are applied later and may be effective even up to the stage of ear

*Table 10.3  Effects of chlormequat on yields and lodging of winter wheat (from Batch, 1981)*

i) Yield (t ha$^{-1}$) of grain

|  | Control | Chlormequat (1600 g ha$^{-1}$) | Per cent difference |
|---|---|---|---|
| Mean of all trials | 7.4 | 8.3 | +13 |
| Mean yield where control plots lodged | 7.4 | 8.5 | +15 |
| Mean yield where no lodging occurred in controls | 7.6 | 7.9 | +4 |

ii) Time of lodging effect on grain yield (per cent increase over controls)

| | |
|---|---|
| Lodging June to July | +21 |
| Lodging August to harvest | +11 |

emergence in winter barley.  The growth retardants shorten the straw by reducing the internode lengths and they may produce thicker stems.  Some of the formulations act primarily as stem strengtheners with very little effect on stem length.

The effects of these growth retardants should be considered in lodging and non-lodging situations.  In the absence of lodging, a number of experiments have demonstrated small increases in grain yields of wheat treated with chlormequat (Table 10.3).  In the example quoted, a 4 per cent increase on a high-yielding crop (7-8 t ha$^{-1}$) is economically important.  The largest benefits from chlormequat are evident with lodged crops where yield benefits, of up to 15 per cent, can result in increased financial returns in addition to allowing faster and easier harvesting.  Table 10.3 shows that the yield depression is greater if lodging occurs in June or July rather than in August or later.  Where early lodging occurs, yield increases of over 20 per cent are possible if chlormequat is used. Similar effects are possible with other retardants on barley.

The yield benefits and the prevention of lodging are obvious advantages of the use of growth retardants on cereals. They have become an integral part of intensive production systems and permit the use of high levels of nitrogen fertiliser to achieve high yields. Other benefits from the use of chlormequat have been reported. The root system of treated plants is more extensive and the crops are more tolerant of drought. Furthermore chlormequat may reduce apical dominance resulting in more ear-bearing tillers and larger ears at harvest. Treated plants also show some increased resistance to foliar fungal diseases and pests.

The use of growth retardants on cereals has a relatively short history (since 1967) but they provide the intensive cereal grower with an invaluable tool to manipulate growth and development towards achieving higher yields. A wider range of chemicals of this kind is likely to be available in the future.

Flowering and seed development

The naturally-occurring growth regulators are involved in the flowering process of plants. Gibberellins can substitute for the vernalisation requirement of biennials and are potentially valuable to plant breeders to accelerate breeding programmes. The promotion of flowering by growth regulators is useful commercially in some tropical crops, e.g. auxin treatment of pineapples. The promotion of fruit development in seedless grapes and pears by gibberellins has also found commercial acceptance.

The control of sex expression in the flowers by growth regulators is a useful tool for the plant breeder where the production of hybrid seed requires the prevention of self-pollination. This is usually done by hand and is time consuming. Careful use of some growth regulators induces male sterility which overcomes this problem.

Ethephon, applied at 1000 to 2000 ppm just before the start of meiosis in the pollen mother cells, produces male sterility in wheat and permits easier hybrid seed production. Maleic hydrazide and gibberellic acid (at high concentrations) can also produce male sterility.

Senescence

The grower may wish to accelerate senescence in crops to allow an early harvest or delay it to prolong the growing season or storage period. Both aspects of senescence can be controlled by growth regulators. Chemicals which accelerate senescence are often referred to as desiccants. The growth regulator diquat is used to destroy the foliage and stems of potatoes in the late-summer and autumn, to stop tuber growth and prevent disease infection of the tubers. Similarly diquat and glyphosate are used to accelerate ripening in cereals and oilseed crops to facilitate harvesting. Further discussion of the use of desiccants is considered in chapter 12.

Delaying senescence in crops may be desirable. An example of this is found in green vegetables which have a short storage life because of the loss of water and chlorophyll. Cytokinins delay senescence in green tissues and are potentially useful here. Similarly it may be desirable to prolong the duration of green leaf in a field crop, e.g. the flag leaf of cereals, to extend the period of grain filling. In neither of these cases have cytokinins been used commercially.

HERBICIDE ACTIVITY

At high concentrations, auxins inhibit growth rather than stimulate it. This property has been exploited in the hormone-type herbicides, e.g. 2,4-D, to selectively control weeds in cereals. Used at high concentrations, auxins produce distorted growth with curling of leaves and splitting of stems. Affected plants may die but weeds vary in their sensitivity to auxin treatment. The great benefit of synthetic auxins such as 2,4-D is that they kill weeds at relatively low concentrations. They are translocated in the treated plants and the effects are rapid. The development of herbicides of this type was a major breakthrough in weed control in cereals and provides a further example of the application of knowledge of growth regulators in practice.

The isolation of growth regulators from plants and the production of synthetic forms are relatively recent phenomena. Developments in this area have been rapid since 1950 but a full understanding of their properties and physiological functions in plants is lacking. Studies have concentrated on individual chemicals, or groups of chemicals, but it is clear that there is considerable interaction of their effects in plants, e.g. the involvement of auxins, gibberellins and auxins in fruit and seed development. A better understanding of these interactions could lead to more widespread applications of growth regulators in crop production. The potential for using growth regulators to control growth and development in crop plants is large. However examples where application of the properties of growth regulators have made a contribution to more efficient crop production are few. The major areas where they are used include: auxin-type herbicides for dicotyledonous weed control in cereals, growth retardants to control stem growth in cereals, the desiccation of crops approaching harvest and the control of the malting process by gibberellins.

REFERENCES AND FURTHER READING

Batch, J.J. (1981)  'Recent developments in growth regulators for cereal crops'.  Outlook on Agriculture, 10 (8), 371-378.

Hudson, J.P. (1976)  'Future roles for growth regulators'. Outlook on Agriculture, 9 (2), 95-98.

Humphries, E.C. (1968)  'CCC and cereals'.  Field Crop

Abstracts, 21, 91-99.

Lenton, J.R. (ed.) (1980) Gibberellins — Chemistry, Physiology and Use. British Plant Growth Regulator Group, Monograph No.5.

Leopold, A.C. and Kriedemann, P.E. (1975) Plant Growth and Development. London: McGraw-Hill.

Luckwill, L.C. (1981) Growth Regulators in Crop Production. Institute of Biology, Studies in Biology No. 129. London: Edward Arnold.

Matthews, P.R. and Caldicott, J.J.B. (1981) 'The effect of chlormequat chloride formulated with choline chloride on the height and yield of winter wheat'. Annals of Applied Biology, 97 (2), 227-236.

McLaren, J.S. (ed.) (1982) 'Chemical control of crop growth and development'. Proceedings of the 33rd Easter School in Agricultural Science, University of Nottingham. London: Butterworth.

Skoog, F. (ed.) (1980) 'Plant growth substances 1979'. Proceedings of the 10th International Conference on Plant Growth Substances, Madison, Wisconsin. New York: Springer-Verlag.

Thomas, T.H. (1970) 'Plant growth regulators and crop production'. NAAS Quarterly Review, 89, 33-42.

Thomas, T.H. (1976) 'Growth regulation in vegetable crops'. Outlook on Agriculture, 9 (2), 62-68.

Wareing, P.F. (1980) 'Plant growth regulators'. Agricultural Progress, 55, 5-16.

Wareing, P.F. and Phillips, I.D.J. (1981) Growth and Differentiation in Plants (3rd edn). Oxford: Pergamon Press, 49-150.

Weaver, R.J. (1972) Plant Growth Substances in Agriculture. San Fransisco: W.H. Freeman and Company.

# 11 Principles of Crop Protection

Losses of yield and quality of temperate crops, from attack by disease-causing organisms and pests, are widespread. It has been estimated that fungal diseases are responsible for a 20 per cent reduction of the potential world food supply from crop plants and losses from pest damage have been estimated at 25 per cent. These estimates are probably too high to be applied to temperate regions where the climatic conditions are less favourable to the rapid multiplication and spread of the organisms. Nevertheless losses from pest and disease attack in temperate crops can be substantial. Powdery mildew (*Erysiphe graminis*) disease of barley can reduce yields by up to 50 per cent in some years. Severe attacks of wheat bulb fly can reduce wheat grain yields by 30 to 40 per cent and, where seedlings of other crops are eaten by pests, the losses may be total.

Crop production systems should therefore make adequate provision for protecting crops from attack by pests and diseases. Growers should be aware of the range of pests and diseases which are likely to affect crops and be able to recognise the symptoms of attack at an early stage. Prevention of attack, rather than a cure, is often the most effective and economic method of control and an awareness of the possible risks of infection or attack is an important aspect of crop protection. This may mean that the grower has to analyse the system over a number

of years, rather than just the current one, to identify
points where conditions may have favoured the build-up of
a particular pest or disease. Reference has already been
made to the importance of cropping sequences or rotations
in this respect (chapter 4).

Crop protection is a large and diverse subject and
full justice cannot be done to it in a text of this kind.
However the purpose of this chapter is to present the
organisms which constitute crop pests and pathogens, to
discuss the ways in which they reduce yield and quality,
and to consider briefly the main methods of control available to the grower. The reference list at the end of this
chapter contains texts dealing with more detailed aspects
of this important subject.

## THE ORGANISMS RESPONSIBLE FOR CAUSING CROP DISEASES

There are three groups of organisms which cause diseases
in plants: viruses, bacteria and fungi. The plant viruses
consist of a single strand of RNA surrounded by a protein
sheath and have the simplest structure of the three groups.
Bacteria are unicellular and occur as individual cells or
as groups or chains. Two main types of bacterial cell are
identifiable: those which are spherical (cocci) and those
which are rod-shaped (bacilli). A further group of pathogens, known as mycoplasma-like organisms, exist which are
intermediate in size between viruses and bacteria.
Mycoplasma-like organisms cause diseases similar to
viruses and are best dealt with in this category. The
fungi are more complex in structure and consist of a
collection of hyphae, which are branched filaments consisting of a row of cells. Reproduction in the fungi is
by the production of asexual and sexual spores.

Fungi are classified according to the method of
sexual spore production and the major groups are listed
in Table 11.1. The Myxomycetes consist of an aggregate of
naked cells and produce zoospores which can survive for a
long period. *Plasmodiophora brassicae* which causes club

272

Table 11.1  *Types of disease-causing organisms*

| Group | | Examples of diseases |
|---|---|---|
| i) Viruses | | Barley yellow dwarf virus |
| ii) Bacteria | | Soft rot of potatoes and vegetables (*Erwinia carotovora* var. *carotovora*) |
| iii) Fungi | Myxomycetes | Club root of brassicas (*Plasmodiophora brassicae*) |
| | Phycomycetes | Potato blight (*Phytophthora infestans*) |
| | Ascomycetes | Powdery mildew of cereals (*Erysiphe graminis*) |
| | Basidiomycetes | Yellow rust of wheat (*Puccinia striiformis*) |
| | Fungi Imperfecti | Wilt of lucerne (*Verticillium alboatrum*) |

root disease of brassicas, is an example of this group. The Phycomycetes produce sexual resting spores called oospores and this group includes the important potato blight disease (*Phytophthora infestans*). The Ascomycetes produce sexual spores in a specialised structure known as an ascus which contains eight ascospores. This group contains a number of pathogens which constitute the powdery mildew, e.g. *Erysiphe graminis*, of cereals. The Basidiomycetes produce spores on a specialised structure known as a basidium and include the important rust and smut diseases. The final group of fungi are those in which no sexual spore production phase is known. These are called Fungi Imperfecti and include a number of wilt diseases, e.g. *Verticillium* wilt of lucerne.

METHODS OF TRANSMISSION

For a disease organism to be successful it must have an efficient method of spreading to another healthy plant, especially if it is an obligate parasite. Facultative parasites can survive saprophytically on decaying vegetation and efficient dispersal is not essential for their survival. Information of the methods by which pathogens are dispersed is helpful in formulating a control programme, as the prevention of the spread of a disease can reduce the need for expensive chemical control measures. The main methods of disease transmission are summarised for each of the main groups of pathogens.

Viruses are non-mobile and rely on some other agent to disperse the particles in the cell sap. In addition, they have no means of entering plants other than through wounds which are inflicted by pests or the mechanical activities of man. Few virus diseases are spread by mechanical transmission of sap. Virus diseases of herbage grasses can be spread by harvesting equipment but this method is rare in arable crops. The main method of virus spread is through the feeding habits of insects, mites and nematodes. Viruses are spread mainly by the group of insects which have mouthparts designed to suck sap from the plant. The aphids are the most important group responsible for spreading viruses. Barley yellow dwarf virus affects cereals and is widespread in grasses. The bird-cherry aphid is often responsible for introducing this virus into a crop and subsequent within-crop spread is carried out by the grain and rose-grain aphids. The aphid may need to feed for up to 24 hours on an infected plant before it acquires the virus and then feed for 4-8 hours on another plant to cause infection. Spread of the disease is greatest in conditions which favour aphid activity and early-autumn sown and late-spring sown crops are at the greatest risk of infection.

The peach-potato aphid is the most important species responsible for the transmission of severe mosaic and leaf roll viruses of potatoes. This is important information to the seed tuber producer who is interested in producing virus-free 'seed'. Several other virus diseases of crop plants are also transmitted by aphids including the pea mosaic virus. Thrips and beetles can also transmit virus diseases of crop plants.

Nematodes can spread viruses by feeding on the roots of infected plants and collecting the particles on their mouthparts. This method of transmission is most common in the soft fruit crops of strawberries and raspberries. Pea early-browning virus is spread by several *Trichodorus* nematode species. Control of viruses spread by soil-borne organisms of this kind is difficult especially where the virus can survive on alternative weed hosts.

A few viruses are seed-borne, e.g. lettuce mosaic virus, but this method of transmission is rare in the major arable crops. Similarly, a few viruses are spread by fungi which have mobile spores, e.g. potato mop top virus.

Where vegetative propagation of infected plants occurs the virus will be transferred in the sap to the next generation. This method of propagation is rare in temperate crop plants with the exception of potatoes. The two important virus diseases of potatoes, severe mosaic and leaf roll, can be spread in this way and healthy stocks must be used for growing seed crops.

Bacterial diseases of arable crops are only serious in a few cases. Blackleg (*Erwinia carotovora* var. *atroseptica*) and soft rot (*E. carotovora* var. *carotovora*) are important bacterial diseases of the potato. They can both be spread in infected tubers and this is the main source of infection. Blackleg can be spread by flies in infected crops by adherence of the cells to the body of the insects. Soft rot is mainly a soil-borne disease and infects tubers through wounds and lenticels. Bacterial diseases which exude cells onto the surface of the plants can be spread by splash-droplets from rain or irrigation.

Fungal pathogens are transmitted by a variety of means. Direct transmission can occur by planting infected seeds or propagation material. Loose smut (*Ustilago nuda*)

of wheat and barley is seed-borne and is not easy to control by conventional chemical seed treatments. Ergot
(*Claviceps purpurea*) is a further example of a seed-borne
fungal disease.

The other main methods of fungal disease transmission
are indirect and require the assistance of some external
agent or vector. Wind is the most important mechanism of
spore dispersal in fungi. Most fungal pathogens, at some
stage in their life cycle, produce spores outside the host
plant. The spores may enter the air currents of the
atmosphere by passive release, as in the case of smuts.
However many fungi display an active discharge of spores
into the atmosphere. The distances involved in active
spore discharge are small, 1 mm to 45 cm, but may be sufficient to ensure efficient dispersal.

Water dispersal is a further method of transmission of
fungal diseases. The motile spores of the club root
fungus can move through films of water in the soil and the
disease is worse under conditions of poor drainage. A
more common method of water dispersal of fungal spores is
from water splash. The impact of raindrops on the surface
of an infected leaf is sufficient to create a splash
effect and the spores can be transmitted in the small
droplets. This is a common method of spore dispersal in
many foliar diseases, e.g. mildews and rusts of cereals.

The spores of soil-borne diseases can be transmitted
in soil particles which are moved round the farm on the
wheels of machines and the hooves of animals. Also those
diseases which survive on crop residues, e.g. take-all of
cereals (*Gaeumannomyces graminis*), can be dispersed by
cultivations and on machinery. A few fungal diseases are
transmitted by animals. Ergot disease of cereals causes
the flowers to exude a sugary honeydew which attracts
insects. The feeding insects pick up the spores of the
fungus and may deposit them on the stigma of a previously
uninfected plant. Passive transmission of fungal diseases
may occur through the adherance of spores to the feathers

of birds and fur of animals moving through the crops.

LOSS OF YIELD AND QUALITY DUE TO DISEASE

Precise quantitative estimates of yield loss due to diseases are difficult to obtain and in any case will vary from year to year and depend on the severity and timing of the attack.   It is more appropriate to consider the effects of the disease on the physiological functions of

**Function**                                    **Disease**

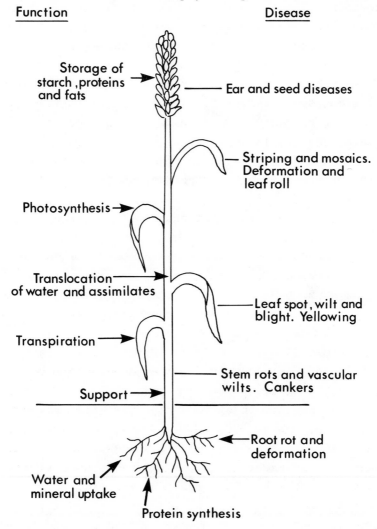

Storage of starch, proteins and fats —————— Ear and seed diseases

Striping and mosaics. Deformation and leaf roll

Photosynthesis

Translocation of water and assimilates

Leaf spot, wilt and blight. Yellowing

Transpiration

Stem rots and vascular wilts. Cankers

Support

Root rot and deformation

Water and mineral uptake

Protein synthesis

*Figure 11.1  Schematic diagram of the basic functions in a plant and their disruption by disease*

the plant and assess how yield and quality loss occurs. Figure 11.1 illustrates the main ways in which diseases attack plants and the physiological processes which are affected.

The root system of plants fulfils an important function in the uptake of nutrients and water from the soil. In addition, the roots are a site of amino acid and protein synthesis. Diseases which infect the root system therefore affect growth and development through their effect on these processes. Take-all of cereals attacks the roots and base of the stem and causes reduced growth of the shoot. Later symptoms in wheat are the production of 'whiteheads' resulting from lack of grain development and premature senescence.

Other underground organs may be subject to disease attack and this is apparent in the potato. Powdery and common scab both attack the tubers from the soil, and other diseases, such as gangrene and dry rot, may subsequently develop in storage as a result of wound damage. Blight of the tubers often results from infection from the haulms.

The stems of plants serve a number of functions. They support the rest of the plant and provide a frame to which the main photosynthetic organs are attached. In addition, stems contain the vascular tissues which are responsible for water transport and the translocation of assimilates. Eyespot disease of wheat attacks the base of the stem and weakens it. As a result the crop may lodge more easily with resulting yield loss. Stem canker (*Phoma lingam*) is a serious problem in oilseed rape varieties which show no resistance to it.

Fungal and bacterial wilt diseases often infect the plant through the root system but have their main effect on stem functions. The organisms responsible produce gums and tyloses which block the vascular system and result in wilting. An example of this is the vascular wilt of peas caused by *Fusarium oxysporum* f.sp. *pisi*.

278

The leaves are the main site of photosynthesis in plants and disruption of this vital function by disease attack can cause serious loss of yield and quality. Virus diseases often cause a loss of chlorophyll from leaves and yellowing is a common symptom. Beet yellows virus is a good example of this and leads to large decreases in yields in severe attacks. Barley yellow dwarf virus is a further example of this type of foliar pathogen. Other viruses produce leaf mosaics or striping as exemplified by cauliflower mosaic virus. In all of these examples photosynthesis is affected adversely by the presence of the pathogen.

There are only a few examples of foliar bacterial diseases of temperate crops. Halo blight of *Phaseolus* beans causes a leaf-spotting and is mainly seed-borne.

There are numerous examples of fungal pathogens which affect the leaves of plants. Winter wheat provides a good example of a cereal crop where a number of foliar diseases are important. These include yellow rust (*Puccinia striiformis*), brown rust (*Puccinia recondita*), powdery mildew (*Erysiphe graminis*) and septoria (*Septoria tritici* and *S. nodorum*). All of these diseases cause lesions on the leaves and eventually produce spores which can be transmitted to healthy leaves. Assessment of the proportion of the leaf affected by the disease can be helpful in deciding if or when to apply a fungicide. Examples of disease assessment keys for cereals are presented in Figure 11.2.

Foliar pathogens are common on other temperate crops. Leaf blight of potatoes (*Phytophthora infestans*) is widespread and can be responsible for very large yield losses in the field and in store. Light leaf spot (*Cylindrosporium concentricum*) can cause yield losses in oilseed rape. Foliar pathogens are some of the most serious diseases of crop plants as a result of their effects on photosynthesis. In addition to the damaging effect on growth and yield, the quality of cereal grains may be

## i) Wheat yellow rust        ii) Barley mildew

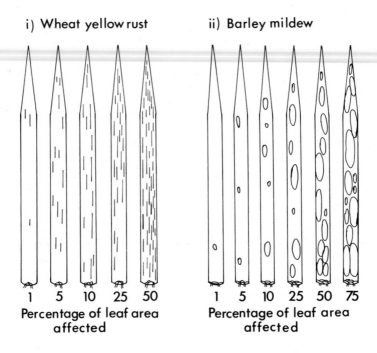

| i) Wheat yellow rust | | | | | ii) Barley mildew | | | | | |
|---|---|---|---|---|---|---|---|---|---|---|
| 1 | 5 | 10 | 25 | 50 | 1 | 5 | 10 | 25 | 50 | 75 |

Percentage of leaf area
affected        Percentage of leaf area
affected

*Figure 11.2  Disease assessment keys for wheat yellow rust and barley mildew*

affected through reduced size due to a smaller supply of assimilates from the leaves.

Diseases which affect the reproductive parts of plants are also important. In cereals, loose smut and ergot render the grain unsuitable for use and, in the latter case, toxicity problems may arise if infected grains are fed to humans or farm animals. Glume blotch (*Septoria nodorum*) of wheat may cause up to 50 per cent yield loss through its effect on grain size. Reproductive parts of other plants are also affected by diseases. Pod spot (*Aschochyta pisi*) of peas and *Botrytis* infection of strawberries and raspberries are examples of this.

The examples quoted illustrate the ways in which plant diseases can reduce crop yields and quality through disrupting physiological processes. The grower should seek

to minimise these effects by good growing techniques and
control measures.

## FACTORS ENCOURAGING DISEASE DEVELOPMENT

If the infection of a plant by a disease is to be successful the correct environmental conditions must prevail.
Most fungal infections occur through the germination of
the spores and subsequent entry of the germ tube. The
conditions required for spore germination and infection
are similar to those for seeds. Adequate moisture is
essential for germination and infection from many diseases
is greatest in moist conditions. Some spores will germinate in atmospheres with a high relative humidity but
most require the presence of liquid water droplets or
films. High temperatures, in association with adequate
moisture, favour spore germination. A knowledge of the
optimal conditions for infection can help in the predic-
tion of outbreaks of disease, in relation to weather conditions. In the case of potato blight, outbreaks of the
disease can be expected when the relative humidity is
greater than 75 per cent and the temperature is above 10°C
for 48 h. Information of this kind helps to plan chemical
control programmes before the disease becomes established.
Environmental factors are important in determining the
success of the infection process in many diseases.

The condition of the plant also affects the susceptibility to a disease. It is not possible to generalise
here as some diseases thrive on weak and senescing plants,
e.g. *Botrytis*, whereas others thrive on vigorously growing
ones, e.g. yellow rust on wheat. Furthermore the reaction
of tissues to pathogens may change with age and this is
associated with changes in the plant's defence mechanisms.
The nutritional status of the plant may also affect its
susceptibility to attack. High nitrogen concentrations
often favour infection whereas high potassium often
reduces it.

The characteristics of the pathogen also affect the

development of diseases. Fungal pathogens often comprise several races which differ in their virulence. The presence of high levels of inoculum of a highly virulent strain results in high levels of infection if the environmental conditions are favourable. The levels of inoculum present depend on the conditions for spore germination and the efficiency of dispersal. In the case of virus and bacterial diseases, the degree of damage to the plant affects the success of infection.

Where animal vectors are involved in disease transmission, the level of infection will depend on the population of the vector and the existence of favourable conditions for its multiplication and movement. Aphids multiply rapidly in warm temperatures in the summer. Weather conditions affect their mobility and they are most active on warm and wind-free days. Control of the vector is the only efficient means of controlling diseases transmitted in this way.

A further factor affecting the development of diseases is the genetic resistance of the crop. The existence of genetic resistance in populations of crop plants has been exploited by plant breeders and the grower can, in many cases, select varieties resistant to specific diseases. Genetic resistance is not present in all crops to all diseases, and even where it exists, it may be short-lived as the pathogen mutates. Nevertheless it is an important method of disease control which will be referred to later.

PRINCIPLES OF DISEASE CONTROL

There are a number of approaches which can be adopted to control diseases. The regularity with which many major diseases occur, the rapidity of their spread and the difficulty of controlling them once infection has occurred, means that many control methods are designed to protect the plant from infection rather than to cure the disease. Chemical control is expensive and in many cases hazardous and should be considered as a last resort.

Tarr (1972) proposes two main approaches to disease
control: immunisation which can be achieved by using
resistant varieties and chemotherapy involving fungicides,
and prophylactic measures. The prophylactic measures include protection, legislation and eradication. All of
these methods are important in the overall strategy for
disease control and should be considered together.

(i) <u>The use of resistant cultivars</u>. Reference to the
success of plant breeders in exploiting the genetic
resistance of plants to selected pathogens has been
made. The grower can select varieties, of many of
the major crops, which are resistant to one or more
of the important diseases. Recommended lists of
varieties of crop plants usually contain information
on their disease-resistance characteristics and the
grower should study these carefully before making
his choice. Considerable success has been achieved
in breeding cereal varieties with resistance to
foliar pathogens. In winter wheat for example, in
the United Kingdom, selection for resistance to mildew, yellow rust, brown rust and Septoria is possible. In addition, varieties of wheat differ in
their resistance to eyespot and loose smut. Unfor-
tunately it is rare to find good resistance to all
diseases in a single variety. A good example of
this is the variety Maris Huntsman which has good
resistance to eyespot but is highly susceptible to
brown rust. Spring and winter barley varieties
differ in their resistance to mildew and rust
diseases and in addition selection for resistance to
*Rhyncosporium* can be made.

Potato varieties exist with resistance to blight
in the foliage and in the tubers and selection of
varieties can be made with this in mind.

Resistance to virus diseases also varies between
varieties within some crops. Potato varieties
exhibit varying levels of resistance to leaf roll

virus, potato virus Y and potato virus X.

In the case of some foliar pathogens of cereals, the fungus exists in a number of different forms or physiological races. Varieties may exhibit resistance to only a few of these races and be susceptible to others. Furthermore the pathogens mutate to produce new races and the disease resistance breaks down. This is the case with yellow rust of wheat. Where the risk of severe yellow rust infection is high it can be reduced by using varieties possessing different resistance factors. Varieties can be classified into diversification groups, each possessing similar resistance factors. The risk of disease can therefore be reduced by growing varieties from different diversification groups in adjacent fields or where the risk of infection is high. This can also be achieved by growing mixtures of varieties possessing different resistance characteristics. The varietal diversification scheme can be used to reduce the spread of mildew in spring barley. The use of disease-resistant varieties is a useful method of control if used wisely.

(ii) <u>Cultural methods of control</u>. There are a number of ways in which cultural practices can influence the development of diseases in plants. The most obvious method of cultural control is the use of rotations to disrupt the life cycle of the pathogen. Club root is a disease specific to certain brassica crops and the level of inoculum in the soil declines in the absence of suitable host. A gap between susceptible crops in the rotation of five years is usually sufficient to control the disease. Club root is very persistent in the soil and similarly wart disease of potatoes can survive for long periods without a suitable host. Continuous cereal cropping encourages the build-up of take-all in the soil but this usually declines again after a few years.

Break crops are useful in disrupting the life cycle of take-all in cereal-based rotations. The major diseases which are controlled by rotations are soil-borne fungal ones with resting stages which persist for a long time.

Weed control is also important in controlling some diseases. Some pathogens survive on a range of host plants which provide a source of inoculum. Several diseases of cereals can survive on weed grasses and be carried over from one season to another on these hosts. Volunteer cereals, from grain shed at harvesting, can also fulfil the same function. It is therefore important to control weeds which can carry diseases from one crop to another.

The drainage status of the soil affects the susceptibility of the plant to disease. Poor drainage leads to smaller and weaker plants which may be more prone to attack from pathogens. Powdery scab of potato tubers for example is worse in wet soils. Adequate drainage of arable land is therefore important in disease control. Irrigation may aid the dispersal of spores of foliar pathogens and encourages powdery scab of potatoes.

The type of cultivations used can affect disease development. Take-all and eyespot of cereals can survive on the stubble, and burial of the residues by ploughing helps to reduce the incidence of these diseases. In contrast, direct drilling may increase the problem. Ploughing is also beneficial in burying weed host plants and volunteer crops of cereals and potatoes.

There is some evidence to suggest that high levels of nitrogen fertiliser increase the susceptibility of cereals to pathogen attack. However the use of low nitrogen levels is not a method of control which is attractive in intensive cropping systems. Maintenance of an appropriate soil pH by

liming provides more vigorous plant growth and dis-
courages the development of some soil-borne pathogens.

The choice of sowing date for the crop may also
influence its susceptibility to disease. Early-
sowing of autumn cereals may lead to higher levels
of barley yellow dwarf virus and mildew. In contrast, early sowing of sugar beet encourages earlier
leaf canopy development and renders the crop less
attractive to aphid vectors of virus yellows.

In some cases, the removal of sources of inoculum can reduce subsequent crop infection. The destruction of discarded potatoes in dumps, and sugar
beet or mangolds in clamps, reduces the risk of
transfer of viruses by aphids to emerging and
developing crops.

There are a number of cultural methods available
to the grower which can help to prevent or control
disease. Many of these are designed to reduce or
eliminate the source of inoculum or to provide unfavourable conditions for disease development.

(iii) <u>Legislative means of control</u>. In many countries,
legislative measures have been introduced to protect
the health of crop plants. Seed certification
schemes are examples of this where the grower is
protected by statutory requirements concerning the
level of disease-infected seeds in samples for sale.
Importation regulations prevent the introduction of
diseased plants from other countries. Other regulations prevent the movement of diseased plants
within a country by the implementation of 'Sale of
Diseased Plants Orders'. Legislative measures of
disease control are important in preventing the
spread and introduction of pathogens which are difficult to control when established.

(iv) <u>Chemical control</u>. There is a wide range of chemicals available for controlling fungal diseases of
crops and a detailed coverage of their individual

characteristics will not be given here. There are
basically two types of fungicide used on crops:
those which eradicate the disease once it is established and those which protect the plant from infection. In both cases there are a number of attributes which are desirable in a fungicide.

(a) Effective fungitoxicity.
(b) Low phytotoxicity, i.e. it will not damage the
plant.
(c) Ease of formulation and application.
(d) Possess satisfactory storage and transport
characteristics.
(e) Not have undesirable side effects such as encouraging the development of insensitive strains
of the fungus.
(f) Have low mammalian toxicity and be safe to use
and handle.
(g) Present minimum environmental and residual
hazards.
(h) Be economical to use.

Ideally, all of these factors should be combined in
the one chemical, but in practice this often is not
the case.

The chemicals for disease control can be classified by several means but it is useful to consider
them under the three main methods of disease spread.
Soil-borne diseases present difficulties of control
because of the large volumes of soil which need to
be treated. Soil sterilants are generally non-
selective and expensive and not widely used in field
crops. Their use is restricted largely to glasshouse soils. Soil protectant fungicides are more
useful and can be applied at the time of sowing or
planting to protect the plants from attack by soil-
borne pathogens. The roots of brassica seedlings
can be dipped in calomel to protect them from club

root infection. Seed protectant fungicides are
applied to the seeds and are useful in controlling
seedling diseases such as damping-off. Thiram and
captan are examples of seed protectant fungicides.
Some soil-borne diseases can be controlled by systemic fungicides applied to the shoot. The chemical
is translocated down into the roots and protects
them from attack by soil-borne fungi.

Seed-borne diseases are a problem in some crops and
lead to infection of the growing plant. Disinfec-
tants are used to control pathogens on the surface
of the seeds of cereals. These chemicals are often
from the organo-mercury group and present problems
of high mammalian toxicity. Systemic fungicide
treatment of seeds is useful for those diseases
which are borne within the seed structure. They are
taken up by the developing seedling and inhibit
internal fungal development, e.g. carboxin for loose
smut of cereals.

Air-borne diseases are the major problem with many
crops and the strategy for chemical control is different. Foliar protectant fungicides are designed
to prevent the establishment of infection and must
be applied before the disease becomes established.
They only protect the parts of the plant with which
they have contact and new growth is not protected
unless further applications are made. Repeated
applications may be necessary throughout the season
and this can be done more efficiently where disease
forecasting systems operate. Examples of foliar
protectant chemicals are the dithiocarbamates (e.g.
maneb) and copper compounds.

Foliar eradicant fungicides are applied to kill
the fungus on the plant and their effectiveness depends on the degree of contact with the pathogen.
They are not widely used on arable crops.

Foliar systemic fungicides are translocated to

the new growth and they do not need to be applied so frequently as the protectants. Systemic fungicides can be applied to seeds to control pathogens situated within the seed or to control air-borne diseases using the treatment as a reservoir of fungicide during the growth of the crop. They can also be applied to the leaves and stems of growing plants and as a post-harvest treatment to apples and potato tubers to control storage diseases. Benomyl treatment of fruit after harvest provides a useful control of storage rots. Triadimefon is used for the control of a range of cereal leaf diseases.

The timing of application of systemic fungicides is not so critical as that for non-systemic types. In general, a disease is most easily controlled when the inoculum level is at its lowest and treating crops early in their life affords the greatest protection. The timing of the application of fungicides is an important aspect of chemical disease control. It is important to apply the chemical before the disease becomes well established. In the case of yellow rust of winter wheat, chemical control should start before the disease covers 5 per cent of the area of the top two leaves at any stage of development and disease assessment keys are a useful aid in this respect. The timing of fungicide application to control disease varies with the individual disease and crop, and advice should be obtained where doubt exists.

Chemicals for disease control are expensive and often hazardous to use but in many crops they are the only reliable method of disease control. Where disease problems are anticipated they should be used according to the advice available. Routine application should be avoided where the economic benefits are uncertain.

## THE ORGANISMS CONSTITUTING CROP PESTS

A pest can be defined as an animal which causes economic damage to crop plants through its feeding habits. A large number of different types of animals are crop pests and these are briefly reviewed below.

*Table 11.2  Groups of crop pests  i) Arthropods*

| Class | | Order | Common name |
|---|---|---|---|
| Insecta | wingless: | Collembola | Springtails |
| | winged: | Hemiptera | Plant bugs (aphids, leafhoppers and capsids) |
| | | Thysanoptera | Thrips |
| | | Lepidoptera | Butterflies and moths |
| | | Coleoptera | Beetles and weevils |
| | | Diptera | Flies |
| | | Hymenoptera | Sawflies, wasps and bees |
| Arachnida | sub-class | Acari | Mites |
| Crustacea | | Isopoda | Woodlice |
| Diplopoda | | – | Millipedes |
| Symphyla | | – | Symphilids |

The largest group of crop pests come from the Arthropods (Table 11.2). This group consists of individuals which are highly mobile and well-adapted to life on land. In addition, they are capable of rapid multiplication and populations can increase rapidly in favourable conditions. The most important class in the phylum Arthropoda is Insecta, the insects. Only seven orders of insects contain pests which cause serious damage to crops.

The Collembola, or springtails, are wingless and soil-inhabiting insects which favour moist environments. They are not very serious pests of crop plants but some species attack seedlings of sugar beet and mangels.

The Hemiptera, or plant bugs, is a large and important

order containing numerous crop pests. Members of this
order display incomplete metamorphosis and both immature
and adult forms feed on cell sap by means of piercing and
sucking mouthparts. Additionally several members of this
group can transmit virus diseases (see earlier in this
chapter). Typical plant symptoms of feeding by this group
include leaf curling, the production of galls and stunting
of growth. The aphid family comprises the largest group
of crop pests. Many of the aphid pests have two or more
hosts in their life cycle. For example, the black bean
aphid (*Aphis fabae*) feeds on the *Vicia* bean in the summer
period and overwinters as the egg stage on the spindle
tree (*Euonymus* sp.).

Aphids are capable of reproduction by parthenogenesis
in the summer period and often give birth to live young.
This means that they multiply rapidly in warm weather.

Other examples of aphid pests include the peach-
potato aphid (*Myzus persicae*) which attacks potatoes,
sugar beet and swedes and the cabbage aphid (*Brevicoryne
brassicae*).

Other members of the Hemiptera do not cause economic
damage to arable crops, with the exception of capsid bugs
on sugar beet and potatoes.

The Thysanoptera, thrips, are small insects with
fringe-like wings and only a few species are of economic
importance. The pea thrip is troublesome in dry periods
in pea growing areas and another species attacks onions.
Cereal thrips are also common on the ears of plants but
the damage caused is often small.

The Lepidoptera, butterflies and moths, display complete metamorphosis through the egg, larva, pupa and
adult stages. The adults cause no damage to plants but
the larvae, with their powerful biting mouthparts, can
cause serious damage. Different parts of plants are eaten
depending on the species involved. The eggs of the pea
moth are laid in the flowers and the larvae feed on the
seeds within the pods, causing serious losses of yield and

quality. Larvae of the cabbage caterpillar group (large white butterfly, diamond black moth and cabbage moth) feed primarily on the foliage and can reduce leaves to skeletons. In addition, the excreta can reduce the quality of horticultural produce. The larvae of several species of noctuid moths are known as cutworms and inhabit the soil. They feed on seedlings and root systems and can cause serious crop losses. Severe damage to potato tubers can be done by this group.

The Coleoptera, beetles and weevils, contain members which feed on crops both in the adult and larval stages. The strong biting mouthparts can cause damage to the tissues and result in crop losses. A good example of this type of pest are the larvae of click beetle (*Agriotes* spp.) which collectively are known as wireworms. These are most prevalent under grassland where the larvae feed for almost three years on the roots and when the pasture is ploughed up there is a risk of damage to succeeding cereal, potato and sugar beet crops. Crop damage becomes serious when the wireworm population exceeds $2,500,000$ ha$^{-1}$. Other beetle pests include the flea beetle, which attacks the young seedlings of brassicas, and the bean seed beetle, which attacks bean pods.

Several weevil pests are of economic importance in crops including the pea and bean weevils, which eat foliage, and grain weevils, which attack cereal seeds in store.

The Diptera (the true flies) is a large order containing numerous crop pests. The adults do not damage plants and it is the feeding habits of the larvae which make them important. The sub-order Nematocera includes the midges and crane flies which can be crop pests. The pea midge is a good example of this group where the eggs are laid inside the flowers and the larvae destroy the developing pods. Other midge pests include the wheat midges and the bladder pod midge of oilseed rape. The larvae of the crane flies are known as leatherjackets and are common in grassland. The roots of cereals and sugar beet are also eaten by leatherjackets.

The sub-order Cyclorrapha includes a number of serious pests of crop plants and the main ones are listed in Table 11.3. All of these pests cause severe damage to plants and control measures are usually necessary.

Table 11.3  Crop pests from the insect order Diptera, sub-order Cyclorrapha

| Pest | Crops affected | Symptoms |
| --- | --- | --- |
| Frit fly | Grass and cereals including maize | Central shoot dies |
| Gout fly | Barley and wheat | Dead central shoot and swollen tillers |
| Carrot fly | Carrots and celery | Root destruction |
| Celery leaf miner | Celery | Mining of leaves |
| Wheat bulb fly | Wheat | Death of central shoot |
| Cabbage root fly | Brassica vegetables | Root destruction |
| Onion fly | Onions | Tunnelling of bulb |
| Bean seed fly | Broad beans and sweetcorn | Seed damage |
| Beet leaf miner | Sugar beet and mangolds | Mining of leaves |

The Hymenoptera (bees, wasps and sawflies), contains insects which are mainly beneficial to man. Some sawfly larvae cause damage of economic importance but these are restricted to fruit crops, e.g. gooseberries and plums.

Other classes of Arthropods also constitute crop pests and the main one of these is the Arachnida containing the class Acari (mites). Most of the mites of economic importance affect glasshouse and other horticultural crops and few are of economic importance in arable crops. The red spider mite (*Tretanychus urticae*) attacks sugar beet and strawberries in hot, dry weather. The grain mite (*Acarus siro*) feeds on the embryos of cereal grains in store and affects germination. The cast skins and excreta of these mites taint the grain and render it unsuitable for human consumption.

Woodlice and symphilids have weak biting mouthparts and rarely cause serious damage to crops in the open. Millipedes are more serious pests and the adults damage seedlings of peas, beans and sugar beet.

Four other major groups of animals contain members which are crop pests (Table 11.4). Snails are rarely a problem in field crops but slugs can cause economic damage. Slugs favour wet conditions and are most active in moist and warm periods. Slugs inflict damage on crops by their rasping feeding action which creates cavities in tubers and storage roots and destroys leaves of young plants. Cereal and oilseed rape crops, which are just becoming established, are particularly prone to slug damage in the autumn. Potato tubers can be severely damaged in wet autumns.

*Table 11.4  Groups of crop pests  ii) non-Arthropods*

| Group | Common name |
| --- | --- |
| Gastropoda | Slugs and snails |
| Nematoda | Nematodes or eelworms |
| Mammalia | Mammals |
| Aves | Birds |

The nematodes or eelworms are major crop pests and most of them are soil-borne. Their activity is highly dependent on adequate moisture in the soil and on the sur- face of plants. They feed on plants by piercing the tissues with their spear-like mouthparts. A number of nematode pests feed externally on plants and these include species of *Longidorus*, *Trichodorus* and *Xiphenema*. Sugar beet and cereals are the most susceptible crops to damage from these types. The stem eelworm (*Ditylenchus dipsaci*) feeds inside plants and damages cells and the race which attacks oats is a serious problem in the United Kingdom.

The most widely known group of nematodes is that which forms cysts. These mainly belong to the genus *Heterodera* in which the female body enlarges and assumes a lemon shape. The female eventually dies leaving a cyst containing eggs. The cyst and eggs can remain viable for a number of years until stimulated to hatch by root exudates from a suitable host. The importance of rotations in controlling this group and the major species causing damage to crops have been referred to in chapter 4. Cyst-nematodes usually only attack a limited number of species.

Several mammalian species can damage crop plants by their feeding habits. Rabbits and hares can cause considerable defoliation by grazing cereal crops and are difficult to control effectively. Field mice and voles attack the seeds and seedlings of crop plants and can reduce establishment. This is particularly important in sugar beet where the wood or field mouse excavates the pelleted seeds and consumes the embryos. This type of damage is most prevalent in early-sown crops in dry conditions. Rats and mice invade grain stores in the winter and can cause considerable damage.

In the United Kingdom a few species of birds cause damage to arable crops. The degree of damage is influenced by the populations of the pest and the season when feeding occurs. Brassica crops are vulnerable to wood pigeon damage in the autumn and winter and this pest can devastate oilseed rape crops. The wood pigeon also feeds on cereals and occasionally on sugar beet leaves. The skylark causes extensive damage to young sugar beet seedlings by feeding on the cotyledons and causes 'gappiness' in crops drilled to a stand.

Other birds which damage arable crops include the rook, starling, house sparrow, pheasant and partridge. Birds are difficult to control because of their mobility and, in some cases, their migratory habits.

It is clear that a wide range of animals can cause damage to crop plants and the foregoing list has presented a few examples to illustrate the type of damage they cause. Crop losses result from the effects of their feeding habits and the plant's physiological processes are adversely affected. Damage to the roots, stems, leaves, flowers, fruit and seeds of plants results in considerable losses of yield and quality. In addition, several pests can transmit diseases of crops. It is therefore important for the grower to be aware of the risks of crop damage from pests and take the necessary preventative and control measures. Effective pest control depends on the ability to classify the pest and have some knowledge of its biology. In this way control measures can be implemented when the pest is most vulnerable.

PRINCIPLES OF PEST CONTROL

The major approaches to pest control are similar to those described for diseases and examples will be given here to illustrate the main methods. It is important to identify pest risks at an early stage so that control measures can be implemented before the populations reach a level where economic damage to the crop occurs. This may mean anticipating the problem and taking preventative measures. Jones and Jones (1974) identify four types of pest:

(i) Regular — these rarely fall below the economic threshold, e.g. frit fly.
(ii) Sporadic — these only occasionally rise above the economic threshold, e.g. millipedes.
(iii) Potential — these might become a serious problem if allowed to become established, e.g. Colorado beetle.
(iv) Pests of special circumstances — these are predictable and can be anticipated, e.g. wireworms after ploughed grass.

It is important to be able to identify the risks to a crop from pests of all of the four groups and make preparations to deal with them.

(i) <u>The use of resistant cultivars</u>. There is less scope for this method of pest control compared with diseases. The feeding habits and nature of the damage caused by pests make it difficult to select plants with characteristics which would make them resistant. Breeding for pest resistance has been most successful for nematode and arthropod pests. Varieties of barley resistant to the cereal cyst eelworm have been developed and similarly oat varieties resistant to stem eelworm are available. The most striking success in breeding for eelworm resistance has been in the production of potato varieties resistant to the potato cyst nematode (*Globodera rostochiensis*). However resistance is restricted to a single or a few pathotypes of this pest and they are not useful in all situations.

Resistance to some aphid pests has also been exploited in plant breeding programmes. The greatest potential for using varieties with resistance to aphids exists in sugar beet, potatoes, brassica crops, raspberries and lettuce. Where resistance to aphids occurs there is subsequently a reduced risk of virus disease transmission.

(ii) <u>Cultural methods</u>. Rotational methods are useful in controlling certain host-specific soil-borne pests. The cyst-forming nematodes can survive for several years in the soil and a five-year break between susceptible crops depletes the populations below the economic threshold level. This approach can be employed with potatoes, peas, sugar beet and cereals. The other aspect of rotational control measures is the importance of identifying the risk of a pest problem in a crop as a result of the way

the previous crop was grown. Reference has already
been made to the risk of wireworms after grassland
has been ploughed up. The risk of wheat bulb fly
damage in winter wheat is greater where the soil has
been exposed to egg-laying adults, such as after
early-lifted potatoes.

Cultivations are of only limited use in controlling pests. There is a possibility that cultivations will bring larvae and pupae to the soil
surface where they die by desiccation or are eaten
by birds, but this is not a reliable method of
control.

Drainage is an important aid to pest control.
The soil-borne pests require a moist environment for
survival and where good drainage exists pest problems can be reduced. Crops should not be left in
the ground too long in wet autumns. Wireworms, cutworms and slugs can all cause great damage to potato
tubers which are lifted late from wet soils.

The factors determining the sowing date of crops
have already been discussed (chapter 6) and these
include the need to avoid sowing when the risk of
pest attack is high. Many of the root flies lay
their eggs around the base of established crops and
are attracted by scent. Delaying sowing until after
the peak period of egg-laying thus reduces the risk
of attack. Delaying carrot sowing until the end of
May reduces the risk of carrot fly attack. In other
cases, early sowing ensures that the crop is well
established and less prone to attack from pests
which emerge later. Early sowing of brassicas
reduces the risk of flea beetle damage to the
cotyledons.

The removal of alternative weed hosts of pests
and of crop debris, which can provide a reservoir of
pests, is helpful in reducing pest populations.
(iii) <u>Legislative measures</u>. Legislation to control pests

is primarily designed to prevent the introduction
of previously unknown organisms. Compulsory notifi-
cation of Colorado beetles on potato crops in the
United Kingdom, under the Colorado Beetles Orders,
has effectively prevented the establishment of this
pest. Other legislative measures are designed to
prevent the build-up and spread of serious pests
which are already established.

(iv) <u>Chemical control</u>. Chemicals used to control crop
pests are collectively known as pesticides. More
specific names are used for these chemicals which
control specific groups, e.g. insecticides, acari-
cides, nematicides and molluscicides. There is a
wide range of chemicals available for pest control
and new chemicals and formulations appear frequently.
The numbers of chemicals involved preclude detailed
discussion of individuals here and the grower should
seek advice on the most appropriate chemical for the
pest problem on his crop. The attributes required
in a successful pesticide are similar to those described for fungicides. Most of them are toxic or
harmful in some aspect to man and wildlife and
appropriate safety precautions must be observed
when using them.

Pesticides can also be classified on the basis
of the way in which they kill the pest. Stomach
poisons are effective through the pest eating
foliage, or other plant parts, to which the chemical
has been applied. Contact poisons enter the pest
through the outer 'skin' or integument, and in this
case the chemical must be placed in contact with the
organism. Some chemicals have a fumigant action and
enter the pest through the spiracles and affect the
respiratory system. Other chemicals kill the eggs
of pests and are called ovicides. Systemic poisons
have a stomach action and enter the organism by its
feeding on cell sap. Several chemicals operate in

more than one of these ways and the most appropriate
chemical should be selected for the pest involved.

The major chemical groups of pesticides are
listed below with a few selected examples.

Plant derivatives constitute a small group of pesticides. Pyrethrin is an example of this group and is
obtained from the flower heads of a *Chrysanthemum*
species. It is effective against caterpillars but
has been largely superseded now by synthetic
pyrethrinoids such as resmethrin. Nicotine is
another plant derivative.

Organochlorine chemicals were some of the first
effective pesticides to be developed and DDT was a
very effective insecticide. However they are a very
persistent and toxic group and are not widely used
except for special circumstances, e.g. aldrin for
wireworm control in potatoes.

Organophosphorus compounds provide a wide range of
pesticides, many of which are systemic in their
action. Examples of this group are chlorfenvinphos,
for use against wheat bulb fly and cabbage root fly,
and demeton-s-methyl, to control aphids. Organophosphorus chemicals are also hazardous and leave
harmful residues and must be used with appropriate
precautions.

Carbamates have a relatively low mammalian toxicity
and are generally safe to use on food crops. Carbo-
furan is an example of a chemical in this group
which is useful for controlling root flies and some
eelworms. Methiocarb is a carbamate molluscicide
for slug control.

The groups of chemicals exist in different
formulations which may be for use as dusts, liquid
sprays, granules applied to the soil or as fumigants.
In all cases the recommended concentration of chemical should be used and care taken with machinery to
ensure a uniform and overall application. The

300

timing of application is also very important to
ensure maximum kill of the pest before it reaches
the level of economic damage. More than one application may be required where there is a risk of re-
infestation, e.g. aphids.

Resistance in pests to some insecticides has
developed and precautions should be taken to ensure
that conditions are not favourable for resistance to
build-up. This means using the recommended concentration of chemical for application and using a
range of different chemicals. The development of
resistance has been most common with organophosphorus compounds.

Chemical control is undoubtedly the most effective way of killing pests of arable crops. Provided
that approved chemicals are used and the manufacturer's recommendations are followed, their use is
relatively safe. Contamination of the environment
and the safety of the operators of the machinery
which applies them are important considerations in
their use.

## BENEFICIAL ORGANISMS

Not all of the organisms found on crops are harmful.
There are two groups of beneficial organisms to be considered when choosing a chemical control programme.
Firstly, crops such as oilseed rape and field beans rely
on adequate pollination for good yields and insects are
important here. Bees are the main insects responsible for
pollinating crop plants although some flies and beetles
are also involved. Care must be taken not to spray
flowering crops with pesticides which harm pollinating
insects.

The second group consists of predators and parasites
which are natural enemies of pests. The insect order
Coleoptera contains a number of species which are preda-
tory on other insects. The adults and larvae of ground

and rove beetles prey on the eggs and larvae of the cabbage root fly and this helps to reduce the populations.
Similarly ladybird larvae and adults consume large quantities of aphids and other insects throughout a season.
A further example of natural control of crop pests is provided by the parasitic wasps of the Hymenoptera. The
female wasps lay their eggs in the body of the host pest,
e.g. an aphid, and the larvae consume the body contents
and kill it. There are numerous documented examples of
natural enemies of crop pests but the exploitation of this
as a control measure has not been effective. Biological
control has been successfully used in glasshouse crops to
control aphids, whitefly and red spider mite but in the
field it is difficult to maintain the appropriate balance
between predator or parasite and the pest.

Biological control of arthropod pests is therefore not
yet a viable method. However the grower should be aware
of the importance of natural enemies of pests and where
possible select an insecticide which selectively kills the
pest and not its predators or parasites.

The use of fungal, bacterial and viral pathogens of
crop pests as a control measure has not been successful in
field crops although this is an area where future developments may occur. Rabbits have however been successfully
controlled by the virus causing myxamatosis.

Pest control should, where possible, be an integrative
programme using chemicals and cultural, biological, legislative and genetic methods.

REFERENCES AND FURTHER READING

Agrios, G.N. (1978)  Plant Pathology (2nd edn).  New York:
    Academic Press.
Chiarappa, L. (ed.) (1981)  Crop Loss Assessment. Supple-
    ment 3.  Slough: Commonwealth Agricultural Bureaux.
Deverall, B. (1974)  Fungal Parasitism.  Institute of
    Biology's Studies in Biology No.17.  London: Edward
    Arnold.

Gibbs, A. and Harrison, B. (1976) The Principles of Plant Virology. London: Edward Arnold.

Green, M.B., Hartley, G.S. and West, T.F. (1979) Chemicals for Crop Protection and Pest Control. Oxford: Pergamon Press.

Horne, R.W. (1978) Structure and Function of Viruses. Institute of Biology's Studies in Biology No.95. London: Edward Arnold.

Jones, F.G.W. and Jones, M.G. (1974) Pests of Field Crops (2nd edn). London: Edward Arnold.

Jones, W.C. (1974) 'Assessment of plant diseases and losses'. Annual Review of Phytopathology, 12, 27-48.

Kilgore, W.W. and Doult, R.L. (eds.) (1967) Pest Control, Biological, Physical and Selected Chemical Methods. London: Academic Press.

Manners, J.G. (1982) Principles of Plant Pathology. Cambridge: University Press.

Marsh, R.W. (ed.) (1977) Systemic Fungicides. London: Longman.

Russell, G.E. (1978) Plant Breeding for Pest and Disease Resistance. London: Butterworth.

Smith, K.M. (1972) Plant Virus Diseases (3rd edn). London: Longman.

Tarr, S.A.J. (1972) Principles of Plant Pathology. London: Macmillan Press.

Western, J.H. (1971) Diseases of Crop Plants. London: Macmillan Press.

Wheeler, B.E.J. (1976) An Introduction to Plant Diseases. London: John Wiley and Sons.

Wright, E.N., Inglis, I.R. and Feare, C.J. (eds.) (1980) Bird Problems in Agriculture. London: British Crop Protection Council.

# 12  Crop Maturity and Harvesting

## INTRODUCTION

The preceding chapters have emphasised the complexity of
crop production systems and considered the various factors
which can affect growth, development, yield and quality.
Considerable management skill is required to control all
of these factors to produce a good crop at harvest. The
next stage in the production system is to harvest the crop
at the most appropriate time, in such a way as to secure
the maximum yield of a high quality product for delivery
to the store or market. Harvesting is as important a part
of the system as any other aspect and due care and consideration should be given to this operation. Losses in
yield and quality can occur at harvest and these should be
reduced to a minimum.

## ASSESSMENT OF SUITABILITY FOR HARVEST

At some point in the production system a decision has to
be taken on when to harvest the crop. The criteria which
affect the suitability for harvest differ for individual
crops and some examples will be explained here. Crops can
be separated into different categories for this purpose.
Those grown for their ripe seeds, e.g. cereals, grain
legumes and oilseeds, constitute one category. Potatoes
and root crops are harvested for their 'fresh' underground
organs and require separation from the soil. A third

category consists of those crops which are harvested fresh for consumption directly by humans and where quality is of paramount importance. This last category includes a range of field vegetables, e.g. cauliflowers, and crops for processing, e.g. vining peas. These crops are harvested before they have matured and yield is sacrificed at the expense of quality.

Cereals exhibit a determinate growth habit and their life cycle is completed within a limited period of time. After anthesis the grain develops and the lower leaves begin to senesce. During senescence re-translocation of assimilates from the leaves and stems to the grain occurs. Eventually the leaves die and the stems turn yellow and brown as the grain ripens. During this ripening process moisture is lost from the grain (Table 12.1). The example shows the changes in grain moisture content for two wheat and two barley varieties over the three weeks before

*Table 12.1 Changes in the moisture content of barley and wheat grains on three dates before harvest (after Manley and Wood, 1978). Data from the south Midlands of England.*

| | Moisture content of grain (per cent) | | | |
| | Winter wheat | | Spring barley | |
| Sample date | Hobbit | Maris Huntsman | Aramir | Mazurka |
|---|---|---|---|---|
| 1-3 August | 47.7 | 43.6 | 38.8 | 44.0 |
| 8-11 August | 41.9 | 44.7 | 26.5 | 25.3 |
| 22 August | 26.3 | 14.2 | 12.3 | 12.8 |

harvest. In wheat, the loss of moisture from the grain is slow in the first week. As the grain ripens moisture loss is more rapid and, in Maris Huntsman, falls to 14 per cent by the end of the period. The loss of moisture from barley grains occurs throughout the period and at the end is about 12 per cent. The moisture content of the grain is the main criterion used to assess the suitability of cereals for harvest. The majority of cereals in temperate crops can be mechanically harvested when grain moisture contents are less than 20 per cent. In many cases, in dry summers, the moisture content is more likely to be in the range 12-16 per cent.

The farmer can easily assess the moisture content of a crop by taking a sample and using a moisture meter. Although the crop can be combined at moisture contents of about 20 per cent or more, the grain has to be dried to 15 per cent or less for safe storage by conventional means.

Assessment of the suitability for harvesting of grain legumes is not so easy as they tend to take longer to ripen and may exhibit an indeterminate growth habit. This means that although some seeds are ripe on the plant others are still immature. A decision then has to be made on a date when most of the pods are ripe. In the field bean, the pods mature first at the base of the stem and last at the top. Seeds are ripe when the point of attachment of the seed to the pod (the hilum) turns black. The field bean ripens very late in temperate climates and the fleshy pod reduces the rate of moisture loss from the seed in cool, wet autumns. Consequently the bean seeds are often harvested with a high moisture content of up to 35 per cent. Ideally the harvest should not start until the stems and pods are black and dry and all the leaves have shrivelled and died.

Peas for combining in a 'dry' condition also mature unevenly. This is complicated by the fact that they invariably lodge and this creates a high humidity microclimate within the crop, retarding moisture loss. There is a danger from delaying the harvest with peas, of losses occurring from pod splitting. Combine harvesting of peas can occur when the grain moisture content falls below about 30 per cent.

Oilseed rape displays an indeterminate growth habit and ripe and immature pods occur on the same plant. The stage of maturity acceptable for harvest depends on the method employed. Crops which are combined direct, either with or without desiccation, should have the majority of pods containing black seeds. Ideally the moisture content of the seeds at this stage should be 12-15 per cent. If the crop is swathed, the seeds in the pods from the lower third of the plant should be chocolate brown in colour and seeds in the middle third should be slightly brown in colour.

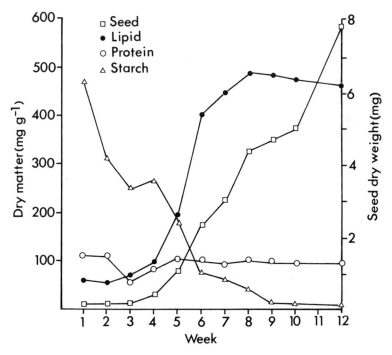

*Figure 12.1  Changes in seed weight and seed protein, lipid and starch content of a winter oilseed rape variety after flowering (drawn from Norton, Harris and Tomlinson, 1977)*

Detailed studies have been made on the seed development and ripening stages of growth of oilseed rape (Figure 12.1). Seed dry weight increases slowly after pod formation but, after four weeks, the increase is rapid and reaches a maximum after twelve weeks. During this period biochemical changes occur in the seed. The starch content declines progressively throughout the period as oil, or lipid, content increases to approximately 50 per cent of

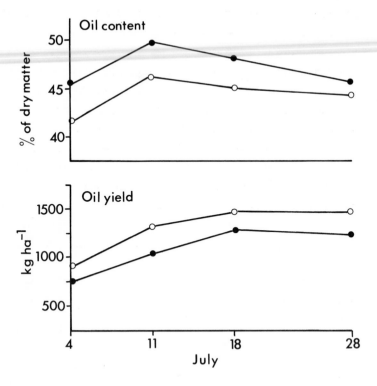

*Figure 12.2  The effect of harvest date on the oil content and yield of a winter oilseed rape variety given 100 (solid dot) and 200 (open dot) kg ha⁻¹ of nitrogen fertiliser (drawn from Scott, Ogunremi, Ivins and Mendham, 1973)*

the seed dry matter.  The protein content remains relatively stable throughout.  It is clear from data of this kind that premature swathing, desiccation or combining will result in lower seed yields with lower oil contents.

Field studies of changes in oil yield and content of a winter oilseed rape variety grown in central England are shown in Figure 12.2.  Oil content increases in the early part of July but then declines slowly through to the end of July.  During this period, oil yield increases initially and then remains stable.  As oil content decreases in the later part of the period, seed yield increases, resulting in smaller changes in oil yield.  The yield of oil doubles over the twenty-four day period

emphasising the importance of selecting the most appropriate harvest date. High levels of nitrogen fertiliser
increase oil yield but depress oil content.

The assessment of suitability for harvesting of
cereals, grain legumes and oilseed depends on the moisture
content of the seed. The choice of harvest date is easier
with crops showing a determinate rather than indeterminate
growth habit. Premature harvesting may result in loss of
yield and quality. Harvesting later than the optimum
period results in losses from seeds being shed onto the
ground in standing crops and from combine harvesting.

Growth of sugar beet roots continues into the autumn
resulting in higher sugar yields from later harvest dates
(Figure 12.3). Maximum yields would be obtained if the

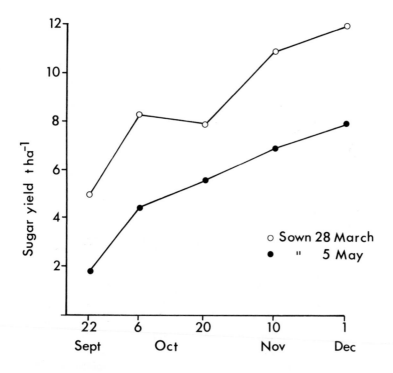

*Figure 12.3 The accumulation of sugar in the beet crop during the harvesting period for crops sown on two dates (from Scott and Jaggard, 1978)*

whole crop was harvested in late-November. However, because of the capacity of the processing factories to handle the crop, the harvesting occurs from September onwards. Delivery to the factory is controlled by contract agreements and farmers are forced to harvest a proportion of the crop early. In addition, sugar beet are difficult to harvest in late wet autumn conditions and there are advantages in this respect from early harvesting.

The harvest date for potatoes depends on the purpose for which they are grown. Seed crops are harvested before they have reached their maximum yield to control the size of individual tubers. This may require the destruction of the haulms to prevent further growth. Maincrop potatoes are grown to produce maximum yields within the ware size grade and the longer the growing season the better. However soil and weather conditions in the autumn may determine the harvest date. Except for early crops, the tubers should have reached their maximum size and have skins which are set, before harvest starts. The risk of disease being transmitted from the haulms to the tubers may enforce earlier harvests than are desirable for high yields. Factors other than yield may therefore have a strong influence on the time of harvest for potatoes.

The time of harvest of vining peas is determined solely on quality considerations. Processors require peas of a certain tenderometer reading and when this is reached harvesting must commence irrespective of yield. This is also true for other crops for processing such as green beans.

Size is an important factor in determining the harvest date for crops for canning, e.g. carrots and potatoes. Size can be controlled by plant population and choice of variety, but harvesting date is also an important determinant. High yield is again sacrificed for quality in these examples.

Quality is also important in other field vegetables. The size, shape and appearance requirements of cauliflowers and cabbages determine the harvest date. In these cases a single harvest may be wasteful because individual plants within crops do not mature at a uniform rate and several harvests may be required.

The factors affecting the suitability for harvest differ with individual crops. Each crop must be considered separately and the best time selected to maximise yield and quality.

ACCELERATION OF 'RIPENING'

It is clear from the earlier discussion that several crops grown in temperate climates display an indeterminate growth habit. This leads to a lack of uniformity of ripening of seed-producing crops and makes the decision of when to harvest difficult. In many oilseed crops grown in temperate climates most of the seeds mature before full senescence of the plant and this makes mechanical harvesting difficult, e.g. sunflowers. Furthermore, wet weather in the late summer and early autumn delays the maturation process and harvest. Hand-harvesting of crops traditionally coped with these problems by accelerating ripening in stooks. Some crops are mechanically swathed, e.g. peas and oilseed rape, to speed up the maturing process.

An alternative approach is to desiccate the crop with a chemical as soon as the seeds are mature. This also has the effect of desiccating any green weeds in the crop which may interfere with harvesting. Chemical desiccants have had a short history in crop production and those used before the mid-1960s were inefficient and toxic. In the mid-1960s diquat was introduced which was quickly adopted as a desiccant. It has the advantages of a rapid contact action and a low residue problem in soil and crop products. Diquat application to sunflowers advances the harvesting date by up to sixteen days, speeds up the harvesting process, lowers the moisture content of the seed and removes the need for expensive drying.

Diquat is recommended for use on oilseed rape as a

desiccant in many countries. The optimum time for diquat application to oilseed rape is when the pods in the bottom third of the main stem are dark-brown to black and those in the middle third are reddish-brown to dark-brown. The remaining seeds may still be green, but firm. To reduce damage to the standing crop, the chemical should be applied with a wide-boom sprayer. Combining should start when all the seeds are black and have a moisture content of 12-15 per cent. Diquat can also be used on linseed with the same objectives.

Desiccants are also valuable for destroying the haulms of potatoes. The objective of this may be to control tuber size in seed crops, to prevent tuber infection with blight or virus disease from the haulm or to set the skin in maincrop varieties for storage. Diquat is widely used for this purpose but sulphuric acid and metoxuron are also suitable. In addition to destroying the haulm for the reasons listed above, desiccation also reduces the volume and water content of stems which facilitates mechanical harvesting.

Desiccants can also be used to accelerate the drying process in lodged cereal crops and seed crops such as red and white clover.

The chemicals available for desiccation of crops all have some hazards associated with their use and caution should be shown when handling and applying them.

METHODS OF HARVESTING

In modern production systems the majority of crops are mechanically harvested. Hand labour is expensive and scarce and the traditional hand harvesting methods have largely disappeared from large-scale enterprises. Mechanised harvesting is a sophisticated business and no attempt will be made here to deal with the details of specific machines and systems involved. This aspect is covered in other texts (Culpin, 1975). However it is important here to consider the principles of harvesting methods.

The method of harvesting differs with different groups of crops. Cereals, grain legumes and oilseeds are usually combine harvested. The objective of this method of harvesting is to thresh the grain from the ear or pod and deliver the residue back onto the field. During this operation there are risks of damage to the seeds if the machine is incorrectly used or adjusted. Also seed losses can occur as they stand in the field, either with or without a desiccant treatment. Wheat, barley and oats are harvested in this way. Alternatively crops may be swathed and allowed to ripen completely before combine harvesting. Oilseed rape and dried peas are frequently swathed before combining.

The choice of the type of combine harvester is important. The size of the machine will determine the work rate. Weather conditions at harvest in temperate climates can be variable and it is vital to select a machine with the capacity to cope with the whole crop area in the limited period available. If the capacity of the machine is not high enough some crops may become over-ripe with resultant losses in yield and quality. Combine harvesters are expensive machines and the cost should be considered in choice of type.

The efficient use of combine harvesters in temperate climates is partly weather dependent and a different system of harvesting cereals has been proposed to reduce this dependency. Whole crop harvesting of cereals with a forage harvester can be carried out even when the crop is too wet for combining. This system also has the advantage of reducing combining losses in the field. The harvested whole crop is threshed in a central processing area and not in the field. This system has the disadvantage of damage to the grain from the harvester which can be as high as 4 per cent. Furthermore a large bulk of material has to be handled with this system and this has proved to be the greatest problem associated with it.

A number of systems for harvesting potatoes exist.

313

The simplest form uses the elevator digger which lifts the tubers and deposits them on the surface from which they are hand-picked. This system is relatively efficient but incurs high labour costs. Other systems involve machines which lift the tubers and deliver them to a trailer running alongside. These machines may be tractor-drawn or self-propelled. One of the biggest problems in potato harvesting is the separation of the tubers from stones and clods of a similar size. Some machines have a platform for workers to stand on to hand separate stones, clods and debris before delivery to the trailer. More sophisticated, and expensive, machines use an electronic device for sorting. These rely on the property of X-rays to penetrate tubers but not stones. Alternatively the separation can be done at the store, which speeds up the harvesting in the field.

The choice of a potato harvesting system depends on a number of factors. The area of crop grown is clearly important. Small areas can be lifted by hand but large areas require large machines. Soil conditions also affect the choice of system. Potatoes are lifted in the autumn when the soil may be wet. Large self-propelled machines cannot work in these conditions on heavy-textured soils but freely drained Fen soils and sands present no such problems and the larger machines can be used effectively. The rate of work of the machine and the cost are also important factors determining the choice of a potato harvesting system.

All potato harvesting systems involve several people and the choice of system must also take account of labour availability. Adequate transport arrangements must be made to deliver the tubers from the field to the store.

Some damage to potato tubers is inevitable during harvesting and precautions should be taken to reduce this to a minimum and prevent subsequent losses in store.

Sugar beet provides a good example to illustrate harvesting methods for root crops. Two main problems are

involved here: the separation of the tops from the roots
and the removal of the roots from the ground. Machines
are available which do both of these operations by topping
one row and lifting another. This is the simplest type of
harvesting system for beet. Other systems are available
which lift more than one row at a time. Multi-stage
harvesting systems also exist which may consist of three
separate machines. The first stage involves topping and
removal of the beet tops from the field. The second stage
involves lifting the beet roots and depositing them in a
windrow. The third stage lifts the beet from the windrow
and delivers them to a trailer. These systems are capable
of high work rates and can deal with five or six rows at
a time.

Clearly there are differences in the harvesting
capacity of the different systems. The system should be
chosen to ensure completion of harvest by mid-December.
It has been estimated that there are only 30-35 days with
good working conditions between the end of September and
mid-December so the capacity of the machinery should be
capable of handling the whole crop area in this time.
Lifting the roots in good soil conditions reduces the
losses and increases the rate of work.

As with all harvesting systems, the correct adjustment
and operation of the machinery is essential for the efficient lifting of beet. Losses in the harvesting of beet
can occur from:

  (i) inaccurate steering of the machine
 (ii) inaccurate setting of the topping mechanism
(iii) inaccurate setting of the lifting mechanisms
 (iv) excessive forward speed
  (v) over-filling of tanks and trailers and in transfer
     from elevators to trailers.

Care in the harvesting process can minimise these losses.
With certain crops there is very little choice in the
method of harvesting. The complexity of separating peas

from pods and haulms for freezing necessitates expensive
and sophisticated machines. There is little choice here
and only a few machines are suitable (these are usually
bought on a group basis).

Systems of harvesting vegetable crops vary. Root
crops are handled in basically the same way as sugar beet.
Cauliflowers and cabbages do not lend themselves well to
mechanical harvesting and hand cutting is involved.
Several harvests may be necessary with these crops to
cater for the different rates of maturity of individual
plants. Brussels sprouts can be mechanically harvested
but hand-picking can be used for varieties which have a
spread of uniformity of maturity up the stem.

To summarise, it is important to choose the right
system of harvesting for the particular crop and conditions to maximise the recovery of the useful product and
minimise losses and damage.

ASSESSMENT OF YIELD

All good farmers should keep detailed records of various
operations in their systems. Such records are an aid to
subsequent management and allow yield data to be related
to management inputs. This is important in intensive
temperate systems where the inputs are high and high
yields and returns are anticipated. It is therefore important to make an assessment of yield at harvest time.
Furthermore, estimates of yield are necessary to decide on
the storage requirements for the crop and to control the
subsequent marketing.

Accurate assessment of yield in the field is difficult, but estimates can be obtained by sampling. This is
easiest with root crops where known areas can be hand
lifted and weighed to give the required information. This
approach is more difficult with cereals because the
samples have to be threshed and cleaned before weighing.
On the assumption that most cereals have a harvest index
of 40-50 per cent, the whole crop can be weighed and an

estimate of grain yield calculated. Yield assessment with
field vegetables is not so useful as the price for the
product is as much dependent on quality as yield.

An alternative approach to sampling for yield assessment is to weigh the loads of produce over a weighbridge
before delivery to the store. Once the weight of a few
loads is known, the number of trailer loads of grain or
roots from a field can be recorded and the yield estimated.
This is an easy and reasonably accurate method of assess-
ing yield. In the case of grain, the yields should be
expressed at a standard moisture content. A further
method is to calculate the tonnage of the crop from the
storage volume occupied. In the case of cereal grains,
bins of known capacity are often used for storage, and
estimates can be made of the total weight in store.
Typical weights for a cubic metre of stored barley and
potatoes are 1.4 t and 1.6 t respectively. With sugar
beet, very accurate yields are obtainable because every
load is weighed on delivery to the factory and the farmer
is informed of the tonnage involved.

In potatoes, only a proportion of the crop is marketable and the best estimate of yield can only be obtained
when the tubers are graded out of the store and marketed.

There are a number of ways in which the farmer can obtain estimates of crop yields. This information can be
obtained for each field and provide the foundation for
improved management in future years.

## THE EXTENT OF HARVESTING LOSSES

Whatever the method of harvesting employed, a proportion
of the crop will be lost at some stage in the process.
Natural losses can occur in the field before harvest resulting from pest and disease damage or the effects of bad
weather. Losses of grain from over-ripe crops can occur
in windy weather and timely harvesting can help to avoid
this. The grower should be aware of losses from various
sources and he should harvest with the aim of reducing

these to a minimum.

The extent of the losses at harvest varies with individual crops and conditions. Losses from combine harvesting of cereals are relatively small but may be financially significant. Sample figures from conventionally combine harvested crops in the south Midlands of England are shown in Table 12.2. Data from six runs through a wheat crop, yielding 6 t ha$^{-1}$, show a range of grain losses from 0.6 to 4.7 per cent of the total grain harvested. The highest loss figure relates to the highest forward speed of the combine indicating one method of controlling these losses. The range of losses from a spring barley crop is similar, 0.1 to 6.4 per cent, and again the highest losses occur with the fastest forward speed of the machine.

Losses in cereal harvesting can occur at various stages. Ear loss can occur at the platform where they are knocked off by the reel and do not enter the combine. Losses also occur through incomplete threshing of the grain from the straw in the drum. Incorrect drum settings are responsible for this. Further losses occur from incomplete separation of threshed grain from the straw on the shakers and straw-walkers. This is usually associated with 'overloading' of the combine. Losses can also occur from incorrect fan settings resulting in grain being blown over the back of the combine with the chaff. All these sources of losses are within the farmer's control and care must be taken to adjust the mechanisms and speed of the combine for each set of conditions. A further source of loss in combines is damage to grain from drums which are set too close. This damage affects the quality of the grain and is very important with malting barley. Sieve sizes in combines should be selected for the size of the grain harvested to avoid this source of loss. Sources of cereal grain loss are numerous and efficient harvesting relies on the skill of the operator, both in driving the machine and in setting it up.

Oilseed rape is prone to losses similar to cereals in

Table 12.2  *Threshing losses of combine-harvested wheat and barley from selected farms (from ADAS, 1973)*

| | | Run number | | | | | |
| | | 1 | 2 | 3 | 4 | 5 | 6 |
|---|---|---|---|---|---|---|---|
| Winter wheat (6 t ha$^{-1}$) | Speed (mph) | 1.9 | 2.5 | 2.9 | 3.1 | 4.0 | 2.5 |
| | Loss (kg ha$^{-1}$) | 35 | 35 | 31 | 80 | 286 | 36 |
| | Loss (per cent of total grain) | 0.6 | 0.6 | 0.5 | 1.3 | 4.7 | 0.6 |
| Spring barley (6 t ha$^{-1}$) | Speed (mph) | 1.8 | 2.4 | 2.6 | 3.6 | 4.0 | 4.8 |
| | Loss (kg ha$^{-1}$) | 6 | 15 | 31 | 83 | 391 | 208 |
| | Loss (per cent of total grain) | 0.1 | 0.3 | 0.5 | 1.4 | 6.4 | 3.4 |

NB  Run numbers for wheat and barley do not correspond and are from different farms combining. However, because of the lack of uniformity of pod ripening, losses may occur from the lower pods splitting and shedding their seeds. The extent of harvest losses in oilseed rape is shown in Table 12.3 for data collected from a study in Yorkshire. The range of losses is great and the value of 1654 kg $ha^{-1}$ for desiccated crops in 1977 represents approximately 50 per cent of the total biological yield. These high losses were associated with high winds and very wet weather which particularly affected the desiccated standing crops, where wind shake caused large shedding losses. Similar conditions prevailed in 1980. Desiccated crops are more at risk from high winds than swathed ones. It has been estimated that 70 per cent of the losses occur up to and at the point where the crop enters the combine. There is some scope for reducing shedding losses by the application of a pod sealant with the desiccant. One such sealant is Di-1-p-menthene.

*Table 12.3  Harvest loss (kg $ha^{-1}$) in oilseed rape (MacLeod, 1981)*

|        | Method of harvesting | |
| Year   | Swathed | Desiccated |
| ------ | ------- | ---------- |
| 1975   | 49      | 293        |
| 1976   | 118     | 89         |
| 1977   | 650     | 1654       |
| 1978   | 99      | 183        |
| 1979   | 50      | 50         |
| 1980   | 80      | 568        |

The combine reel settings and forward speed are the major determinants of harvester losses with oilseed rape. In normal weather conditions the losses are similar from crops combined direct after desiccation and from a swath.

Additional losses can occur from swathed crops under certain conditions. Where crops are badly lodged, it may

*Table 12.4  Losses from mechanical harvesting of sugar beet and potatoes (from ADAS, 1972 and 1974)*

i) Sugar beet

| Type of harvester | Total loss ($t\ ha^{-1}$) | Surface loss (per cent of total) |
|---|---|---|
| Trailed tanker, chain | 3.3 | 33 |
| Trailed tanker, belt | 2.5 | 67 |
| Self-propelled tanker | 3.7 | 41 |
| Two-stage, multi-row | 2.3 | 37 |
| Three-stage, 5-row | 2.0 | 54 |
| Three-stage, 6-row | 2.3 | 30 |

ii) Potatoes

| Type of harvester | Total loss ($t\ ha^{-1}$) (tubers > 40 mm diameter) | Per cent of total yield |
|---|---|---|
| One-row trailed | 1.8 | 5.1 |
| One-row self-propelled | 3.6 | 9.2 |
| Two-row trailed | 2.7 | 6.9 |
| Two-row unmanned | 1.4 | 3.2 |
| Electronic | 2.4 | 6.0 |

be difficult to leave a high enough stubble to allow air movement through the swath.  In these conditions, the swath remains damp and the seed may germinate in the pod. Additionally the crop is prone to bird damage while in the swath.

Harvesting losses from sugar beet and potatoes are generally higher than those from cereals and other grain crops.  Survey data on sugar beet show that total root losses may be as high as 3.7 t $ha^{-1}$ (Table 12.4) representing a large financial penalty.  Root losses are to some extent dependent on the type of harvester used but all types leave a large proportion of the crop in or on the ground.  With most harvesters, the greatest losses result

from roots, or pieces of roots, left below the ground.
However surface losses range from 30-67 per cent of the
total. Sugar beet are often harvested in difficult soil
conditions which are not ideal for machine harvesting but
there is still scope for improving the efficiency of
harvester use. The losses quoted here represent about 8
per cent of the total root yield. Root losses are higher
where the plants are irregularly distributed and of
variable size; a situation typical of crops drilled to a
stand.

Sugar beet harvesting systems employ a topping stage
and losses can occur from overtopping of the roots.
Machinery should be set to reduce overtopping losses to a
minimum. Similarly undertopping should be avoided as this
results in excessive top tare for which the grower is
penalised financially.

Potato harvester losses are also substantial (Table
12.4). The data presented are for losses of tubers over
40 mm in diameter estimated from digging the ground after
harvesting. The type of machine influences the extent of
the loss and total values can be as high as 9.2 per cent.
Losses of the marketable product may occur subsequently
from damage to the tubers during harvesting. Tubers can
be bruised by careless harvesting and cut by lifting-
shares and this type of damage may cause rejection of the
product for some market outlets. Indirectly, further
losses result from additional water loss in store and
higher disease incidence. Losses from direct harvesting
damage can be as high as 10 per cent.

It is apparent from the few examples quoted that substantial losses in crop yield can occur at harvest. These
represent a biological and financial loss to the system
and the grower should take precautions to reduce them to
a minimum. Modern crop production systems are based on
high inputs with high costs and it is important to secure
as much of the yield as possible to give the necessary
financial returns. The harvesting aspect of crop

production is often not carried out with enough care and insufficient importance is attached to it.

DELIVERY TO THE STORE

Once the crop has been harvested the useful product is usually stored for a period of time before it is marketed or utilised. The period of storage may range from a few hours or days to several months. Crop storage and conservation is not dealt with in detail here as this subject is extensively covered elsewhere (Nash, 1978). Crop storage is a very important aspect of any crop production system and needs careful consideration. It is sufficiently different from the field aspects to be considered as a separate subject. This text is concerned with the production of the crop up to the delivery to the store stage.

Harvesting of crops is usually carried out in a short period of time when weather conditions are favourable and it requires a high degree of management skill to organise the operation efficiently. Speed of operation is usually critical at harvest time and adequate labour and machinery should be available. Because of the speed element involved in harvesting, there is potentially a risk that crop losses and damage will occur in delivering the crop to the store.

One point of loss or damage is at the stage of delivery of the product from the harvester to the trailer or lorry. With grain crops care must be taken to avoid spillage at this stage. There is a risk of damage to potato tubers at the delivery point and the falling height should be reduced to a minimum. Transporting vehicles should not be so overloaded that losses occur on the way to the store. The sight of sugar beet roots, potato tubers and grain on roads is all too common.

Losses can occur on the way to the store from inadequate sealing of trailers. Cereal grains can escape from small gaps and holes in trailers and represent a large source of loss. Flowering rape plants on roadside

verges are an attractive sight in early summer but they
represent a financial loss from last year's crop. Every
effort should be made to eliminate these sources of loss
and damage. With a few exceptions there is no great
urgency to get the crop to the store, if adequate transport facilities are available for the capacity of the
harvester. It should therefore be possible to drive
slowly enough to minimise losses and damage in transit.
An exception to this is vining peas where the product has
to be delivered for freezing quickly before spoilage
occurs. Most field vegetables for the fresh market have
a limited storage life after harvesting. In these cases
adequate provision must be made to process and grade the
products quickly so that they can be delivered to the
market in good condition.

At the point of delivery to the store some pre-
treatment of the crop may be necessary before storage. In
grain crops, this involves some pre-cleaning to remove
stones, soil, weed seeds and debris so that problems do
not arise in store. Similarly with potatoes, the removal
of stones, soil and haulms will help to prevent losses in
store. Sugar beet are often clamped after harvesting
before delivery to the factory. Dirt tare is a problem
for the farmer and the use of a machine to remove soil,
either on delivery to the clamp or from clamp to lorry,
can help to reduce this.

In some crops, the application of crop protection
chemicals before storage is necessary to prevent pest and
disease problems.

The delivery of crops to the store is a further important stage in crop production. Losses and damage at this
stage should be minimised so that storage and subsequent
marketing of the product can be done effectively.

DISPOSAL OF CROP RESIDUES

After the useful part of the crop has been removed there
are often residues in the field which have to be disposed

of. These can interfere with cultivations for the subsequent crop and in some cases provide a reservoir of pest
and disease organisms. Some crop residues are useful and
are removed with a purpose in mind. Others have no direct
use and merely need to be disposed of as quickly and
cheaply as possible.

Cereals dominate the cropping programmes of many temperate areas and they serve as a good example to illustrate some of the methods of residue disposal. On the
all-arable farm straw is of little value to the farmer unless he has a local market for it with a neighbouring
livestock farmer. If the straw is to be used, then it can
be baled and transported off the field. If it is not to
be used then there are two methods of disposal available
to the farmer. Firstly, he can chop the straw behind the
combine and plough it in. The attraction of this approach
is that in theory it will increase the organic matter content of the soil. In practice, any increases in soil
organic matter are very small, even if it is carried out
over a number of years. The incorporation of straw may
adversely affect the growth of the subsequent crop by
reducing the availability of nitrogen and through the production of harmful organic acids from straw breakdown
which inhibit seed germination. On balance, there is no
great benefit to be gained from ploughing in straw.

The second method of straw disposal available is
burning. Provided that weather conditions are favourable,
and the operation is carried out correctly, good disposal
of straw can be achieved by burning. This operation
leaves the field clear for subsequent cultivations or
direct drilling. Burning has the added advantages of
being quick and relatively cheap and of killing surface
weeds and weed seeds. Dormant weed seeds, on or near the
surface, may be stimulated to germinate after burning and
they can then be killed by chemical means or cultivations.
There is little evidence to suggest that cereal diseases
such as eyespot and take-all are significantly reduced by

burning straw.

Clearly there are dangers to other crops and vegetation and nearby buildings from burning operations and safety precautions must be taken. Smoke and ash drifting over the countryside are disliked by the public and may cause road accidents. Provided that appropriate safety precautions are taken, burning is a good and quick way of disposing of cereal straw and other crop residues, e.g. rape and field bean trash.

Straw has a number of uses in addition to being a valuable source of food and bedding for livestock. It can be used as a medium for growing horticultural crops, for mulching, erosion control and the manufacture of pulp, paper and board. In addition, it is a potentially valuable source of energy and of chemicals such as alcohol and methane. Many of these uses have not yet been developed commercially and are not available to farmers as outlets for straw disposal.

Other crops present different problems of residue disposal. The tops of sugar beet constitute almost half of the total crop weight and have to be disposed of. Some harvesters have top-saving mechanisms which allow them to be deposited in heaps or into trailers for subsequent removal to feed to livestock fresh or for ensiling. Alternatively, the tops are left in the field where they can be grazed, if livestock are available. If there are no livestock, then the tops can be ploughed in after they have wilted. The tops should be well buried otherwise they may re-grow and present a weed problem in the next crop.

The potato crop leaves very little residue especially where the haulms have been destroyed mechanically or with a desiccant. Winter wheat can therefore be sown after potatoes with minimal cultivations.

Other crop residues can present problems of disposal. The haulms of vining peas can be ploughed in after they have been spread over the field. Alternatively they can

326

be removed and ensiled. The residues of several brassica vegetable crops may need to be rotovated before they can be incorporated into the soil. Brussels sprouts provide a good example of this where the tough woody stems would cause problems of cultivation and drilling in the next crop unless fragmented. Cabbage and kale stalks and, to some extent, oilseed rape stubble present a similar problem.

The disposal of crop residues is the final field operation in the cycle of crop production. It needs to be done effectively to prevent problems occurring in the next crop. Timely removal of residues allows early cultivations and drilling of the next crop in the cycle.

REFERENCES AND FURTHER READING

ADAS (1972) 'The utilisation and performance of potato harvesters, 1971'. Farm Mechanisation Studies No.24. London: Ministry of Agriculture, Fisheries and Food.

ADAS (1973) 'The utilisation and performance of combine monitors, 1971-2'. Farm Mechanisation Studies No.25. London: Ministry of Agriculture, Fisheries and Food.

ADAS (1974) 'The utilisation and performance of sugar beet harvesters, 1973'. Farm Mechanisation Studies No.26. London: Ministry of Agriculture, Fisheries and Food.

ADAS (1982) Peas for Combine Harvesting. Leaflet 801. Alnwick: Ministry of Agriculture, Fisheries and Food.

Christensen, C.M. (ed.) (1974) Storage of Cereal Grains and Their Products. (2nd edn). St Paul, Minnesota: American Association of Cereal Chemists.

Culpin, C. (1975) Profitable Farm Mechanization (3rd edn). London: Granada Publishing.

MacLeod, J. (1981) 'Harvesting'. In Oilseed Rape Book. Cambridge: Cambridge Agricultural Publishing, 107-120.

Manley, A.C. and Wood, R.S. (1978) 'The analysis of fractions of cereal crops on three dates prior to harvest'. Agricultural Progress, 53, 71-76.

Nash, M.J. (1978)  Crop Conservation and Storage in Cool Temperate Climates.  Oxford: Pergamon Press.

Norton, G., Harris, J. and Tomlinson, A. (1978)  'Development and deposition of protein in oilseeds'.  In Plant Proteins, ed. Norton, G.  London: Butterworth, 59-80.

Sanderson, J.F. (1976)  'Pre-harvest desiccation of oilseed crops'.  Outlook in Agriculture, 9 (1), 21-25.

Scott, R.K., Ogunremi, E.A., Ivins, J.D. and Mendham, N.J. (1973)  'The effect of fertilisers and harvest date on growth and yield of oilseed rape sown in autumn and spring'.  Journal of Agricultural Science, Cambridge, 81, 287-293.

Scott, R.K. and Jaggard, K. (1978)  'How the crop grows — from seed to sugar'.  British Sugar Beet Review, 146 (4), 19-23.

Staniforth, A.R. (1979)  Cereal Straw. Oxford: University Press.

Staniforth, A.R. and Collins, F.C. (1979)  'Changes in weight and quality of wheat grain and straw over a 21-day period around normal harvest date'.  Agricultural Progress, 54, 28-32.

# Index